KU-498-556

SNOWBOUND WITH THE PRINCE

CARA COLTER

MILLS & BOON

All rights reserved including the right of reproduction in whole or in part in any form. This edition is published by arrangement with Harlequin Enterprises ULC.

This is a work of fiction. Names, characters, places, locations and incidents are purely fictional and bear no relationship to any real life individuals, living or dead, or to any actual places, business establishments, locations, events or incidents. Any resemblance is entirely coincidental.

This book is sold subject to the condition that it shall not, by way of trade or otherwise, be lent, resold, hired out or otherwise circulated without the prior consent of the publisher in any form of binding or cover other than that in which it is published and without a similar condition including this condition being imposed on the subsequent purchaser.

® and TM are trademarks owned and used by the trademark owner and/or its licensee. Trademarks marked with ® are registered with the United Kingdom Patent Office and/or the Office for Harmonisation in the Internal Market and in other countries.

First published in Great Britain 2021
by Mills & Boon, an imprint of HarperCollins*Publishers* Ltd,
1 London Bridge Street, London, SE1 9GF

www.harpercollins.co.uk

HarperCollins*Publishers*
1st Floor, Watermarque Building,
Ringsend Road, Dublin 4, Ireland

Large Print edition 2022

Snowbound with the Prince © 2021 Cara Colter

ISBN: 978-0-263-29444-6

WEST DUNBARTONSHIRE LIBRARIES		
020427956		
ULV	MB	
AF	£17.99	

Cara Colter shares her home in beautiful British Columbia, Canada with her husband of more than thirty years, an ancient, crabby cat, and several horses. She has three grown children, and two grandsons.

Also by Cara Colter

Tempted by the Single Dad
Cinderella's New York Fling
Matchmaker and the Manhattan Millionaire
His Cinderella Next Door
The Wedding Planner's Christmas Wish

Cinderellas in the Palace

His Convenient Royal Bride
One Night with Her Brooding Bodyguard

Discover more at millsandboon.co.uk.

To all those kindred spirits who have found sanctuary and salvation through imagination.

CHAPTER ONE

VALENTINE'S DAY TOMORROW.

Was there a worse day to be single? Particularly newly single? Somehow, Erin O'Rourke had thought Valentine's Day, this year, was going to be extra special.

After the disappointment of no ring at Christmas, she thought Paul had decided on the much more romantic Valentine's Day to spring the question.

Erin had pictured wine. Roses. And maybe, just maybe, a ring, small diamonds sparkling, tucked into the red velvet petals of one of those roses.

But she couldn't have been more wrong. How could she have missed all the signals? How could she have interpreted a situation so incorrectly?

Two weeks ago, Paul had announced, *It just isn't working.*

Erin had been stunned. It wasn't?

While she was indulging a fantasy of commitment—wedded bliss; a little house; some-day soon, a baby—her boyfriend of two years, Paul, had been moving in the opposite direction. How to get out of it. How to escape the traditional values—the ones she had adored—of the family he had been raised in.

So, instead of celebrating her new engagement, here Erin was on the eve of Valentine's Day. Free. Well, basically free. There was always, thank goodness, Harvey.

She patted the bulge of precious cargo at her tummy, pulled her toque down even lower over her brow and her ears, her hair all tucked beneath it.

She had just gotten off the Lonesome Lookout chairlift, the highest chair at Touch-the-Clouds ski resort. Her grandfather had started the Rocky Mountain resort more than fifty years ago.

The resort had come a long way from its humble beginnings. It had once had a single chairlift and a T-bar, a simple, cavern-ous lodge heated by a stove made from a salvaged oil barrel.

But Touch-the-Clouds had some of the best deep powder in the world and, over the years, it was a secret that had gotten out. It had grown in popularity, particularly with the rich and famous. Finally, it had grown beyond her grandfather's capacity to keep up.

It now consisted of an entire village with bars and hotels, shops, restaurants and condos. It offered a dozen different chairlifts and hundreds of runs. While it was still the preferred ski retreat of the rich and famous, everything depended on snow. They'd had a bad few years.

And a bad review in *Snow Lust* magazine. The resort had been called "tired and over-rated."

Although it was owned by a big corporation now—as were most high-end ski resorts that wanted to be viable—Erin was employed in the accounting department, and she knew the resort had spent several years in the red. How long could they keep that up? She lived at an apartment provided for her in the ski village complex, and she still had exclusive use of her grandfather's original cabin, Snow Daze, but for how long? The cabin was well off the beaten track, and the snowy trail to it could only be accessed from this chairlift.

She had decided that Snow Daze was where she would spend Valentine's Day, taking the day off tucked away in the rustic cabin. She hoped the intense quiet of deep snow outside and the crackle of a fire inside, and a cat on her lap, would soothe something in her, as they always had.

That way, tomorrow, she would not be on the receiving end of sympathetic looks from her coworker, Kelly, as she acted surprised and gleeful over the delivery of flowers and a gooey card from her husband.

Erin had, so far, managed to keep her humiliating breakup to herself.

See? There was a good side to Paul never producing a ring. A suddenly naked ring finger was like sending out an announcement card.

However, so was *nothing* arriving for her at the office on February fourteenth. It would be the equivalent of posting a group email around the office, its message the opposite of a valentine. *I'm a failure at love. It didn't work. I'm single.*

Erin regarded the mountain in the waning light of a cold winter day. She knew it as few people did, and the snow was now coming so thick and fast that she could no longer see the peaks of the mountains that surrounded this bowl.

She had caught the chair as the old attendant, Ricky, was turning everyone else away for the day.

"You're cutting it close," he'd warned her. "I sent the ski patrol up twenty minutes ago to sweep the mountain for stragglers. You're only about thirty minutes from full dark. I don't think you can make it all the way down in that time."

"I'm not going all the way down. I'm heading to the cabin," she'd said. "Lots of time for that." She'd patted her front pocket. "I've got a satellite device. I'll let the patrol know when I get there."

He'd cast a look at the thickly falling flakes of snow. "Okay, but be careful."

She had actually laughed. "Going to that

cabin for me is as routine as an afternoon commute for most people."

"I know," he'd said. "I helped your grandpa build that place. I know you're as at home here as anywhere else. But it's still a mountain, and Mother Nature can still surprise you. That looks like one doozy of a storm building. I don't think we could mount a rescue in it."

"You won't be rescuing me," she had assured him.

His concern for her had been a comfort.

On the chair, she put a hand on the warmth radiating from her belly and said out loud, "*This* is our family. Touch-the-Clouds is our home."

And that, Erin was determined, would be enough.

Now, at the top of the run, in absolute solitude, Erin pulled her hood up as extra protection from the heavily falling snow, and slid her goggles over her eyes. She used her poles to shove off and heard the wonderful hiss of her ski edges cutting into the new powder.

She crouched, picked up momentum and

speed, and felt her heartaches blow away as she became fully immersed in the exhilaration of the moment.

Snow, wind, the skis beneath her. Since she was a child, those things had filled her heart with a euphoria that nothing else had ever replicated.

Including her love for Paul, she realized.

She had also been going to Snow Daze since she was a baby. Her memories of the cabin were of multigenerational family gatherings. She had grown up to ducking through strings of clothes drying by the fire, wet from sledding and building snowmen. Her memories were hot-chocolate scented, rambunctious card games won and lost around a beat-up wooden table, books devoured in a rump-sprung easy chair, waxing skis on the kitchen counter.

Still, realistically, hadn't those moments been few and far between? Her father's pro racing, and then his coaching career, had sent him all over the world. Her mother, exhausted from his inability to say no to anyone who was charmed by the combination of fame and extraordinarily good looks, had finally left him when Erin was eleven.

The remainder of her childhood had been spent between their two households, with their ever-changing international backdrops. And partners.

She had longed for the things other people's families stood for and that they seemed to take for granted.

Stability. Connection. Loyalty. Love.

Those were the things she had hoped for when she'd started dating Paul… Erin shook it off. The entrance to the trail that led to the cabin was difficult to find at the best of times. Part of the healing power of the mountain was that it forced you to stay focused.

There was no room up here for daydreaming. There were consequences for errors. It would be too easy in these conditions, even for someone as familiar with the mountain as she was, to swoop by the trailhead and have to do the arduous, sidestepping climb to backtrack up to it in the growing dark and the thickening storm.

She skidded to a halt, loving the wave of snow that shot out from her skis, the familiar ache of muscles used hard. Between wind gusts, it was deeply silent. Even the rumbling hum of the chairlift was gone, shut off for the day.

Still, the snowfall, she realized, was developing a different quality, becoming shardlike. She squinted through ice-crusted goggles up the hill and then slid them onto her forehead. She caught a single glimpse of the sky. It was taking on the ominous purplish tint that said, to those who knew the mountain, a storm was coming.

A doozy of a storm, just as Ricky had predicted.

She might end up at the cabin for more than a day, but that suited her. The cabin was always well stocked, plus she had, in her backpack, a special Valentine's feast for one. She could check in with the resort by her sat device to let them know her plans.

Paul, not much of a skier, had never been to the cabin, so there was nothing there to remind her of him.

Had she deliberately saved it? Thinking it would be the most delightful place in the world for a honeymoon? Thinking, if they had a summer wedding, they could hike into that secluded place, untouched by modern technologies, and have a few blissful days all to themselves?

No phones. No computers. No interruptions.

Paul and his phone: the constant checking, tapping away, shutting out the world, shutting out her…

Again, she shook off her sudden awareness of the insult of it. Instead, Erin looked toward the tree line. Barely visible was the tiny opening that marked a secret trail. Nailed above it was a small sign, faded, nearly covered with snow, that said Private. No Entrance. It was a largely unnecessary warning since only someone looking for this narrow gap in the wall of silent, snow-covered fir could find it.

She slid the goggles back down, tightened her hood, and pointed her skis toward the opening. She was just about to plant her poles when a voice stopped her. Was it a voice? Or just the storm announcing it was intensifying with the odd howling wind gust?

She had thought she was alone on the mountain. She turned and squinted up into the driving snow. She saw nothing.

But then she heard the voice, louder than before. Definitely not the wind.

"Alisha, wait." The voice was deep and masculine.

Alisha? Did that mean there were two people still out on the slopes in the storm? She couldn't see anyone, the snow was so thick. Erin noticed it was beginning to blow sideways rather than drift straight down.

Then the veil of snow lifted and she saw him, making his way down the mountain toward her. It was a steep section and the visibility had gone extraordinarily flat, but he was a good skier, very technical, and she could see a natural athleticism in the aggressive way he tackled the challenging slope and traversed the ground between them.

He swooshed to a stop in front of her, covering her in a cascading wave of snow as powdery as icing sugar. As she shook it off, she was irritated, not because he had covered her with snow, but because he was still on the mountain after it had been swept.

Still, her annoyance abated somewhat as

she became aware of his sheer physical presence. The storm seemed to pause around them. The wind and snow stopped abruptly. Was it possible it was going to blow over? Not likely.

He was much taller than she was and for some reason she noted that, probably because for two years she had been trying to shrink, as if her being taller than him was some sort of slight to Paul.

The athleticism she had seen in the way this man navigated the hill was even more apparent at close range. His shoulders were broad under a very expensive ski jacket and he wore the tight, flexible pant of a ski racer. Those pants molded the large muscles of powerful thighs. He carried himself with such sheer confidence that the reprimand she wanted to give him—what the heck was he still doing on the mountain—died before she spoke it.

It felt as if he, not she, had been born to this mountain, as if he owned not just it, but all the earth.

His eyes were covered by mirrored goggles. Below those goggles, he had chosen to be unprotected from the conditions by not pulling his neck gaiter up over his face. Was there something vaguely familiar about him? Probably. She had likely seen him around the resort village. He was the kind of man you would notice—and then quickly *not* notice—if you had recently been devastated by a long-term relationship exploding in your face.

Or fizzling, as the case might be.

She had to ground herself. She could not let the lull in the storm distract her from the seriousness of his situation, or that of his still missing companion, Alisha.

But instead of feeling grounded, Erin felt compelled to look at him again. A renegade tingle went up and down her spine.

It was just the wild unpredictability of the winter weather, Erin assured herself. It was increasing the intensity of her awareness of everything, including the stranger who had come out of its understated prelude.

Coming storms did this, infused the air and the earth with a humming current, both powerful and mystic. The awareness she was feeling because of the storm was transferring to him, it wasn't *because* of him.

If she thought about it, she was also aware of the feeling of each snowflake falling on her face, the deep, muffled quiet, the scent that always rode in with strong weather. Indefinable. Pure. Untamed.

"Alisha," he said. "I thought I had lost you."

Any illusion Erin had that the intensity of her awareness was caused by the mountain preparing to unleash its savagery around them evaporated.

His voice was like warm honey. It was deeply and deliciously exotic. He had the faintest accent that carried her far away from the storm, to sun-drenched places that smelled of spice and flowers.

She wished she was Alisha.

Slowly, with a sigh, she lifted her hand, flipped down her hood and then raised her goggles off her eyes.

CHAPTER TWO

PRINCE VALENTINO DE OSCARO STARED, shocked, into the greenest eyes he had ever seen. The shock was intensified because he thought he had finally, in this lull in the snowstorm that was in equal parts terrifying and exhilarating, been reunited with his head of security.

"You're not Alisha," he said.

It was stating the obvious. The ski jackets, the height—unusually tall for a woman—were similar enough that he had made the initial error of thinking it was Alisha, particularly since that was who he had been looking for. What were the chances, after all, of two women of similar appearance being out in this storm?

But his head of security, Colonel Alisha Del Rento, was the antithesis of this woman: her life experiences honed into her face, unapologetically tough and weathered. The colonel was as dark as this woman was pale.

The prince realized the word *pale* did not do justice to the woman in front of him. *Fair* might be better. There was the wholesome glow of the outdoors dusted on her skin, giving her a look most women would want but that could never be attained out of a makeup bottle.

These observations were peripheral. Where was Alisha? Though she took pride in the fact that she could handle anything that life threw at her, neither she nor the other two members of his security team were familiar with this mountain.

They had, he knew, trained for winter conditions, but still he felt concerned. This was on him. He had insisted, despite the worsening weather and against his security team's wishes, on one more run, the new snow making the powder too exquisite to resist.

The woman might not physically resemble the colonel in any way, but that tight-lipped look of disapproval was familiar.

"What on earth are you doing out here?" the woman asked.

Valentino was unaccustomed to sharpness of tone and, despite his worry for his team, he felt oddly delighted by it.

Just as he felt oddly delighted by the storm. It was so real. A man and a mountain, pitting his strength, his abilities, his intelligence, against the elements.

Of course, he had two women, now, who were really annoyed at him. The one before him, whose green eyes were sparking with an intriguing inner light, and his head of security, who had strongly advised, given the weather, they not make this final run.

But he had insisted, *loving* the challenge of it.

Only one of those women would feel free to express her chagrin, and that was the one in front of him.

He felt himself rising to the challenge of her, too. He answered her question by repeating it.

"What on earth are *you* doing out here?" he shot back.

Her look of disapproval intensified. Who, besides his mother, had ever dared be disapproving of him?

"I live here."

He glanced around. "Where? Under one of the trees?"

She failed, apparently, to see the humor. "I also work here. You shouldn't be on the mountain in this storm."

"But you should?" he asked mildly. "Besides, it seems to be letting up."

"I thought so, too, but don't underestimate mountain weather. It's possible it has barely hit yet."

Could that be true? The snow had paused but was coming again, though lighter than it had been before. The wind had died down almost completely.

Glaring at him, as if he was a horrible inconvenience to her, she planted her poles and pulled off her gloves. He was not sure why he noticed her fingers were ringless. She unzipped an outer pocket of her jacket. He noticed a slight bump at her waistline and something in him went cold.

Was she pregnant?

Valentino felt suddenly and astonishingly protective of her—and also in way over his head. As he looked at her, the bulge in her stomach area *moved*.

Good grief, was she going to have a baby? Out here in a storm that, according to her, had barely hit yet? With him, of all people? He wasn't wholly loving the challenge of the mountain—and of her—quite so much now.

Thankfully, she produced a cumbersome item that looked like some kind of phone, and he felt the relief sigh within him. Signals on his own cell phone had been intermittent since arriving at the resort.

She held her apparatus up to the sky and shifted her glare from him to it. She took a few sidesteps up the mountain, and he recognized, despite her condition, how at ease she was on the skis.

She held up the device again.

"What are you doing?" he asked.

"Searching for a signal. It's a satellite device," she said without looking at him. Her face brightened. She quickly lowered the device, punched in numbers, and put it to her ear.

"What's your name?"

Valentino simply was not accustomed to being snapped at like this: as if he were some sort of nuisance, causing aggravation to someone. Despite the fact that he was somewhat lost, with a storm apparently nowhere near over, with a woman who was pregnant, he contemplated how what should have been an insult instead felt oddly refreshing.

Had he ever, in his entire life, had someone have absolutely no idea of who he was?

And so, he didn't want her to know. Not just yet. He would enjoy this anonymity for a little while longer by just giving his first name. Of course, once she got someone on the other end of that phone, she was bound to find out the Crown Prince of the Kingdom of Lorenzo del Toro was missing.

"Valentino," he said. He wanted to say something more North American. Like Fred. Or Joe. But there was the security team to consider. They would be frantic with worry for him, wherever they were. So, as delightful as it would be to remain anonymous, his duty to others came first. As always.

"Seriously?" Her green eyes narrowed skeptically on him, as if he *had* given her a pseudonym.

"Excuse me?"

"Your name is Valentino?"

"It is," he said.

"What are the chances?" she muttered.

"Excuse me?" he said again.

She sighed heavily. "What are the chances that I would find a man named Valentino on the mountain on the eve of Valentine's Day?"

"It had completely slipped my mind that tomorrow is Valentine's Day," he told her. Then, before he could ask her name in return—and if she shouldn't be with her husband to have her baby on Valentine's Day—she moved on, snapping another question at him.

"And your companion? Alisha? When's the last time you saw her?"

"We were on the chair together. There were actually four of us total."

"Four?" she said, and her green eyes widened in alarm. Now was probably not the time to notice how thick her lashes were, the snowflakes—the snow *was* deepening again—crusting on them like tiny diamonds.

It might reduce her alarm to tell her his team were all specialists in a number of areas that would likely more than prepare them for the challenges of the mountain. But then, he was concerned about them himself, and admitting to being accompanied by a "team" of specialists of any kind would certainly give clues that she had not run into just an ordinary joe on the mountain.

The prince was not yet ready to give up his taste of anonymity.

"Yes, we were skiing together. They're very accomplished."

Her look of skepticism was not reduced. Again, it was novel to have someone doubt him.

"To be honest," he offered, "I don't know how we were separated. It seems impossible."

Given his team's absolute devotion to his protection and safety, it really did seem astonishing that somehow they had lost each other. One moment he had been swooping down the mountain, elated, and the next he had been aware of the deepening of the storm and that he was alone.

"The mountains love to make fun of what people think is possible and impossible," she said and then turned her attention to the phone.

"Hi, Stacy. This is Erin."

Erin. He contemplated that name and how well it suited her. In his world, women had feminine names, so this added to his sense of being let loose in a different time and place.

Erin's voice drifted to him. For all that her name wasn't particularly feminine, her voice was.

"I've come across a guy up here on the Lonesome runs. Valentino."

He was irrationally glad he hadn't told her he was Joe or Fred, because he liked the way his name sounded coming off her lips.

"Four total in his party," she said then raised her voice. "Four."

She listened and then pulled the phone away from her ear. Even with a bit of distance between them, he could hear a hissing and crackling on the line. She waited, patiently, until it subsided, and put the device back up to her ear.

He expected his moment of anonymity was about to be lost. She would be told she was with a member of the royal family from a small Mediterranean island kingdom. Everything would change. She would look at him with deference, a new respect, but it would be because of his title, not because of who he was. He felt unreasonably deflated by that.

She was squinting at her device, disgruntled. She held it up, sighed, then shoved it back in her pocket.

"The signal evaporated," she said with a shrug, none the wiser to who he was. "Which is not so surprising in this weather. But I understand that the rest of your party is accounted for, thank goodness."

His sense of relief was instant. Despite the fact the soldiers of his personal guard were experts who had trained in survival from the Italian Alps to the Arctic Ocean, he still had known it was because of him they'd been out in the storm. If anything had happened…

"Good," he said. "I'll meet them down there."

She looked pensively at the weather, took in a deep breath of the air, as if it gave her clues.

"We aren't going down," she decreed.

We? And who had placed *her* in charge of *him*? He raised an eyebrow. In his world, that was all it took.

But she knew nothing of his world.

"I think it's too close to dark," she stated. "We can't make it all the way down to the village, especially if the storm gets worse, which I think it is going to."

"Do we have an option?" he asked. He did not want to be trapped on a mountain, in a storm, with a woman who looked like she might be about to have a baby. His gaze drifted to the terrifying bump at her belly. He thought he detected a slight motion again. A baby at any moment!

Again, she considered the weather. "I don't think so."

"What exactly does that mean?" Valentino asked. "That we have to shelter up here?" He had kidded her about living under one of the trees, but now it didn't seem funny.

She was silent and preoccupied, pulling the goggles back over her eyes, fastening her hood tight around her toque.

"We can build an igloo," he proposed. He couldn't have predicted that this morning. That he would be building a shelter, a storm raging, a baby coming. His life rarely handed him surprises. But he didn't feel trepidation about the challenge.

Instead, he felt ready. Protective. And fierce, as if a warrior spirit he had not known he'd possessed had stepped up to do battle with these elements.

He felt the huge weight of the responsibility to get her through this, but he also felt ready to test himself against the mountain, to not be pampered and protected. But instead to be the protector. He felt astonishingly alive, vibrating with urgency.

"An igloo?"

He frowned at her. The one who claimed

to live here didn't seem to be getting the peril they were in since she had decided they couldn't make it back to the village. It was probably a form of protective denial. Because of the baby.

"Yes, you know," he said, keeping his voice calm, patient, reassuring. "We'll have to find some crusted snow. And cut blocks from it. It will protect us from the elements until morning."

"I know what an igloo is." For the first time, a smile tickled her lips. He noticed they were unglossed and generous. And gorgeous.

What kind of man made that kind of note about a pregnant woman's lips? It seemed like something you might have to admit to in the confessional!

Besides, he had to keep the priorities straight, since she was obviously not going to. How could she not know how dangerous this all could become in the blink of an eye?

Still, that smile changed everything about her. The sternness left her face and she looked very youthful and wholesome, not to mention extraordinarily beautiful.

And then she laughed.

He might have enjoyed the sound of that more if he hadn't had the annoying sense she was not just making light of their predicament, but laughing *at* him. Not *with him*—because he was not laughing.

This was an extraordinarily novel experience. Not at all enjoyable, like his anonymity had been.

"An igloo," she snorted between chortles.

He frowned at her. Was she mocking him? A frown from him had always been enough to bring instant respect. She, however, did not take the frown as a reprimand, as he had intended. Not at all.

"And you know how to make one?" she asked, the music of her laughter still tinging her voice. "An igloo? Or do you think I know how to make one? A mandatory part of being Canadian?"

She was continuing to be amused at his expense! The novelty of her not knowing who he was, was thinning rapidly.

"I'm sure I can figure it out," he informed her stiffly. "I saw it on a documentary once."

She managed to contain, finally, her awful chortling, though her lips still twitched. "Well, that would certainly make you an expert," she said. Her tone was not sarcastic, but soothing, which made it twice as insulting, as if she were speaking to a child who had told her he knew how to build a rocket ship to the moon.

"I could, in a pinch, put together a rudimentary shelter from the elements."

"Yes, of course, you could." There was the patronizing tone again. "But we aren't going to need your igloo expertise."

As much as the prince wanted to be mistaken for a normal person, he didn't want this stranger on the mountain thinking she was going to patronize him, and worse, be in charge of things. She seemed to think she was going to protect him, not the other way around. The insult of it was grating.

"We need to think about the baby," he informed her sternly.

She looked astonished. And then she glanced down at the bulge under her jacket, as if she had forgotten her delicate condition. That annoying *amused* smile deepened. Thankfully, it was not accompanied by the chortle, though she looked as if she might be biting it back.

"I have a cabin up here. That's where I was heading. We're ten minutes from there. Let's move."

She had a cabin? A young woman alone on the mountain? A young woman who was about to have a baby? Because of the gathering twilight and the intensity of the snow, the light was growing stranger around them by the moment.

Between that, and the prince standing on the unfamiliar ground of being both unprotected and with someone who had no idea who he was, this whole incident was beginning to have the faint, hazy texture of a dream.

Or a fairy tale.

And then, before his very eyes, the baby bulge her jacket was stretched across moved quite violently!

If that baby decided to arrive, the dream could turn into a nightmare very quickly!

CHAPTER THREE

As VALENTINO GRAPPLED with all of that, Erin set her poles.

"Follow me," she ordered, all business, borderline bossy. "We have to make time. We're losing the light. Try to keep up."

There was that hint of an insult again, both at being given an order and at her instructing him to keep up.

But when he looked down the slope, he was a little shocked by how conditions had diminished suddenly. The snow had thickened to nearly zero visibility, as if the two of them existed alone after being dropped into a milk bottle.

Apparently, she had been right about the storm barely hitting before. Now, it descended on them with its full force. The wind suddenly screamed into the silence, stopped, then screamed again.

He had to raise his voice to be heard above it. "Let's go."

Valentino had been taught by some of the best instructors in the world since he was a small boy. He had skied some of the most exotic places in the world, including the alps of Italy and Switzerland. Skiing to him was like riding. Both activities came as naturally to him as breathing.

He thought Erin should probably be worried about keeping up with him! Particularly in her delicate condition. She would need to protect herself.

But she did not seem to have those concerns. And she quickly proved him wrong about who would be keeping up with whom. She found an almost invisible trail through some trees. Valentino knew he skied well, and maybe extraordinarily so.

But she skied differently than anyone he had ever seen before. Despite the fact she was carrying quite a large pack on her back—and a baby on her front—her movement was both powerful and seemingly effortless. She wasn't conquering the slope of the mountain, she was melding with it, dancing with it, celebrating it.

It was an extraordinary thing to witness, at the same time he was terrified of her falling! He would have shouted at her to slow down, but he never got close enough to make his voice heard above the storm that howled and pulsated around them.

It was also humiliatingly hard to keep up to her. Between the speed she was traveling and the heavily blowing snow creating a blanket between them, it took all his considerable skill to keep her in his sights.

As their passing disturbed them, heavy snow dropped in clumps off the needled branches of the trees. It was like being in a war zone: a sense of life-and-death urgency coupled with the relentless whistling of the wind, snow now dropping from branches like bombs on both sides of the trail.

And then it was over.

Not the storm.

But the sense of urgency and peril. The trail abruptly ended in a small clearing. They had beaten the storm.

Barely visible through the driving snow and ebbing light was a structure. With towering trees at its back, a tiny cabin faced the clearing. It was like something off a Christmas card, the kind of place he thought probably only existed as nostalgia, a figment of imagination, a longing for simplicity and sanctuary in a busy, complex world.

With one last huge effort, he launched himself toward the cabin's promise. They had arrived at safety.

As Valentino stopped at the steps to the cabin, Erin was already stepping out of her bindings and tossing her skis over her shoulder. He felt like a man who had crossed the desert in search of water and could not be certain that what he was seeing was not a mirage. He took it all in.

Constructed of logs, long since weathered to gray, the cabin was anchored on one side by a sturdy chimney made of round, smooth river rocks in varying shades ranging from gold to mauve. In the shadow of a large porch that wrapped around the entire structure, a brightly painted red door welcomed. There were red shutters around the square-paned glass of the windows. The snow, stacked up on the roof, was at least two feet deep.

Valentino was a man who had been raised in grandeur and opulence. The palace of his family was often compared to the Palazzo Brancaccio in Rome, though, as his mother liked to point out to anyone who was interested, it predated that structure by several hundred years. Their house, Palazzo de Oscaro, was arguably the most photographed palace in the Mediterranean.

He followed Erin's suit and kicked off his skis, and then tumbled, grateful, through the door of the cottage. He had to put his shoulder against it to close it. It was as if the storm was an intruder, demanding to come in with them.

With the storm closed out—howling as if angry at its exclusion—Valentino became aware of a feeling he'd never had before when, at this moment, he felt it for the very first time.

As he leaned his back against the door, he was enveloped in a sense of warmth, a sensation of arriving, finally, after a long, long journey, at the place called home.

But then, sharing the small entryway with him, Erin yanked off her toque and a cascade of hair tumbled out as golden as ripened wheat. She ran her hands through it, tossed it over her shoulder with a shake of her head. He could smell some heady scent.

His sense of having found a safe place, a place called home, evaporated. As someone who had grown up royal, he had had it drummed into him from the first small hop of a hormone: do not *ever* put yourself—and therefore your family—in a compromising position.

In a world that was always under a microscope and always under control, he had never encountered a situation quite like this one.

He was going to be snowed in, alone and entirely unchaperoned, with a woman. A very beautiful woman.

A strange sense of danger, every bit as intense as what he had felt on the mountain and from the storm enveloped him.

A very pregnant woman, Valentino reminded himself. *Thank the gods.*

Valentino on Valentine's Day, Erin thought as she yanked off her toque and ran her hands through her hair, contemplating the option that someone was punking her.

She glanced over her shoulder at the stranger to see if he was amused. An igloo? It had to be a trick of some sort.

But the man looked only relieved to be inside. Besides, who could have put such an elaborate trick in play? It would mean someone had known about Paul breaking off with her. It was possible, given that it had happened two weeks ago, that he was slowly letting people know, even if she was not.

But really? She didn't know anyone in their circle of friends, thank goodness, who was cruel enough to make a joke out of that.

Besides, the whole premise rested on a chance encounter on the mountain. And Valentino seemed to genuinely think she was pregnant. So, no, it had to be the universe having a snicker at her expense.

Well, at least she'd managed to punk back a little bit by letting him believe she was pregnant. And by besting him at skiing. He had skied beautifully, but Erin allowed herself a small snippet of satisfaction that, even so, he couldn't keep up to her.

She patted the bump under her jacket, just to get a reaction from him, but it backfired. The reaction was hers.

Because Valentino lifted his goggles from his eyes.

Any brief satisfaction she had felt by besting him at skiing evaporated like mist before the sun. His eyes were utterly astonishing. A deep, deep brown flecked with gold.

Now that she wasn't, well, taken, and now that they had found sanctuary and safety from the storm, it gave her permission to really look at him as he leaned over and released the buckles on his boots.

She fought the temptation to look at him longer. Instead, she took out the satellite device and tried for a connection. No go. She typed in a quick text to let people know they had arrived safely. Generally, it would send the next time the device found a signal.

She accidentally jostled him as she bent over her own boot buckles.

"Oh, sorry," she said, annoyed that she was blushing as he regained his balance and kicked off the boots.

"I'll set those outside," she said.

He passed the boots to her and his hand brushed hers. She still had her gloves on; he did not. It was impossible that she felt the heat of his touch, wasn't it?

She was so close to him. In the fading light, his golden-toned skin seemed to glow. She could not help but notice his nose: perfect, strong and straight. He had high, commanding cheekbones. He was clean-shaven, which accentuated a faint cleft in his chin, a feature Erin had not realized she found attractive until this very second.

A hint of a dark shadow on his cheeks—added to that exotic skin tone—suggested he might have dark hair beneath the custom-painted ski helmet that complimented the rich navy of his jacket and pants.

For some reason, once her eyes found them, she could not look away from his lips, which were firm and wide. The bottom one was enticingly puffy, the faintest line dividing it in two. What form of madness was this?

Aside from the fact they were going to be stranded together for at least one night, she was freshly heartbroken! This jolt of pure awareness his lips were causing in her seemed entirely inappropriate.

It felt as if, given the circumstances, she should be ashamed of her awareness of the sensual fullness of his lower lip. She tried to muster that feeling.

Instead, Erin was aware of feeling free, like someone who had been inside a house too long suddenly being let out to breathe fresh air.

It felt liberating, and exhilaratingly so, to just look at a man and appreciate him. It felt good to *not* be taken, spoken for, committed.

Erin was shocked at herself and a new and niggling awareness of how superficial she was capable of being. She turned quickly away from him and put the sets of heavy ski boots outside the door. Snow blew in, right up under the porch. When she stepped back in the door, Valentino had not moved, but was studying the interior of the cabin.

The look on his face was extraordinary. It was as if he was lit from within. Her eyes moved to the puffiness of that lower lip again.

Then he threw back his head and laughed. Was it because he had noticed her fixation on his lips?

"Encantado," he declared softly, his accent unconsciously seductive. And then his eyes came to rest on her. He had spoken in Spanish, so he translated. "I'm enchanted."

She felt as if her breath stopped.

Was he referring to her? To her gazing at his lips? She quickly looked away, over the broadness of his shoulders, and tried to quiet the fluttering of her heart.

All her life she had lived with her father's unending appeal to women, and her mother's bitterness over it. But until this moment, she had not experienced a pull toward someone that felt so compelling. She was shocked to feel something primitive and powerful stir within her.

She had not felt this before—a naked animal awareness of a member of the opposite sex—and it shook her. After all, she knew nothing about this man who was looking so intently at her with a gaze that set fire in her blood.

Wanting.

Wanting what? Erin asked herself primly. She just wasn't the kind of girl who went around lusting after strangers on the ski hill.

Erin did not like weakness. And she particularly did not like *that* weakness. She sighed inwardly. The universe had not only provided her with a Valentino for Valentine's Day, but one that was going to challenge everything she believed about herself.

For instance, that she was not in the least impulsive.

She did not believe people had instincts they could not control.

She certainly did not believe in love at first sight.

He took off his jacket and reached to hang it on a peg behind her. He was very close, in fact, and his presence was so electrical that some of her hair reached out and attached to the sleeve of his white, long-sleeved undershirt.

When she reached out to yank her errant hair back, she realized the undershirt was not wool, but something finer, like alpaca or cashmere. The texture of it made her want to sink her fingers in to it. Or maybe that was the scent that tickled her nostrils, every bit as invigorating as the scent of the coming storm she had detected earlier.

It was faintly spicy, faintly cold, faintly pure man.

Then Valentino removed his ski helmet and reached by her again to put it on a peg. Despite ordering herself not to, Erin could not help but stare at him.

A cascade of damp curls, as black and as shiny as the wings of a raven, had been released from underneath that helmet.

He shook them and then ran a hand through the tangled mop of his hair. He was so gorgeous, it felt as if her heart would stop.

She suddenly was not so sure she did not believe in love at first sight.

That was a thought that had to be resisted wholeheartedly!

"When's the baby due?" he asked, a certain tender protectiveness in his tone that could melt a susceptible person's heart. She was determined she would not be that person.

"I'm not pregnant."

Valentino looked quizzically at her stomach. And then a blush changed the tone of his golden skin. He thought he'd *insulted* her.

Harvey, no doubt recognizing they were home, wanted out. Valentino's eyes widened at the violent wave of motion under her jacket.

She stepped by Valentino into the main room and unzipped her coat to reveal the rounded hump of baby carrier underneath it.

"You skied with a *real* baby?" he breathed, aghast, apparently not familiar enough with baby paraphernalia to realize a head should have been visible if she was, indeed, carrying a real baby.

"Well, my baby."

"But that's not safe!"

"This is the same baby carrier my father used to put me in to come here when I was just a baby," she said. "My family skis as easily as most people walk."

"Still," he said, appalled, "you could have fallen. On your baby."

"Think of it like people in Europe riding bikes with babies in the carriers."

"It's not the same—"

At that moment, Harvey decided he'd had enough. His paws emerged first, over the lip of the carrier. And then he hefted himself up, poking his gray furry head out of the carrier He eyed the stranger in his domain balefully through slitted amber eyes.

Valentino took a startled step back. "That is not a baby!"

"Really?" She looked down at Harvey with pretended astonishment. "Where did he come from?"

Valentino eyed her with such annoyance, a shiver went up and down her spine. He had that look of a man far too certain of himself, a man that people did not cross.

"You're not pregnant," he said, something edgy in his voice.

"Is there any reason you would sound disappointed by that news?"

"You let me believe it. You let me think I might be delivering a baby in an igloo."

"I'm in no way responsible for other people's absurd conclusions!"

"You're skiing with a cat and you call me absurd?" he shot back.

"I don't think I would have been out here skiing by myself if I was that close to having a baby. What do you take me for? An idiot?"

"I feel as if I've been the one played for the idiot," he said stiffly. "You could have told me right away. Plus, you could have seriously injured your animal."

"Not just an idiot! An irresponsible idiot! Believe me, if I had fallen on Harvey, I would have come out of it in worse shape than him."

Valentino looked at her with narrowed eyes. She could feel a spark in the air between them. She didn't like sparks between people! She liked calm.

But look where that liking had gotten her. Paul had told her, in his little breakup speech, that their relationship was boring. It reminded him of his mother and father's relationship. It was obvious—look at her relationship with Harvey—that she wanted children. Soon.

He wasn't ready. Kids and family felt like jail to him.

Erin's focus moved again to the intrigue of that puffy split in Valentino's bottom lip. She contemplated the feeling that rippled through her. Whatever it was, it was not boring.

She was annoyed with him. He was aggravated with her. And still, underneath that ran a current of…something. Something she could not encourage, or investigate, given their circumstances.

Not that she would want to under any circumstances. That kind of spark was dangerous! It could burn a whole forest down before you even blinked.

They were about to be snowed in here, together, for who knew how long. There was no room in that equation for *wanting*.

CHAPTER FOUR

THERE WAS NO room for wanting, Erin told herself sternly, no matter how delectable Valentino's lips were. Part of her, to her own disgust, sighed. *What would one little taste hurt?*

There would be no such thing as a *little* taste of those lips. It would be like trying to have only one little bite of fantastic chocolate.

And there was no room for attractions or sparky arguments, either, even if it did make her feel faintly invigorated.

"Let's call a truce," she suggested. *And not look at each other's lips.* "I'm sorry I let you believe I might be pregnant."

"For your own amusement," he said.

"You obviously did not get the script," she told him with elaborate and sarcastic patience. "This is the part where you say, 'I'm sorry I insinuated you were an irresponsible idiot.'"

Valentino was silent. He looked stern. Almost forbidding. A man who rarely had to give an inch to anyone and who didn't plan to now.

"I have food," she told him. "And wine. And I'm not above bribing you for a truce."

"I'm bigger than you. I could just take them." But finally the stern line around his mouth softened.

"But you wouldn't," she said.

He cocked his head at her.

"I can tell by looking at you. And since we're stuck here together for a while, it would probably be better if we made an attempt to be civil. So, truce?"

He considered. He nodded. "Truce."

Having won that reluctant concession from Valentino, Erin released the cat from the carrier and set him on the floor. Harvey would have normally headed straight to his dish and complained loudly at finding it empty. Instead, he marched over, tail high, and wound himself around Valentino's legs.

Despite her call for a truce, she couldn't believe her cat.

Traitor.

She could usually count on Harvey to be an equal opportunities hater. He had held Paul in utter contempt for the entire length of their relationship.

Valentino squatted and scratched under the scruffy cat's chin. "You look like an old warrior," he said.

She was suddenly not so sure how wise calling a truce had been. Valentino's deep voice, roughened with affection, sent a tingle up and down her spine. If she was not mistaken, her cranky cat was reacting about the same way. He rounded his back as Valentino's hands moved from his chin to his tail.

Erin stared at his hands. They were not the hands of a working man, but rather beautifully shaped and manicured while still being entirely masculine. He must be an executive. Actually, given that take-charge, brook-no-nonsense demeanor, she was willing to bet he owned and ran a very successful company.

He was doing something with those hands—

caressing—that made that *wanting* leap to the fore more powerfully than when she had first fought it back.

The cat preened under his touch.

"How old is he?" Valentino asked, not the least bit aware, thank goodness, that she had become entranced with his hands.

"I've had him since I was eleven," she said. "And he wasn't a kitten, then, so he's at least fifteen, maybe older."

"And you travel with him?"

Was she eager to let him know she was not some eccentric single woman who could not be separated from her cat? It would seem so. But, wait a second, wasn't she the one who had decided to embrace the single life?

Looking at Valentino's hands on that cat, she was embarrassingly aware she didn't want to be perceived as a career single person and a crazy cat lady!

"He's going slowly blind," Erin explained. "And deaf. He's nervous when I'm not around, so I've increasingly found ways to keep him close to me. He sleeps most of the time now, so it's no problem to have him under my desk at work. I'm in accounting at the resort."

"Accounting?"

Was she relieved at the surprise in his voice? When had she started being a person who didn't want to look like she was in accounting?

About half an hour ago!

"Yes, accounting. Harvey is kind of the office mascot, even though he has a nasty streak."

"A nasty streak?" Valentino said, giving Harvey's chin another scratch before straightening. "I don't believe it."

Harvey cast her a look that clearly said he'd been *seen*.

"That's an unusual amount of dedication to a pet on your part," he said.

Paul had thought it was distinctly weird, not admirable.

"I owe him one," Erin said. She went over to the kitchen counter and removed some long matches from a jar.

"That's interesting. How can you owe a cat something? I would think it might be the other way around. You provide for him. Food. Shelter. Tummy rubs."

"No, it's definitely me that owes him." She began to move around the room, opening the valves on the wall lamps and lighting them, one by one, until the room took on a soft glow. It was full dark outside now and the lights made the cabin seem like a cozy nest in the middle of the storm that raged right outside the windows.

"What can I do?"

"Could you feed Harvey? His food is in the top drawer over there and his dish is beside the fridge."

Valentino crossed the room, telepathic cat on his heels, and Erin could not help but notice the grace and athleticism she had seen on the mountain was still very evident in the way he moved. He carried himself with supreme confidence. He found the one-serve cat food and broke one open.

Harvey, at the sound of the package opening, yowled as if he hadn't been fed for a week. Valentino, somehow at home, rummaged around in another drawer until he found a spoon, leaned over the dish and scraped the food into it.

Harvey, impatient, kept pushing his hand out of the way, until Valentino laughed.

Erin retrieved her backpack and began taking its contents out. She left the bakery box with the heart-shaped cake in the pack. She had bought a candle for it that was shaped like the number one. She had planned a defiant celebration of finding herself single by having a Valentine's Day feast for one. Now, she didn't know what was going to happen. If the storm abated overnight, in the morning she would be taking Valentino down the slopes. Would she come back up? Somehow, celebrating being single on Valentine's Day had lost its appeal.

And if he was still there, she was not sure a Valentine's Day feast would be appropriate.

It occurred to Erin that it had been a long time since she had shifted a plan spontaneously. A long time since things had gone out of control in her world.

She told herself she liked it that way, the plans and predictability. That's why she worked in accounting. The world of numbers was safe and regulated. You applied formulas and got expected outcomes.

And yet, if she were honest, wasn't she rather enjoying this scenario?

Of not knowing what would happen next? Of things being slightly out of her control? Wasn't life suddenly and unexpectedly infused with a sense of adventure? Didn't it feel oddly and wonderfully exhilarating to be ensconced inside the cabin—stranded— with a gorgeous stranger?

Maybe that had been missing from her life.

Maybe Paul was correct when he had declared it all a little too dull and predictable, too boring. Maybe they had been—she had been—too young for that, to be acting like his parents.

"Steak it is," she muttered. Some of the items needed to go in the fridge and again she found herself in close quarters with Valentino.

The problem was, was her sanctuary ever going to feel the same after this? Or would his substantial presence—his laughter—leave a mark here, like a shadow?

He watched, grinning, as the cat gulped down the food. "There's no possible way you owe him," he decided.

"I do."

"Like he saved you from a burning building or something like that?"

"Something very like that," she said. "I've heard that you do not choose a cat, a cat chooses you."

Because of Paul's almost instant animosity to the cat, Erin had never told him that part, never trusted him with her vulnerability around the cat. Harvey wasn't just her pet. He was her family.

She moved quickly out of the kitchen, adjusted the thermostat in the living room and heard the comforting chuff of the propane-powered furnace kicking over. She finally shrugged off her coat and removed the carrier.

"Electric heat," he said, his surprise evident in his voice. But when she glanced at him, he didn't seem that interested in the furnace.

His eyes rested for a moment on her and she was glad for her choice of this sweater—white angora—this morning. It flattered her, a sweater that said—if sweaters could say such things—*Is this the sweater of a woman who has just been thrown over by her boyfriend?*

"Propane, but it does the trick. It's quite a modern igloo," she told him, annoyed at herself for being glad about the sweater. "We even have an indoor bathroom."

"Okay," he said, holding up his hands, cowboy surrender. "I think we've moved on from the igloo stuff. It's in the terms of the truce."

"I'll have to see a written copy."

His laugh, again, was so delightful. Warm. It filled the space with its richness and vibrancy.

"Anyway, I get it," he continued. "All the modern conveniences. No igloo stereotype. It actually seems more like something out of a fairy tale than an igloo."

Valentino was looking around with very real interest, and Erin followed his gaze, trying to see the familiar space through the eyes of a stranger.

"You mustn't be much of an expert on fairy tales," she told him, trying for a light tone. "Don't they usually take place in castles?"

With a prince, she reminded herself. It was embarrassingly easy to envision him, with his very evident confidence and composure, and with that exotic lovely accent, as the kind of prince who rode through the pages of fairy tales rescuing damsels in distress.

That, given her recent breakup, she might qualify as.

"Ah, castles," Valentino said with a shake of his head, pretending to be a man weary of such things. It was her turn to laugh.

He grinned back at her.

"This seems much preferable. The gingerbread cottage that Hansel and Gretel found in the woods," he elaborated.

She was sure her place on the mountain was just like thousands of other Canadian cottages, and yet she loved this space so much. A big stone fireplace dominated the room, the rough-hewn timber mantel littered with dusty ski trophies. Cozy furniture, covered in carelessly tossed plaid throws, circled around it, and stuffed bookshelves flagged both sides. An L-shaped kitchen with knotty-pine lower cabinets and open-shelving uppers took up one corner of the not very big space.

The main living area of the cabin was all one room, but this expanse inside the door had a large square of tile that could handle snow melting off clothes better than wood. On the wall behind the door was an abundance of pegs to hang wet clothing.

Still, the kitchen space suddenly seemed very tight. Erin was aware, again, of his size. Not just that he was taller than she, but that the sizzling masculine energy of him made her feel almost small and decidedly feminine. Small was something she had rarely felt! She had been five foot nine inches by the time she was fourteen.

His gaze fell on her and he smiled. "Minus the wicked child-eating witch, of course."

"Don't underestimate Harvey."

Just like that, they were laughing together, the soft light from the lanterns illuminating his skin tone, his mouth, his hair.

The man was absolutely, stunningly, gorgeous.

Gorgeous, and yet Erin was aware of that feeling again, that she had seen him before. She must have caught a glimpse of him in the village, though that didn't feel quite right. He did not seem like the kind of man a person— even one who'd had her dreams of a ring for Valentine's Day dashed—would forget seeing.

"What?" he asked her softly, and she realized, embarrassed, she was not just staring but being very obvious about it. She looked away quickly.

"I'm not sure. You look familiar," Erin admitted, glancing back at him.

"Do I?" he asked. Did the faintest of shutters lower over those amazing eyes? Was he being deliberately unforthcoming, as if he was accustomed to being recognized?

She realized he might be a model: that's

how gorgeous he was. Maybe she had seen him in a glossy magazine, in one of those supersexy ads for men's cologne or out-of-reach holidays on tropical beaches.

Except his sexiness was threaded through with a distinct dignity she was fairly certain was not for sale.

A film star, then? No, that wasn't quite right, either. Though he definitely had a star quality, a presence, he simply did not seem, in their short acquaintance, like a man who could pretend to be someone else for a living.

"You're probably mistaking me for Sebastian Avio," he said, naming a famous Mediterranean opera singer. His tone teasing, he said, "Lots of people do."

Only if Sebastian were thirty years younger than Valentino was, Erin thought.

"You should take off your pants," she said, trying to shift her awareness of him and seeing they were shedding a puddle on the floor.

"I bet you only say that to guys who remind you of Sebastian Avio," he said, his tone still teasing.

She could feel heat moving up her cheeks.

Surely, she could have thought of another way to word that? She didn't have to act as if she was a gauche schoolgirl in the presence of her secret crush.

"I'll expect you to serenade me later," she said, hoping to hide her discomfort with a bit of banter.

She didn't think she'd succeeded. He seemed faintly amused by her lack of composure and though he dropped the suspenders off his shoulders—making her even more aware of the broadness of them—he made no move to take off his ski pants. She realized, the heat growing in her cheeks, that if he only had an undershirt on under the jacket, that might be all he had on under the pants, too.

She turned away from him, vacating that tight-shared square of space as if she were in danger of catching fire. And it felt like she was!

"Go in to that second bedroom over there." She gestured at one of the doors off the main room. "There should be some clothes that will fit you in the closet."

"Thank you," he said.

"I'll just get the fire going," she said. "It will help warm it up more quickly in here and save on propane."

Not that she felt chilly. Embarrassingly warm, actually.

She busied herself with that, not looking at him as he moved by her, concentrating on preparing the paper and the kindling as if her life depended on it.

Something tingled at the back of her neck and Erin was aware that Valentino had not gone through to the back bedroom.

"'Enrique O'Rourke,'" he read off the trophies. "Wow."

"You know him?" she asked carefully.

"Of him. Who doesn't? A legend."

"My father," she admitted. "My grandfather started this resort."

"That explains it."

"Explains what?"

"Being allowed to keep a cat under your desk, for one. Your access to this Hansel and Gretel cabin in the middle of nowhere, for another. But more than that, how you ski. To be honest, when you first told me to try and keep up, I almost laughed out loud."

She turned to look at him and allowed herself a small smile. "I know. I could tell."

"Then that must have made it extra delightful for you to leave me eating your snow all the way here."

"It did," she said. And then they both laughed. The shared laughter, again, should have eased some tension she was feeling but it did not. It made her more aware of him, how easy and natural it felt to laugh with him. "You made me work at it, though. Leaving you eating my snow."

"I can swallow my pride for Enrique O'Rourke's daughter. I've never seen anybody ski like you. Except maybe him, now that I think about it."

"Thanks," she said. "He taught me, so our styles should be similar."

"It's as if you're folding yourself into the mountain somehow. Not on top of it, but part of it."

Was it his accent that made the words feel

like pure poetry? Whatever it was, it was lovely to be admired.

She felt hungry for it. Almost pathetically so. Her father had been stingy with compliments. And so had Paul.

She frowned. Was there a connection there?

"My father really never forgave me when I didn't want a career in skiing," she said then wondered what on earth had made her say that. It seemed way too personal.

But she glanced over her shoulder at Valentino again. He seemed to be contemplating her words gravely.

"I think maybe it is the nature of growing up to want different things than our parents," he said. "Be grateful you had a choice."

And then he, too, looked regretful, as if he had said too much or revealed too much.

Valentino left the room quickly. But no matter how she tried to concentrate on the fire in front of her, it felt as if another fire was starting.

Deep inside her.

Ridiculous, she told herself. She would

not be so weak and facile as to drown her sorrows over her recently shattered dreams in the deep and inviting sea of a stranger's charm.

She would not see it as a gift from the universe that she was stranded on the eve of Valentine's Day with someone named Valentino.

No. More like a test.

A challenge.

A trial of her strength of character.

One that she was resolved to pass.

CHAPTER FIVE

VALENTINO MADE HIS way down the hall to the bedroom. He was glad to be leaving the room that Erin was in. He was so *aware* of her. Her scent, the melody of her voice, the way that spun-with-gold hair tumbled over her shoulders, the sweet cling of that sweater.

But perhaps that awareness served as a distraction, because he was dealing with extremely weighty issues. He had escaped to Canada, to the Touch-the-Clouds resort, to make a decision.

In two weeks, his engagement to Angelica, princess of the neighboring island kingdom of Sorrento, was to be declared. The engagement event would be huge: a dinner where the formal announcement would be made, followed by a ball.

The palace had been in a frenzy of preparation for a month. And the people of Lorenzo knew it was coming. Never had there been a people so eager to celebrate life, and this would be their day, as well as his and Angelica's. Families would be picnicking on the palace grounds in anticipation of the balcony door opening, the king and queen stepping out onto it, he and Angelica following... They would cry for that first kiss, and their applause and cheers when it happened would be like a tidal wave of sound.

Angelica and Valentino had known each other since they were children. Their union was expected—it had been negotiated at her birth. He was now twenty-seven; she was twenty-two. The pressure had been building for two years. It was *time.*

He liked Angelica, and she liked him, in that comfortable way of old friends who had common ground and much of it. With her massive dark curls and her ready smile, she was beautiful, she was smart, and she was funny.

As far as arranged marriages went, Valentino was aware he had hit the jackpot.

And yet...he was chafing against this

choice being made for him. Still, he had been raised with a sense of duty and service. The needs of his island kingdom came before his own, and the alliance with Sorrento was imperative.

So why was he here? Why had he run away for a break in Canada? What good could it do? His fate was cast.

Valentino knew he would have accepted that. It was Angelica who had made him need to get away from it all. To clear his head. To gain perspective. To make a decision.

Their encounters, since they had hit puberty, had been closely chaperoned, and that day a week ago had been no different. Angelica had suggested a ride so that they could speak privately, the chaperone trailing behind them on a forest path.

Angelica loved to ride. She rode well and aggressively, but that day she had been subdued. He could tell Angelica's spark was being snuffed. She was *so* unhappy.

He had probed the unhappiness and, casting a guarded glance back, she had admitted she didn't feel ready to get married. She didn't feel ready to surrender to the expectations, which would be to produce a royal heir as soon as humanly possible.

"Don't take it personally," she had pleaded with him. "I love you, Valentino, but like a brother. I want to *feel* things. I want to feel so in love that it's as if I can't breathe when I'm not with that other person. I want to feel passion so hot, I become the flame, consumed by the heat of another person's touch."

It was his turn to cast a wary glance back at the chaperone. Because it was evident to him that Angelica already had met someone who made her feel exactly those things.

If she was already acting on them—and because of the flush in her cheeks and the smoldering in her dark eyes, of that he was fairly certain—she was going to do something rash.

If he called off the engagement before it was announced, could he protect her, a least a little bit, from the outrage and disappointment such a breakup would bring on the instigator? Would such a move actually free her or would her parents make new arrangements for her immediately?

Where did the good of his own kingdom fit into all of this? He was an only child. He knew—and was reminded constantly—the royal legacy fell on him.

He sighed, rolled his shoulders, trying to relieve the weight on them. He opened the closet door and looked at the clothing offerings, which seemed to lean toward plaid shirts and blue jeans.

A few minutes later, feeling as if he was in the most ridiculous costume, he went back out to the main room.

Erin, who had pinned her hair up into a loose bun, was in the kitchen. She glanced at him and grinned. He had the renegade thought that he wanted to free her hair, to pull those pins from it, one by one.

Valentino had always prided himself on his intense discipline, and so the wayward thought took him aback.

"You look very Canadian! You could pass yourself off as a lumberjack."

"My greatest ambition," he said, his tone

deliberately dry with no hint of *I want to pull the pins from your hair* in it. "I thought we were going to avoid Canadian stereotypes?"

She seemed to think about it. "Hmm. Is it in the agreement? Because, at the moment, you actually look like someone who could make an igloo."

He frowned at her. "I thought we had decided to leave that behind us?"

"I still haven't seen a written version," she teased him.

He contemplated that. Being teased. He decided he liked it, even as it made keeping a cool distance between them more difficult.

She glanced at him. "Okay, Val, come and make yourself useful."

Val? Make yourself useful? Again, Valentino was not sure he had ever been addressed quite like that in his life.

"How can I assist?" he asked.

"You can open the wine, and then I've got ingredients for a Mediterranean salad. You look like you'd be an expert on both those things."

Valentino was not sure what would make

him look like an expert on such things. The truth was, he had never opened a bottle of wine himself and he had certainly never made a salad. Mediterranean or otherwise. He was aware of a strange tension at the back of his neck, as if this were a test he needed to pass.

He went over to where the bottle of wine was on the kitchen table, trying to appear casual, like this was a workaday event for him. He regarded the bottle. It felt like the enemy.

He picked it up, trying to buy some time, studying the label. "A white," he said. "Sauvignon."

"It's a Canadian wine. From a British Columbian vineyard. I try to buy local. And I avoid screw caps."

All the more shame, he thought as he tentatively peeled away a silver-foil seal that revealed a cork firmly embedded in the neck of the bottle.

"The corkscrew is in the drawer over there." Erin gestured with her head.

The drawer was on the other side. He moved by her. Her scent tickled his nostrils.

She was seasoning a steak. Thank goodness, it looked as if one of them knew what they were doing.

He opened the drawer she had pointed to. It was full of items he didn't recognize, most of which looked like they had been designed to compel confessions in the torture chamber. The corkscrew, thankfully, was easily recognizable as the instrument used by the palace sommelier to open wine at the table.

Valentino grabbed it and went back to the bottle. He'd seen wine opened a zillion times, even if he had never done it himself. Confident now, he jammed the sharp tip into the cork. Then, putting a bit of weight on it, he twisted. Instead of coming out, the cork seemed to recede deeper beneath the lip and down the neck of the bottle. He must not have made sure the corkscrew was seated firmly enough. He pressed harder. The cork moved in the wrong direction.

The last time he'd opened a bottle of wine, it had been to smash it across the hull of a ship he had been invited to christen.

He had, on several official occasions, seen champagne uncorked with a sword. Valentino slid Erin a look. She wasn't paying the least bit of attention to him.

He bet uncorking a champagne bottle with a sword would impress her.

Did he *want* to impress her?

What man didn't want to impress a beautiful woman? And maybe, in that realization, he had already made up his mind about Angelica and what he needed to do. Because his entire life, he had been *taken,* and so had not felt awareness of women the way he now felt it about Erin.

Was it because of their circumstances? Escaping the storm, followed by the intense solitude of the situation he found himself in with a woman who was a stranger to him?

Or was it because, somewhere along the line—maybe from the moment he had stepped on the royal plane headed for Canada—he had already known what he'd needed to do.

"How's that coming?"

He put more weight into the corkscrew. The cork groaned down the neck of the bottle, letting loose suddenly and splashing into the wine, where it floated, baleful evidence of his failure.

"Um…done," he said, turning to her, blocking her view of the bottle with his body.

"Great. Can you start the salad? I'm just going to run out and turn on the grill. Unless you'd rather do that and I'll do the salad?"

He looked at the heap of ingredients on the kitchen counter at her elbow: colorful peppers, cucumbers, tiny tomatoes, olives, a block of white Feta cheese.

Everything was whole. He wasn't sure where to even begin tackling the vegetables. On the other hand, a grill? It sounded like a good way to blow them both up.

"I'm fine with the salad," he lied.

"Knives are in the block there."

She picked up the steak and opened the side door to a small porch. Wind tossed snow in before she quickly stepped out then nudged the door shut again with her hip.

He went over to the block and took out a knife. It was a huge, heavy thing that looked as if it might be good for a beheading. A pepper? Not so much. One by one, Valentino took out the knives and studied them. Finally, in the interest of self-preservation, he chose the least lethal-looking one.

Carefully, he cut the pepper in two and was astonished to find *stuff* inside it. He'd been unaware peppers contained *contents*.

Were the contents—tiny seeds and feltlike bits—part of the salad? He didn't recall ever seeing anything that looked like that in a salad before. He tested a seed and pared off some of the felty substance. He sampled that, too. It tasted just like a pepper to him. Was it possible he hadn't seen it in a salad before because of some form of *snobbery*? Surely common people ate everything that tasted good? Having revealed his own privilege to himself, he carefully chopped up the remainder of the pepper, including all its parts, and tossed it in the bowl Erin had provided.

The wind shook the cabin. He wished she would come in out of it. He should have volunteered to do the grilling. He didn't like it that she was out there and he was in here.

He abandoned the salad and went to the door. The wind pulled it out of his hands.

"Can I help you?" he asked her. "We could switch, if you're cold."

"No, almost done," she said, apparently unbothered by the wind and snow whistling around her. Delectable smells drifted to him. "How's the salad?"

"Great," he said, "I could probably have my own cooking show."

Wouldn't that give his mother conniptions? Still, Erin laughed, and he liked that.

He returned to the kitchen and focused on the block of Feta cheese. He was feeling quite pleased with how easy it all was when his knife hand slipped. He stared down at the cutting board in a kind of paralyzed horror.

Unless he was mistaken, that was a tiny tip of his finger sitting there among the crumbled cheese and red-pepper juices. He looked at his finger.

Blood was gushing from it.

The door opened. "Steak is done," she sang.

He turned to her, slowly, holding up his hand.

"I seem to have had a small mishap. It

doesn't bode well for my cooking show," he said.

She dropped the platter holding the steak. It landed on the floor with a clatter, and she rushed to him. She took his hand in her own.

He considered how all he should have felt was pain. But the pain had not set in yet and what he felt was her touch. Cool. Comforting.

"Let's just get that up," she said, guiding his hand to a more elevated position. Then she led him over to the couch. "Sit down. I'll get the first-aid kit. I think it's in the medicine cabinet. Don't worry. It's nothing."

He didn't feel worried at all, but he heard something shrill in her voice.

Erin tossed a dish towel at him. "It's clean," she said, "wrap it around your finger."

She looked pale and shaky as she disappeared down the hallway. Meanwhile, the cat had launched himself on the steak that had fallen to the floor and greedily had his face buried in it.

He got up and rescued the steak from the cat, who was clearly furious to have his prize taken from him. Valentino set the steak on the counter.

"Here it is," she said, coming back, waving a white, tin first-aid kit triumphantly. "What are you doing? You need to be sitting down." The shrillness in her voice had increased.

"It's just a scratch," he told her mildly.

"It's not!" she said. "Sit!"

He sat. She knelt at his feet and placed the kit on a hassock. She rummaged through it. He studied the top of her head, the sun-threaded gold of her hair. One of those pins that was holding that bun together was loose. Just the tiniest nudge with his finger...

"There," she said. She had items laid out on the hassock like a field doctor preparing to do surgery. She closed her eyes, inhaled a deep breath, and opened them again.

She took his hand in hers. She was trembling as she peeked inside the dish towel. He was the one who was hurt!

The towel had become quite saturated with blood in a very short time and, if it were possible, Erin paled even more.

"Are you afraid of blood?" he asked.

"I'm afraid you're going to bleed to death," she said, but the denial was weak.

"You're afraid of blood."

"I don't think *afraid* is the right word," she said, not denying it this time. Well, how could she? Her face was as white as that snow outside and she was trembling. "But—"

She took another deep, fortifying breath and finished unwrapping the dish towel from his hand. Blood spurted out the end of his finger. She hastily wrapped it again.

"I can do it myself," he said.

"No! I'll do it." She took off the towel again. This time she had a wipe ready and quickly cleaned the wound. It looked as if he had managed to remove the entire pad from the tip of his finger.

"Hey," he said, "that'll be handy if I commit a crime. No fingerprints."

She did not seem amused at his attempt to distract. Her face determined, her tongue caught between her teeth, she began to wind gauze tightly around his entire finger, crisscrossing the tip. His finger was beginning to look like a marshmallow, but she was being so brave—for him—that he said nothing.

Finally, she reached for her carefully laid-out medical tape, leaned close and began to wind it around his finger. He couldn't help it... He reached for that errant pin, felt the silk of her hair under his fingertips.

Pulling that pin was like pulling one card from a shaky house of them. Her hair tumbled down.

Much better, he thought.

She glanced up at him, wide-eyed, her eyes as green as a piece of perfect jade catching the light.

"It was falling out," he lied.

He immediately felt contrite. She looked even worse than before, shaky as an olive tree leaf in a faint breeze. Of course she would look like that! A strange man removing pins from her hair. It was a terrible faux pas.

"Here," he said, getting up, crouching beside her, putting his shoulder under her. "Your turn to sit. Let me look after dinner."

"You're the injured one," she protested, though her protest lacked vehemence.

He held out his gigantic white-wrapped finger to her. "All fixed. I'll take it from here. You relax. Thank you for doing that. Especially since you are afraid of blood."

"Since I was a child," she admitted.

Thank goodness! Her current state of wooziness seemed to have nothing to do with his fingers, acting separately from his brain, reaching for her hair.

Given the intensity of the circumstances, he had to make sure he didn't do anything so inappropriate again.

Valentino spun away from Erin, eager to put a bit of distance between them while he regained his sanity.

CHAPTER SIX

ERIN WATCHED AS Valentino moved away to the humble kitchen. She should protest his offering to get dinner, especially now that he was handicapped with a giant, white-wrapped finger. Maybe she had gotten a little carried away with the first aid—but she hadn't wanted any blood to leak through that bandage. She felt woozy enough already.

Embarrassingly, she had been dizzy even before he had touched her hair. Good grief, she had gone from faintly light-headed to full swoon in the blink of an eye.

Harvey stalked him into the kitchen and waited, hopefully, under the counter for a drop. There was something endearing about watching Valentino in the kitchen. For a man with such grace and athleticism on the ski hill, he now looked like a duck out of water, completely unsure of himself.

After contemplating his options for a moment, he started with the steak, which he inspected. He rinsed it under the tap and then blotted it. She remembered it had fallen on the floor.

"You were planning this meal for yourself only," he noted, cutting the steak, which was not large, in two. "Thank you for sharing your supper with me."

"Of course!" she said. She was glad the heart-shaped cake with its embarrassing *"1"* candle was still hidden in her pack. "The dressing for the salad is in the fridge."

As she watched, he finished up the salad and then plated the food and poured them each a glass of wine. He found a metal tray and put everything on it. Balancing it carefully, he brought it over to her. He shoved aside her first-aid supplies on the hassock, set the tray down and settled on the couch.

The couch wasn't large—more like a love seat—and his thigh touched hers. An electrical current of awareness jolted through her.

"M'lady," he said. He leaned over and took a wineglass off the tray with the hand that was not bandaged. He awkwardly handed it to her. He took the other one.

"A toast," he said.

She lifted her glass.

"To surprises."

"To surprises," she agreed.

They clinked glasses and she took a sip, as did he.

"This is really a nice wine," he said. "It's dry but fruity. I almost get an overtone of lime in it."

He seemed to know quite a bit more about wine than she did. To her distress, Erin felt something chunky in her mouth. She tried to figure out what it was and what to do. She had an awful decision to make. Spit it out or swallow it?

"Ah, there was a little problem with the cork," he said, noticing her expression just as she made a decision to swallow.

"It happens," she said, setting down the glass. He handed her a plate and some utensils. She regarded his offer solemnly, took her fork and poked through the pepper part of the salad. It seemed, like the wine, to have foreign components in it.

He was watching her, eager for her to sample it.

"Oh, sorry, I was just wondering—"

"Yes?"

"What exactly is this?"

He regarded the item she was holding on her fork. "Pepper insides." He blinked at her with elaborate innocence. "Don't you use them?"

"Not generally."

"We do. In my country."

She felt her lips twitch at so obvious a lie. "Don't take up poker," she suggested.

"I happen to be an excellent poker player!"

"Have you ever made a salad before?"

"I have not," he admitted. His lips twitched, too.

"Or cut vegetables?"

"No."

"It's a good thing I didn't ask you to chop wood," she decided. "You probably would have lost a hand."

"Except for the fact that's true, I'd be insulted," he said.

"What exactly were you planning on doing if I had a baby?"

"Boil water!"

And then they were both laughing.

The steak, despite his running it under the tap, had grit in it, The wine had the odd piece of cork, and the seed-ridden salad was possibly the chunkiest she had ever eaten.

But with the storm deepening and howling outside, and the warmth and the wine inside, it felt so good. As good as anything in Erin's life had felt for a long, long time.

Valentino took away their plates and fetched the rest of the wine. He refilled their glasses.

"Tell me about where you're from," she invited. A voice inside her added, *And what you do, and who you love. Valentino, tell me every little intriguing thing about you.*

"I come from a small island in the Mediterranean, Lorenzo del Toro. Have you heard of it?"

Had she? She thought so, but the wine and

the warmth of the fire, her stomach full, his gaze touching her face, made her not very sure of anything about the world. "I'm not sure."

"Ah, well, let me take you there." And just like that, his voice swept her from the little cottage and the storm that raged outside the door.

They were in a sun-drenched land of olive groves and vineyards, ancient buildings and quaint stone cottages and cobbled streets. The flowers were so colorful and so abundant that the air was perfumed by them. Donkeys pulling carts and shepherds herding sheep blocked narrow country roads.

"And what do you do there?"

"I'm in the family business," he said. Did she hear a note of caution in his voice?

"And what is your family business?"

Again, did she sense hesitation?

Valentino took a sip of wine. He refilled her glass. He looked at the fire. "We manage a number of enterprises," he finally said. "The business is hundreds of years old."

"Do you like it?"

He thought about that for a minute. "I'm not sure I've ever thought of it in terms of liking or not liking. It is what I was born into."

"That's what you meant when you said to be grateful I had a choice about whether or not to follow in my father's footsteps? That you did not? That you were expected to go into the family business?"

"Yes," he said. "That's what I meant. But enough about me now. Tell me about you. About growing up with a father like yours."

Maybe it was because of the wine. Or maybe it was because their experience was a little like being trapped with a stranger on an elevator given the relentless storm outside, but there was a kind of instant intimacy developing between them. However, there was a time limit on this.

He lived around the world in a place she was never likely to go. After the storm abated, she was probably never going to see him again.

Why did that feel, already, like a sadness?

Still, Erin found herself confiding in him

about growing up in the crazy world of professional skiing with a very famous father.

"I had skis on practically as soon as I could walk. And I loved to ski—and still do. It's my place where I feel one hundred percent engaged. Present. Alive.

"But, to my father's great disappointment, I wasn't interested in putting my natural ability, which I had inherited from him and my grandfather before him, to work for me. I'd raced since I was tiny. When you're small and everyone gets a trophy, it was fine, and fun.

"But I grew to hate it," she said softly. "There was too much pressure on me because I was the great Enrique's daughter.

"Remember when Sebastian Avio's daughter wanted a career in music? And everyone kept comparing her to him? It was like that. I mean… I was just a kid and I was being interviewed on the evening news after a race.

"Plus, even at the junior levels—we're talking under ten—racing brought out this horrible competitive side in my dad. He became my mentor and my coach. I could do nothing right. If I won a race, he started dissecting how I could have done better immediately. If I lost, he'd be furious, pouting and sulking.

"It took what I loved the most and changed it into something I could barely recognize. So, at age eleven, I stood firm and told him I was leaving my career as a ski racer behind me. I quit. Nothing was ever the same between us after that, as if he couldn't handle it that my life didn't belong to him.

"In retrospect, with everything going on in the family, I think ski racing had become just one more pressure. One I was ill-prepared to handle."

"What was going on in your family?"

Erin thought she had really said quite enough. And yet there was something about the way he was looking at her and listening to her that felt like an elixir: if she drank of this cup, she would feel better.

That was astonishing because she hadn't been aware she *wasn't* feeling okay. Harvey jumped on her lap and she scratched his ears. Valentino reached over and scratched his ears, too.

It was such a nice moment. It had a lovely intimacy to it. Their total isolation from the whole world made her feel as if she could tell him anything.

Not just as if she could tell him anything, but as if she had carried a burden too long by herself and this stranger had come along and unexpectedly offered to share it.

During the tumultuous years of her childhood, and just before they'd called it quits for good, her parents' relationship had been more volatile than ever.

"My mother," she said softly, "had just discovered my father had yet another love interest. The days were filled with the sounds of slammed doors and shouted arguments. So many accusations and so much pain. Love that had burned too hot had finally consumed everything in its flame, destroying everything around it."

Erin cast a look at Valentino. That's where mooning over someone's lips got you. That was where passion led.

"That's why I said I owed the cat," she confessed. "Harvey chose me. He showed up on our doorstep and became my shadow, just when I needed him most. Even back then, when he was young and handsome, silky-furred and svelte, Harvey hated absolutely everyone. Except me.

"This silly old guy reserved his absolute devotion for me, at the time in my life when I could do nothing right in my father's eyes and our family unit was exploding around me. Maybe some people—maybe most people—would see my loyalty to the cat as odd, but he gave me hope when the world seemed utterly hopeless.

"The cat was my constant as I moved between my parents' ever-shifting households, partners, locations.

"I fell asleep at night, in whichever house I was in, often with my pillow soaked in tears. But the cat curled in close to me, his purr reassuring and solid."

Solid. Stable.

She cast a glance at Valentino. His hand had gone still on the cat's fur. He was frowning at the fire.

She had said *way* too much.

But when he looked away from the fire and at her, his dark eyes were even darker, shadowed with sadness, as if he had, indeed, taken some of her burden as his own. Erin felt something she had not felt for so long.

A trust in this man beside her unfurled within her.

"And tell me," he said softly, "what all this has to do with you and your cat bringing a feast up here to have Valentine's Day alone."

She wasn't sure if she hated it or loved it. That he saw, immediately, how her tumultuous childhood and being alone right now were linked.

"Naturally, after all that excitement and chaos growing up, I longed for what other people seemed to have. Family as a place of refuge. Calm.

"I thought I was going to build that with my boyfriend, Paul, because his family was the polar opposite of mine. A mother and father who never seemed to say a cross word after thirty years together. Who had roast chicken on Sunday nights. Who belonged to the bowling league.

"What I didn't realize was that while I'd been enchanted with all of that, Paul had felt oppressed by it, as if his family's solid life was a trap he was being walked into. By me."

Her voice dropped to almost a whisper. "His parting words to me were that it was all just too boring."

Valentino stiffened beside her. "Boring?" he said, his voice soft and deliciously incredulous. And then indignant. "Boring?"

"Which I inferred meant *I* was boring. He certainly acted like it. I mean, near the end, he would barely look up from his phone."

Valentino snorted with an outrage on her behalf that Erin found quite sumptuous. "He wouldn't look up from his phone and he thought *you* were boring?"

"Well, I mean I know I'm not exactly a barrel of excitement. Look at me, a career accountant."

"Look at how you ski!"

"He wasn't a skier."

"You were with somebody who didn't share that passion with you? It *is* you."

It would be easy to just lap up his defense

of her, but she felt driven to prove Paul might have had a point.

"I do have a kind of unusual attachment to my cat."

"He didn't like your Harvey," Valentino intoned with a sad shake of his head. "How could he not love the cat who saved you?"

Erin realized she had never shared Harvey's role in her life with Paul. A few hours in, this man already knew more about her secrets than Paul had in the entire length of their relationship.

Wasn't that telling her something?

As was the look on Valentino's face as he gazed at her. It felt as if she was being *seen* and, whatever Valentino saw, he did not seem to think it was boring. His hand left the cat's fur. It cupped her chin. His thumb scraped across her cheek. His eyes held hers.

"A man who could be bored with you is not even a man," he said firmly, his soft, accented voice as sensual as the touch of lips on the back of her neck.

She laughed a little nervously. Despite the snowed-in-together confidences, there was a larger truth here they both needed to acknowledge.

"You don't even know me, Valentino."

Still, she didn't try to move away from his hand, and he looked stunned that she would suggest that!

"I do," he said fiercely. "No man could look into your eyes and not know you. And no man could look into your eyes and ever have a moment's boredom. Not unless there was something lacking in him."

"I'm not the kind that inspires great passions," she protested. But she was aware of how suddenly, and dangerously, she *wanted* to be that woman.

Valentino snorted, moved his hand from her cheek, tucked her hair behind her ear.

"Not inspire great passions?" he said, his hand still smoothing her hair. "A painter would die to paint you. The sun in that hair. That look on your face. A man could get lost in your eyes. He could dive into them as if they were a cool pond on a hot summer day. He could let what is in them fold over him, soothe him, hold him, heal the parts of him that are wounded."

Erin stared at him, her heart hammering so hard she thought it would break from her chest. This close, she could see the faint stubble beginning on his chin and cheeks. She was aware of the scent of him, as crisp, as exotic, as she imagined the land he came from would be.

Everything he was saying about her eyes held true for his own. Fringed with an incredible abundance of sooty lash, they were as rich as dark chocolate, melted. They held depth and compassion, and mystery. A mystery a woman could spend her whole life solving...

He dropped his hand from her hair and abruptly created some space between them on the sofa.

"I'm sorry." His voice was a scrape of pure gravel. "That was way too personal. I'm not generally—" he looked genuinely abashed "—given to poetry." Then his eyes found hers again and he sighed with a kind of surrender.

"But that is what your eyes do," he said softly. "They call out to the poet in a man."

Oh, God, something in her was absolutely melting. They'd had too much wine, obviously. Both of them. Too much wine, and the feeling of being safe inside, together, as the storm raged on, was creating a natural affinity between them.

Even knowing those things, even knowing what they were experiencing was akin to being shipwrecked on an island together, it felt as if she was being seen in a way she had not ever been seen before.

And she wanted, suddenly and urgently, to be a person she had never been before.

Not boring.

But the one Valentino had just seen. Fully a woman. A sensual woman who called to the painter in a man, and the poet.

She wanted to embrace the adventure of finding out who she really was, if there were hidden facets of herself that she had never discovered.

It felt as if maybe she never would discover those hidden things if she did not say *yes* to what was right in front of her, in this moment in time. She wanted, not to shrink away from the power he said she had, but to embrace it, to uncover it, to unleash it.

She wanted to get lost in his eyes and say *yes* to whatever hid in their dark, compelling depths. Empowered by what he had said, she reached out and traced that plump split in his lip. At that touch, her heart felt as if it had slumbered.

Not just now, but with Paul, through her entire life, a protective layer around it that fell away like a thin layer of ice tapped with a hammer.

Valentino went very still. His eyes were steady on her face, full of knowing, full of hunger. And then he opened his mouth ever so slightly, just enough to nibble the finger that explored his lip.

A kind of insanity overtook her. A delicious loss of mind. Years of careful control evaporated as if they had been a muddy puddle waiting for the heat of the sun. Years of feeling as if she knew exactly who she was vanished like a mirage in the desert.

This was who she really was.

This was who she was always meant to be.

She leaned into him. And she took his lips with her own. His hands came up and bracketed each side of her head, tangled in her hair. He pulled his mouth away from her and whispered endearments in her ear in another language, his words soft with the poetry of the heart.

Then his mouth found hers again. Urgent. Questing.

And Erin's world was changed for all time. Even as she took his lips, she knew whatever was happening, she could never, ever, go back to the way it had been—and she had been—before this moment.

"Love me," she whispered against his lips. In her tone, things she had never heard before. Urgency. Desperation. Hunger. "Please."

"How could I do anything but?" he whispered back.

CHAPTER SEVEN

VALENTINO PICKED UP ERIN, cradling her against his chest as he strode down the short hallway into the darkness of the bedroom. She wrapped her arms around the beautiful column of his neck. She did not consider herself a small woman, and her ex had consistently made her feel as if she came from the land of the giants.

Yet, in Valentino's arms, in the effortless way in which he had lifted her and now carried her, she felt light as a feather, exquisitely feminine and desirable. She felt cherished. She felt he was like a warrior who had found his way home to the maiden who had waited, her candle lit, believing he would come, even before she had known his name.

If they wanted light, the lamps would have to be lit. But she liked the room as it was, the atmosphere dimly lit and dreamlike.

He set her tenderly into the billowy embrace of a white down comforter. The bed was a beautiful, intricately carved antique that had come with her great-grandparents from Norway in the eighteen hundreds.

It felt right and good. That this bed that had been woven into generations of her family's love stories, was where she would come to know Valentino in every way possible for a woman to know a man.

He stood over her and as her eyes adjusted to the deep shadows, she saw that he was staring down at her with a gaze both tender and fierce. His hand moved to the buttons on his shirt.

He had forgotten his bandaged finger and so had she, and they both laughed, breathless with anticipation and delight, as she scrambled to kneeling and he came to the edge of the bed. She undid the buttons of the shirt one by one, her eyes never leaving his face.

When she was done, she got off the bed to stand before him. She peeled the plaid fabric off him, over his shoulders, caressing the naked skin beneath the shirt as it was revealed to her. Finally, she tugged each arm out of its sleeve. The shirt dropped from her fingers to the ground, leaving her to stare with stunning avarice at what she had unveiled.

Valentino was absolutely perfect. The weak light from the gas lamps in the other room outlined the carved lines of his arms, powerful triceps and biceps, illuminated the broadness of his back, and spilled over the wideness of his shoulders. She had thought, because of his abundance of curls, that he might have a hairy chest, but he did not.

His skin was taut and golden, hair-free, molded to the perfect plain of a deep chest, the pebbles of his nipples, stretched over the slight rise of his ribs and the slender, hard curve of his belly.

She reached out tentatively and laid her hand, splayed, across his heart, and the sensual silk of his warm skin made her mouth go dry. She could feel the steady, strong beating of his heart under her fingertips.

He captured her hand, pulled it to his

mouth, anointed the inside of her wrist with his lips and then tugged her yet closer to him.

His hands found the hem of her sweater and he hesitated.

His voice low, he asked, "Are you—?"

The sentence did not need finishing. Was she sure? Was she ready? She had never been more sure or more ready in her life.

Her tongue flicked to lips that suddenly felt dry and his eyes fastened there. She nodded.

There was nothing clumsy now, not even with that bandage on his finger. He peeled the sweater up and over her head, her hair hissing from the static as her head popped free. He tossed the sweater away and smiled, taking in what he had revealed.

Slowly, tenderly, he smoothed her hair with the fingertips of his unbandaged hand, owning her in some way with that possessive gesture that made her mouth even drier, her breath even more ragged, her need even more acute.

Valentino looked at her, a man who could never get his fill, a man with eyes that would paint her. Words spilled from his lips, tender, soft, in a language so universal she did not need to know the words to appreciate their meaning.

He had come to worship at the altar of her femininity.

And she at the altar of his masculinity.

They had entered a dance as ancient and as sacred as the earth itself.

Little by little, slowly, with reverence, the rest of their clothes fell away, until it was just the two of them, at the beginning of time, exploring each other with wonder. With curiosity. With awe. Exploring the miracle and the marvel of a man and a woman.

Together.

Finally, when the urgency would not be denied any longer, they tumbled together deep into the embrace of the bed. Their bodies met, fused, entwined, melted. They climbed, and climbed, and climbed, exploring the jagged, endless precipices until finally they stood on the edge of a cliff.

And then, unhesitatingly, they leaped off.

Falling into the abyss of pure sensation. Joining the motes of cosmic dust that made up the stars. Joining what had always been; that place that did not acknowledge space or time.

Exhausted, content, they folded their arms around each other and, despite the storm that screamed under the eaves and at the windows, they slept the deep sleep of two people completely satiated.

Erin awoke in the morning to the sound of the storm still raging outside, as if it wanted to pick up the cabin, twirl it in the air and smash it down somewhere else on the mountain.

Her confidence in the sturdiness of the cabin strengthened her sense of contentment, her awareness of how her skin felt under the deep warmth of the down comforter and beneath the heat of Valentino's arm. It felt as if her whole body was tingling; the way it might feel going from a hot shower into a snowbank.

Valentino was on his side, one arm thrown possessively across the nakedness of her midriff, one leg pinning her legs as if, subconsciously, he had wanted to hold her to him, prevent her escape.

But she was a willing captive.

Erin turned her head to study him, aware that a smile amused her lips as she took in the wild corkscrew of messy curls, the stubble on his chin, the flawless perfection of skin that looked perpetually sun-kissed.

She waited for the sense of recrimination to come.

She had, after all, just spent the night—made wild love—to a complete stranger. And yet what she felt as she looked at Valentino was not recrimination. She did not feel that he was a stranger, but that she *knew* him as deeply and as completely as she had ever known another person.

She certainly did not feel any sense of shame. Or guilt.

But freedom.

Tenderness.

Delight.

She was marooned on a desert island with him and she had given herself, completely, to what the moment offered. And she was glad. It was very much like giving herself to the mountain when she skied.

It was a surrender. A great knowing that nature was, always, a more powerful force than you. But the surrender was such a joyous one, it became a dance.

Remembering what had passed between them last night, Erin was aware she felt grateful. She had almost given herself over to a life where this side of her—playful, passionate, curious, sensual—might have gone undiscovered.

Valentino stirred against her. His warm breath tickled her skin. She watched as the dark tangle of those lashes flicked open and revealed the melted-chocolate sensuality of his gaze.

She held her breath. Would he be the one who returned them to sanity? Would he be the one who pointed out that they were strangers? Who questioned if they had gone too fast, too far, too soon? Who asked if they were acting like survivors, exhilarated by the nectar of life, of being alive, without any care for tomorrow?

But when his gaze found her face, the drowsy smile—of welcome, of recognition—lit him from within.

His hands found her neck and tugged her to him, and he wished her good morning with a kiss that held back nothing.

Despite the fact they were in the tiniest of cabins—trapped here, really—with the storm still raging around them, it felt as if the whole world opened to her.

Embraced her.

Sighed for her.

This, then, was how it was meant to be.

Valentino was a man who had collected exhilarating experiences like other men might collect stamps.

He had skied some of the highest and most inaccessible peaks in the world. He had—over the objections of his security team and his family—embraced the sport of skydiving, throwing himself into the endless, vast blue of the sky. He had raced his horse at breakneck speeds over polo fields and along forest paths. He had a powerboat that, at optimum speed, would lift its nose and skim the water as if it were flying.

Valentino had experienced every thrill that being born to his station in life would allow.

And he was aware, now, as he watched Erin move through the kitchen with such grace, that every one of those things had been superficial compared to the exhilaration he felt, trapped by a snowstorm, and just being in the same room with her, sharing the same air as her.

Her hair was in a glorious mess and she had on a man's housecoat that would open every now and then to give him an enticing glimpse of long, long legs. There was a glow about her that could warm a man, as if he had come into a welcoming hearth on a cold day.

Which I have, Valentino told himself. The fire was spitting in the hearth, throwing heat. He had put on only the jeans from yesterday; his chest was bare. It was a kind of freedom to walk around in a state of half dress. And besides, just as he kept sneaking peeks at Erin's legs, she kept sneaking looks at him.

She leaned over and fed Harvey, murmuring to the cat, her fingers caressing his willing ears for a moment before she straightened.

Even that small gesture told Valentino who she was. Gentleness in her. A connection to living things. An ability to immerse herself in the simplicity and gifts of each moment.

And coinciding with those things, the incredible contrast of a passionate fire that burned white-hot within her.

Should I tell her who I am?

It felt as if he should. Right this moment, before it went any further. She needed to know what she was getting herself into. She needed to have a choice.

But it would be the worst kind of distraction. It felt as if she already knew who he was. Better than anyone else, because she did not know about the titles, his position in life, his family. The mantle of royalty. For the first time in his life, Valentino felt *seen*.

He was not aware he had waited his entire life for that.

Until now. Until it happened.

She came and put coffee in front of him. His senses were so heightened that the aroma felt as if it could overwhelm him. But then that sensation receded as her hand found his hair and she combed it with her fingertips, tenderly, possessively. He turned his head and nipped at her hand.

Telling her the truth of who he was faded from his consciousness. It could wait. With the storm continuing outside—the snow so thick when they looked out the windows, they could not see across the clearing this morning—it felt as if there would be plenty of time for everything that needed to be said between them.

She laughed at his playful nip, and that glow intensified. She was alight with life.

"Breakfast," she said. She put a tiny heart-shaped cake down in front of him and sank into the chair beside his.

It was obviously a cake that had been made

for Valentine's Day. It had a candle on it, shaped like a number one.

"What does the candle represent?" he asked.

"Me, alone on Valentine's Day," she said. Her laughter deepened, the light flowing out of her to embrace the whole room. And him.

"But now you're not," he teased her, pointing out the obvious. "So, should we throw the candle away?"

"No." She lit it. "It can represent firsts of all kinds. Make a wish before we blow out the candle."

"I wish," he whispered, "that this could last forever."

She was silent for a moment, her brow furrowed.

"What?"

"You're not supposed to tell anyone your wish. Then it doesn't come true."

He was taken aback by this North American superstition, but then realized how deeply he was under a spell. Because, obviously, it could not come true regardless. This could not last forever. Nothing could.

The storm that rattled the cabin, that made him a grateful prisoner, would end.

"You make the wish, then," he said.

"I think you're only allowed one wish per cake."

"Too many rules," he decided, and the solemn moment evaporated, replaced by their laughter.

They blew out the candle together, their breaths mingling. She took up a knife she had brought over to the table with her.

Even he, with his inexperience at all things domestic, could see the knife was too large for the task.

"Hey, be careful with that thing," he said.

"Don't worry, I'm not about to trust you with it."

And then, to his surprise, instead of cutting the cake, she lowered that cleaver-like knife as if it were an ax. She chopped the cake into chunks instead of slices.

"I'm taking a lesson from your salad making," she told him.

"But I was going to start a cooking show," he said as he gazed at the mess of chocolate cake and icing on the plate.

She laughed. "Things don't have to be perfect to be…well, perfect."

She proved how true that was. Instead of getting plates and forks, she picked up a chunk of the cake with her fingers and shifted herself onto his lap. He opened his mouth to her then licked the icing off her fingers. The massacred confection tasted of ambrosia, dreams and promises.

Following her lead, he dug his fingers into the rich darkness of the cake and fed it to her. And then he licked the icing off her lips.

Her turn. She took a chunk of that cake and pressed it into the nakedness of his chest.

Valentino groaned as she lowered her head and cleaned it off with her lips.

Soon there was cake everywhere and they were chasing each other around the small cabin, the cat hiding under the couch, miffed.

And then they were in the shower together.

And then back in bed.

He knew he had to tell her. But again, with the storm unabated outside, it felt as if time would expand endlessly and present him the perfect opportunity.

Obviously now, with the fires stoked in both of them, would be absolutely the wrong time.

Erin woke for the second time that day. She stretched like a cat, feeling luxurious, content, satiated. She was not sure she had ever felt this *full*.

She glanced at Valentino, sleeping on his back, his profile beautiful, his lashes as thick and sooty as a chimney brush, the whiskers darkening yet more on his face. She studied that yummy split in his full bottom lip. How could he seem so familiar already? How could it already seem as if she could not lead a life without him in it?

Crazy thoughts. This kind of thing, whether she wanted to acknowledge it or not, was a fling brought on by the intensity of circumstances, a powerful chemistry between a man and a woman stranded alone.

There was no point in contemplating the future. It would just ruin everything. For once in her life, she was going to give up her need to be in control, to figure out what happened next, to try to make her world safe and predictable.

For once in her life, Erin would do the unthinkable: go with the flow. Just see what happened next. Have no plan. She would immerse herself in the moment.

Her eyes drifted to the window. Still snowing. Still snowing hard. But she detected a difference in the ferocity of the storm, an abatement of the wind. Few people would attempt the mountain on a day like this, but she was so familiar with the slopes, she knew she could find the way down, effortlessly, to the ski village at the bottom of the mountain.

But she did not feel ready to let go. Not just yet.

His wish filled her. *I wish that this could last forever.*

Wrapping herself in the sheet, she got up and gave Valentino's bare skin a smack with her hand.

"Get up, lazybones. We can't sleep all day."

He opened his eyes and looked at her idly. With such frank appreciation, it made her skin tingle.

"I have awoken to a goddess," he murmured and then, pretending he was cranky, added, "Why can't we sleep all day?"

He wagged his eyebrows at her with wicked meaning that had nothing to do with sleep.

"We'll be awake all night if we sleep all day," she said.

He lifted that wicked eyebrow a little higher. "I can think of things to do if we're awake all night."

She smacked his bare skin again and he winced with exaggerated hurt.

"Get up. We should go outside and play. You told me about your island home. It's warm there all the time. How often do you have opportunities to play in the snow? Have you ever built a snowman? Had a snowball fight? Made a snow angel?"

"I have not done any of those things," he admitted.

"Then you must."

Before the spell is broken. Before the reality of nothing lasting forever sets in. Before the storm ends. A voice inside her insisted on reminding her, despite her intentions, of a future that loomed ahead, unknown.

"To tell you the truth, I'd rather—" he waggled his eyebrows at her.

"Stop it." She smacked him again. He held his arm with pretend hurt.

"Okay, okay. A snowman it is," he grumbled. "But this had better be good."

"Oh," she promised, "it will be."

And it was. Erin had never been with someone who had not experienced snow as a matter of course, as a life reality for four or five months of every year.

Valentino had skied, yes, but, just as she had guessed, he had never *played* in snow. They couldn't get a mitten over his bandaged hand, so she had carefully wrapped it in a scarf. And then, laughing, she'd had to unwrap it so he could get his jacket on.

She put Harvey's cushioned basket outside on the covered porch so that he could hear that she was near, and he settled into it contentedly.

The snow was still falling thickly, but the wind had stopped and it had warmed since yesterday. The ground cover was turning from the dry powder that everyone came here to ski, to the heavy, wet snow that was perfect for winter activities.

"First," she said, "Snowman Building 101."

"I think, in the interest of equal opportunities, we should build a snowwoman."

She scowled at him with feigned fierceness. "Are you going to be difficult?"

"Of course!"

"You take a little ball of snow—"

"Snowwomen don't have—"

"Stop it," she warned him, but she was snickering. "You take some snow and you shape it like this."

"That looks like a ball. I thought we had decided—"

"This is serious!" she scolded him. Of course, it was anything but.

She showed him how to put the ball in the snow and push it. Because the snow was so sticky and wet, it stuck to itself and the ball she was making got very large very quickly. She had to get down on her knees and put her shoulder into it.

"A girl who likes big balls," he said approvingly, and she took a rest, scooped up some snow and tossed it at him. It hit him right in the face. He wiped it off with elaborate carefulness. And then he scooped up some snow and stalked toward her.

She got up from her snowball and took off running, aware that nothing was going to go as she'd planned, not even building a snowman. She gave herself over to the simple joy of being open to the moment and to whatever direction the energy between them turned itself in.

Erin did what had been demanded of her since the moment she'd met him. She gave up control.

Screaming with laughter, she tried to put distance between them, but the snow was just too deep. His legs were so much longer and more powerful.

He caught her easily, took her arm, spun her around. He pulled off her toque and smooshed his handful of snow into her hair. Then he tried to put the toque back on over it.

"That wasn't even a proper snowball," she said, wiggling away from him.

"You know, you seem preoccupied with the subject of balls."

She chortled. He threw back his head and laughed. The snowflakes danced around them, shimmering, as if they were the universal manifestation of the rhapsody unfolding between Erin and Valentino.

CHAPTER EIGHT

ERIN SCOOPED UP a handful of snow, smoothing it into a hard sphere with her hands. The cold sank through her mittens, making her fingertips tingle almost as much as they had as they'd explored the heated surface of Valentino's skin.

"Do you know what this is?" she asked him, trying for menace in her tone.

"Um, the item of your preoccupation?" he asked, grinning boyishly. When he smiled like that—carefree, mischievous, charming—it melted her.

"Wrong! Deadly missile."

She let fly. He ducked. The snowball whistled harmlessly by him. He straightened and the boyish expression was put away. He looked at her with pretend sternness—a look at least as sexy as his boyish one—and held up his scarf-wrapped hand.

"Do you think that's fair? Throwing things at a one-armed man?"

"All is fair…" she said, stopping herself just short of finishing the expression. *All is fair in love and war.*

She was certain that Valentino completed the phrase inside his head, just as she did. Because, suddenly, standing there, the snow collecting on their hats and coats and eyelashes, the world became very silent. And very, very still.

It felt as if a huge secret had just whispered itself out of the realm of mystery and into the realm of reality.

She broke the spell. She scooped up another handful of snow, and he took her cue, running, shouting taunts at her in two languages with a smattering of French thrown in for good measure. She let fly with the snowball. It hit him in the middle of his back. He fell as if he had been shot, and Erin dissolved into giggles. Then he rose and turned to her with yet another sexy look. This time, the warrior ready to win the battle.

He caught on to the art of the snowball

fight very quickly, soon making deadly snowballs and aiming them at her with accuracy born of natural athleticism. The clearing soon echoed with their shouts, their taunts, their laughter.

They chased each other through the snow until they were breathless, panting for air. Until they could not run one more step.

Erin surrendered first, flopping into the snow on her back. He lay down his snow weapons and collapsed into the deep snow beside her, his shoulder just touching hers. She stuck out her tongue at the sky.

"Try this," she said. "Catch a snowflake."

He stuck out his tongue. She watched a fat snowflake fall on the sensual pink curve of his tongue and melt instantly.

He laughed, low in his throat, delighted. "It's like capturing a single bubble of champagne."

After they had rested for a while, catching snowflakes with their tongues, she rolled away from him then swept her hands up over her head in a wide arc, and then her feet.

"Snow angel," she told Valentino when he

looked askance at her. She rose and stepped carefully out of the impression she had made to inspect it. He got up and stood beside her.

"That's quite remarkable."

And then he threw himself to the ground, on his back, and made a snow angel right beside hers, the wings touching. Having caught their breaths, their energy renewed, like children they raced around, throwing themselves in the snow, filling up the entire clearing with a veritable army of snow angels.

Sometime, while they were doing that, it registered with Erin, peripherally, that the snow had stopped. A watery light was trying to pierce the clouds around them.

Done with snow angels, Valentino was executing a new idea. Dragging his feet, he used them to draw a huge line through the snow, around almost the entire clearing, encircling the angels. After a moment, she saw that the line he was pounding out in the snow was taking on a heart shape.

She moved inside the heart and, with her feet, stamped out letters in the snow. Big letters, at least two feet high.

VALENTINO
ERIN

The sun burst through the clouds. The clearing turned into a fairy-tale land of white, the sun's glint making it blindingly bright, as if the snow had been threaded through with millions of sparking blue diamonds.

She could not stop the laughter when she was finished imprinting their names in the snow. With absolutely no planning on her part, the strangest thing had happened.

Erin O'Rourke was having the best Valentine's Day ever.

Valentino stood, his arm thrown around Erin's shoulder, looking at the valentine they had made. With the warmth of the sun on his face, the clearing sparkling with fresh snow, and her at his side, he wasn't sure if he had ever felt so happy.

A sound penetrated his happiness. The clearing was so silent that any noise would have seemed like a violation, but this one seemed particularly intrusive.

At first the sound was at a distance, but

then there was no denying that the steady thrum was coming closer and closer.

Erin looked off in the direction the sound was coming from, puzzled.

"That's a helicopter," she said. "They wouldn't usually put it in the air unless there was an emergency." She went very still as she considered that. "I hope someone else wasn't caught in this storm. Shoot. I'm going to go get the sat device and check in. We might have to help with a rescue."

Just like that, she was running toward the cabin.

As she ran, the helicopter broke over the trees and hovered. A sinking feeling overcame Valentino. Not someone else caught in the storm.

Him.

The helicopter—the rescue—was for him.

With desolation in sharp contrast to his happiness of moments ago, he realized, just like that, it was over.

Foolishly, he thought, *I should have never spoken that wish—that this could last forever—out loud.*

His freedom was over.

And suddenly, guiltily, he saw he had enjoyed his freedom at her expense. She had no idea what was about to happen and he had no way to warn her. He watched as Erin froze on her way to the cabin, turned and shielded her eyes as the helicopter began to descend into the clearing.

For a moment, it was a complete whiteout as the wind generated by the blades kicked up a great cloud of white.

And then the cloud settled, the helicopter seesawed down, planted itself in the snow, and the engine was turned off. The blades slowed. Out of the corner of his eye, Valentino could see Erin, puzzled, coming back toward him.

The door of the chopper opened and Colonel Alisha Del Rento stepped out. Though she was not wearing a uniform, she was every inch the colonel in charge of his protection. And close behind her, the rest of his security team. They weren't wearing uniforms, either, but they might as well have been. They looked tense and ready to do battle with whatever they needed to.

"Your Highness," the colonel said just as Erin arrived at his side.

He felt Erin go very still. He turned and looked at her. Her baffled eyes went from him, to the colonel, to the rest of his men, and back again.

At first, she looked bewildered, but then something shuttered in those eyes that had been so open to him.

"'Your Highness'?" she said, her voice flat.

"Erin—"

She cast a glance at Alisha and leaned in close to him. "You lied to me," she said, fury in every clipped syllable she spat out.

His position suddenly felt indefensible, which drove him to want to defend it.

"Isn't finding out an ordinary man is a prince the best of surprises?" he asked her.

"No," she said without a moment's hesitation. "It isn't."

"I was going to tell you."

"Well, you know what they say about the road to hell." She stepped back from him.

"We have much to talk about," he said.

"That's your opinion. I don't feel we have anything to talk about."

Out of the corner of his eye, he registered the shock of Alisha and his security team at the tone Erin had used to address him.

Reasonably, he said, "Let's gather up our things and Harvey, and get on the helicopter. We can talk."

"I'm going to go down exactly the way I came in," she said. "I don't think we have anything to talk about, *Your Highness.*"

He heard something in her tone—particularly in the way she'd said *Your Highness*—that he was not sure he had ever heard before in his life.

Contempt.

The colonel had heard it, too, drawing in her breath with sharp and unmistakable disapproval.

Erin gave her a withering look.

"Don't go yet," she called, turning her back on him. "I have something for you."

Hope fluttered in him. Something for him. A memento. The wax number off the cake. Her phone number. Anything to cling to.

But when she strode out of the cabin moments later, she had two black-plastic bags. When Alisha tried to intercept her, she quelled her with a look.

She handed him the bags.

He peered in the first one. His clothes from yesterday. He looked in the other.

He realized, shocked, she had just handed him the garbage. Then she turned, nose in the air, and marched back to the cabin with as much dignity as the deep snow would allow. She did not look back. She scooped her cat out of his basket by the door, went in and slammed the door behind her with such force that the windows rattled in their panes.

Valentino found himself on the helicopter, lifting in that same cloud of snow. But as the cloud settled, before the nose of the helicopter was pointed downhill toward the resort, he saw it.

Their valentine.

Despite the clearing being so disturbed by the arrival of the helicopter, it was still there, even more spectacular from the air than it had been from the ground.

A lopsided heart encircled all those snow angels. And their names. His and hers, linked together. He cast a look at Alisha. She was staring down at the valentine. She glanced at him and then quickly away, her expression deliberately impenetrable.

But he had not a doubt that she and every other person on the helicopter knew that something had happened when he and Erin had been stranded in that cabin together.

The evidence was right there, printed in the snow.

He had forgotten, put aside, that he was not allowed the whims of ordinary men. He never had been. He had a role to play. An example to set. His was a life guarded against compromising situations. He was on duty all the time. He was not allowed slips. He was not allowed inappropriate liaisons. Not ever.

He waited for regret to come.

And found, in its place, defiance.

Erin stood with her back braced against the cabin door as if she were trying to hold out a band of marauders.

She waited until she could not hear the helicopter anymore before she moved away from the door. She thought she might cry, but she didn't. She was too angry to cry. She cleaned the cabin with a vengeance, doing dishes, putting bedding in the laundry, stuffing her backpack with her things.

"A prince?" she said to Harvey. "Family business, indeed. No wonder I thought I recognized him. His ugly mug is at the grocery store checkout all the time."

If she was recalling it correctly, the paparazzi *loved* Valentino.

He's not ugly, a voice inside her insisted on protesting.

"Huh," she answered out loud. "Ugly is as ugly does."

Valentino was one of those men—just like her father—skilled in the art of seduction. All of it—the ineptness, the poetry—had probably been an elaborate act to get her into bed. And she had fallen for it! No, not just fallen! Hurled herself into it!

She felt angry, with Valentino and herself, and the anger was much better than feeling sorry for herself. It felt powerful. And passionate.

That passion—and the feeling of practically vibrating with energy—made her realize she was not even the same woman that she had been less than twenty-four hours ago.

Then she had been a *victim,* retreating from the world to lick her wounds, to feel sorry for herself about being dumped so unfairly by a man she had invested two years of her life in.

She didn't feel like that at all right now.

The truth was, she probably had Valentino to thank for this passionate, powerful side of her rising to the surface.

Harvey was hiding under the couch, eyeing her warily, not at all used to this kind of energy crackling off her.

Finally, bedding in the dryer and cottage looking for all the world the way it had always looked—as if nothing exciting or unexpected had happened there—she was ready to go.

She strapped on the baby carrier, stuffed her cat inside it, pulled on her coat, her toque, her gloves, her backpack.

She closed the door behind her.

Was she going to be able to come back here? Or would this place—that had always been her sanctuary—be haunted now?

The ghosts of his smile, his touch, his eyes on her, taking up residence here and never leaving?

She gave herself a shake, turned away, got her skis ready.

The snow wasn't the feathery powder everyone came here for. It was heavy, wet. The kind that was perfect for making the snowman they had not made. Still, even with the snow so challenging, she attacked the downward slope. Threw herself into it.

The passion translated to the way she skied. She could feel it. She embraced the intensity and singleness of focus that mountain required.

Once she got to the village, she made her way to her apartment and dropped off her things. She was stunned that it was only early afternoon. It felt as if years had gone by. In fact, it was still Valentine's Day.

Rather than sit around her apartment sulking, ruminating, going over every detail of the events that had just unfolded, Erin decided to go to work. It was her hidey-hole, after all. She popped Harvey back in his carrier and headed across the resort, enduring the smiles of people who thought she was carrying a baby.

"I thought you weren't coming in today," her office mate, Kelly, said, looking up with surprise when Erin came through the door.

Erin noticed that Kelly's desk sported a vase with at least a dozen red roses.

"I changed my mind," she said, trying to slide through to her office.

"I assumed you and Paul had something romantic planned," Kelly said, shamelessly probing. Her eyes slid to Erin's ring finger, hopefully.

Erin pulled back her shoulders and lifted her chin.

"Paul and I are no longer a couple," she said.

She wondered why she had dreaded this moment. Why she had thought *her* failure would be, humiliatingly, on public display.

Because she didn't feel like that at all.

She felt free. And strong.

She felt like a woman who had heard a man say to her, his tone as touching as a caress, *No man could look into your eyes and not know you. And no man could look into your eyes and ever have a moment's boredom. Not unless there was something lacking in him.*

"I'm so sorry," Kelly said. "Perhaps it's just a spat?"

Erin lifted a shoulder, not prepared to go into the details with her workmate. She found the refuge of her office and shut the door. She took Harvey out of the carrier. He went gratefully under her desk and curled up right on top of her feet.

That was how easy it was to get back to normal. With the cat purring steadily at her feet, soon she was immersed in the world she loved. A world of numbers and formulas. When done correctly, there were no surprises.

Surprises. It triggered a memory of Valentino's voice. In her mind's eye, Erin saw him lift that glass of wine to her and offer a toast.

To surprises.

Is this what her life was to be like now? Was she going to constantly be remembering a man she had spent so little time with?

Oh, but that time!

She shook it off.

Erin had just succeeded at immersing herself in that soothing world of work when her office door suddenly burst open. No knock.

Kelly, nearly lost behind a huge arrangement of flowers, said breathlessly, "See, I told you it was just a spat."

But Erin stared at the flowers, her mouth open, knowing this kind of extravagant arrangement was just not the sort of thing Paul would ever spend money on.

"I think its birds-of-paradise," Kelly said, setting them down and handing her a card. She stepped back to gaze admiringly at them. "And some kind of exotic lily. I don't think I've seen that before."

A tantalizing fragrance tickled Erin's nostrils.

"So beautiful!" Kelly declared, reaching out and touching the white, waxy petal of one of the lilies. She waited for Erin to say something, but Erin was stunned into absolute silence.

"Where do you get flowers like that at this time of year? They aren't from Berkley's Flowers. In fact, there's no tag on them at all. Just that card I handed you. Believe me, I looked! The delivery man wasn't what you'd expect. For some reason, he reminded me of a soldier. He said he'd wait for your reply. He had quite the yummy accent."

"My reply?" Erin managed.

"I think Paul's outdone himself. Open the card!"

If there had been any doubt who the flowers were from, the fact that a man who looked like a soldier and had a yummy accent was waiting in the front office, erased it in Erin's mind. She thought of the men and the woman who had tumbled out of that helicopter ready to rescue their prince.

Definitely soldiers.

Erin remembered his description of his land: the colorful flowers everywhere.

But even he could not have had flowers brought from there this quickly. Still, even without Kelly telling her, Erin knew that the small florist shop in the village could not have produced anything like this bouquet.

Of course, money would be no object for him. He'd probably had some staff member order the flowers and then sent a helicopter to pick them up.

The card was probably a brush-off. *Thanks for a memorable time.* But then, why would the messenger be waiting for a reply?

"Are you going to open the card?" Kelly asked anxiously. She turned and peered out the office door. "Yes, he's still there. I think Paul wants to set up something special. I bet he's going for forgiveness!"

Erin's fingers fumbled with the creamy envelope. She slid out a thick card and stared at it.

Kelly was absolutely correct. On one count, anyway.

She had the message right.

She just had the wrong man.

CHAPTER NINE

ERIN HELD THE creamy-white card. Who on earth had stationery like this on hand, particularly when they were traveling on a vacation? Silly to be seduced by the feel of paper, but it was so thick and rich. Possibly handmade. It was also ever so subtly embossed. The royal crest rose out of the paper and she explored the soft ridges with her fingertips.

That was who had stationery like this. A prince.

The card was handwritten, which made it harder to dismiss. His writing was strong, masculine, spiky.

Please forgive me. Give me an opportunity to explain. Would you come to my suite for dinner tonight?

It was signed *Valentino.*
That newfound sense of herself and her

strength faltered. She felt weak with wanting to see him. Just like that, she could imagine his eyes on her eyes, his hands exploring her skin, his lips claiming hers. It made her feel as without strength as a newborn kitten.

But that helpless sense of weakness was just one more reason to say no. What would be the point of seeing him, of hearing his explanation? Where could such a liaison as the one they had shared possibly go?

There was no future in it.

Does everything have to have a future in it? A voice inside her whined. *Does everything have to have a point?*

She thought of the lovely intimacies they had shared: bandaging his finger, eating together, being in his arms, waking up beside him, exploring every inch of him, chasing him through the snow.

She could feel the blood rising in her cheeks. The desire to see him again was unbelievably strong.

She read the final line.

Please bring Harvey.

For some reason that tested her resolve even more than remembering Valentino's lips on hers. He had *heard* her. He understood that she tried to keep the cat with her as much as possible; he understood what Harvey meant to her. Nobody had ever included Harvey before.

Paul had barely tolerated the aging cat and the feeling had been mutual. He had *hated* her attachment to her beloved pet. "Weird," he had cuttingly pronounced it.

But before she gave in to all this temptation, swirling around her like a storm trying to suck her into its vortex, Erin took a black felt marker out of her desk drawer and wrote *NO!!* across the entire invitation.

Under Kelly's horrified eyes, she stuffed it back in the envelope and passed it to her.

"Give this to the man who is waiting."

The great prince couldn't even come himself? Obviously, he had used his resources, and very rapidly, too, to sort out where she worked at the resort.

No. Their worlds were too far apart. If this was that important to him, he could have come himself. He had lied to her already. She had made love to an imposter.

Not that she had to explain her refusal to herself or to anyone else. *No*, according to a self-help book she was reading, was a complete sentence.

"But—" Kelly said. Her voice drifted away when she saw the look on Erin's face. She turned, reluctantly, and left the office, shutting the door quietly behind her.

Valentino put his phone down and went to the window. From his penthouse suite, he looked out over the Touch-the-Clouds resort. The quaint mountain village was snow-covered, bustling with the after-storm activity of colorful parka-clad skiers. The mountain cradled the resort in its bowl.

And tucked away in those mountains, a secret place, where it felt as if he had left his heart. He had just spoken to Angelica.

She had cried with relief when he'd told her he was not going to ask her to marry him. She had been so grateful but worried, too, knowing the brunt of the breakup would be borne by him.

He sighed and rolled his shoulders. He had told her, truthfully, that he was grateful, and prepared to pay the price. Whatever it might be.

There was no mistaking the sense of freedom. Of shaking off the harness he had worn since the day he was born. He was scheduled to leave tomorrow, and he felt he had to get home as soon as possible. The whole betrothal celebration must be canceled before any more work went into the preparations. Even at this point, it would probably be akin to trying to stop a runaway train. But it had to be done.

Valentino returned his attention to the card his guard had returned to him while he was on the phone.

He took a deep breath and slipped it out of the unsealed envelope.

He stared at it, incredulous.

Erin, in thick, black felt marker, had scrawled *NO* across the surface in two-inch-high letters, adding two exclamation points just to make sure he got it.

The feeling of incredulity died. He was not sure why he was smiling. He should be insulted. But just like that bag of garbage she had handed him, he didn't feel insulted.

Intrigued. A tiny bit tickled. Now that she *knew* who he was, she was not treating him any differently than she would any other guy who had hurt her feelings.

He thought of them in her bed together and admitted to himself that it went a little further than hurt feelings.

Where was it going, then? An apology and a goodbye on good terms?

But why? He was free of the matrimonial expectations that had been placed on him. Why couldn't he—they—see where it all could go?

The truth was, it had been many years since anyone had said no to him. Still, he'd obviously gotten it wrong. You didn't, apparently, beg for forgiveness by way of royal summons.

He had so much to learn.

And he realized he was hoping Erin would be his teacher. But first he had to get her to see him again!

Erin looked at the clock. Time to go home. But why go home? All she would do was think about things she could not change. The only thing that mattered to her—Harvey—was here with her. She could stay in the office, order supper and keep working.

She could be having dinner with a prince. But, no, she'd be sharing a ham sandwich from the staff cafeteria with Harvey…

A knock came on the door. Kelly, no doubt, to remind her it was quitting time. But Kelly came in, slid the door shut and leaned on it. Was she trembling?

"Kelly?"

Kelly opened her eyes. They were wide with shock. "*He's* out there."

"Who is out there?" Erin asked, trying to keep her voice calm. Of course, she already knew what kind of man would elicit this kind of reaction. Of course, in his world, he would not take no for an answer. Why hadn't she anticipated this and gone into hiding?

"The Prince of—" Kelly glanced at the card she held in shaking hands "—Lorenzo del Toro. I've seen him in magazines. But nothing could prepare me for him in real life." She sighed with so much feeling that Erin feared she might faint.

But then she pulled herself together. *"You know him."* This was said with faint accusation, as if Erin had willingly withheld a secret—that Kelly's survival depended upon—from her.

"Casually," Erin said then felt her cheeks burn. She knew full well why she had not gone into hiding. Because part of her—even with all the evidence that such things were naïve and foolish—hoped.

"He's asked me to announce him," Kelly said and giggled. "I feel as if I should have a trumpet. Toot-doodle-loo! Announcing—"

"Just let him in," Erin interrupted her.

Kelly opened the door wide and called, "You've been announced," then dissolved into girlish giggles as Valentino brushed by her, giving her an indulgent look.

Erin folded her arms over her chest and did not stand.

Kelly looked from one to the other and, sensing the tension in the room, scuttled out. Valentino closed the door behind her.

"What do you want?"

"I wanted to tell you I'm nearly completely recovered from my injury. See?" He held up a finger. Her first-aid attempts had been replaced with a very neat and tidy—not to mention, small—bandage.

He seemed—adorably—like he didn't quite know what to do now that he found himself there. For a man who commanded a nation, and stood so strongly in himself, it was seductively charming that he was off balance, unsure.

She had to fight an urge to get up and go look at his finger. To take it, and maybe to touch it with her lips… Erin shook off those thoughts, absolutely appalled with herself. She glared at him.

He cleared his throat, dropped his hand into his pocket.

"I wanted to tell you how sorry I am. Since you won't have dinner with me, I have brought the message to you. I should have told you who I was. I never meant for you to be shocked like that."

The very sound of his voice—deep, tender, genuine—weakened her. As did his eyes on her face.

Pleading.

A prince was pleading with her, Erin O'Rourke, for understanding. She felt a lump in her throat. He elicited so much feeling from her. It was dangerous. It was a feebleness.

"All right," she managed to say. "Apology accepted. Your conscience can be clear. You can go now."

A touch of a smile tickled the line of his lips. She ordered herself not to look at that bottom one.

"Is something funny?" she asked.

"It's just no one talks to me like that." He made no move to go. "Please, come have dinner with me tonight. It's my last day here. I fly out tomorrow. I have urgent matters to deal with."

"I get it," she said. "*Princely* duties call you. This will shock you, but I have a life and obligations, too. I can't just drop everything because you have summoned me."

This was so patently untrue that if she was Pinocchio her nose would grow about six feet right now.

"You have a previous engagement," Valentino said. He looked so crestfallen, she felt that dangerous softness for him inside her intensify. If she was not careful, she would be like Kelly, nearly fainting from his nearness.

"But it's been nice meeting you," she said coolly.

"Erin," Valentino said, his voice hoarse, "I just, for once in my life, wanted to be a man like any other. I wanted to be liked for myself and myself alone.

"Whether you forgive me or not, that is the gift you have given me."

She digested that. She felt her position compromised. She hadn't thought of it from his perspective. She hadn't thought how hard it would be to never be sure if someone liked you for you or because you were a member of a royal family.

She had not thought how someone, who had never had it, might long for normal.

"All right," she said, "I accept your apology. And I forgive you. Now, you can go."

He still didn't move. His look of relief was so genuine. "Would you have dinner with me tonight? Please. Perhaps your other engagement can wait, since I'm leaving first thing in the morning? I feel there are things we need to discuss."

"What kind of things?"

"The future."

One thing being an only child of warring parents had taught her was that hope—especially hope that love could win—was the most dangerous thing.

Love?

The intensity of what they had experienced wasn't love. It was a survivor's euphoria of some sort. The isolation, the storm, had led to impulse. A sense of embracing the moment. Infatuation. Passion.

She was going to say no to his dinner invitation. She really was. It would take all of her strength, every single bit of it, and still, the rational part of her knew there was only one answer.

There was no future for an ordinary, common Canadian girl with a prince.

But just as she was forming the word—how could a one-syllable word prove so difficult to get out—Harvey roused himself, stretched and came out from under her desk. He peered around the corner in the direction of Valentino.

The cat was mostly deaf. He was partly blind. He was antisocial.

And yet, somehow—perhaps by that thing called instinct that was so well-honed in the animal kingdom—he knew exactly who was there.

He shot across her office floor with more speed than Erin had seen in him in years. He wound himself around Valentino's legs, "talking" loudly.

Valentino laughed and picked up the cat. He lifted Harvey over his head and then brought him down to his face and planted a kiss on the tip of the cat's nose. He then hugged him into his chest and held him there.

It was the way somebody might handle a baby. She didn't want to think about Valentino with babies.

Babies. That's what she had wanted with Paul. In fact, she had wanted it so badly, it had taken away her discernment, her ability to tell the difference between fantasy and reality. And, of course, there was the fact Valentino was a prince. There would never be any babies with him.

And yet, seeing him with the cat, there it was nonetheless. A longing so powerful it nearly took her breath away.

"Are you going to come for dinner with me tonight, my old warrior?" he asked. He looked to Erin for the answer.

Baby thoughts should have put her defenses up higher. Instead, whatever was left of them crumbled. "Okay," she said, "we'll come."

The fact she was having unexpected longings for babies should provide ample protection against temptation to have another tumble with him. Having a baby was a serious enough business without adding the complication of a prince!

Besides, he was probably surrounded by a veritable army of people at all times. No wonder he had enjoyed his time on the mountain. It seemed to Erin that would be a perfectly awful way to live.

An hour later, standing in front of her mirror in her own apartment, she knew she had been put under a spell and that it was wearing off. Because, really? The dress she had on was terrible. Never mind that she had loved it when she had bought it to attend an awards dinner her father was being honored at. It was the fanciest thing she owned—jade green that matched her eyes, off-the-shoulder, short and sassy. Now, it felt as if she was trying too hard. Way too hard.

She had been in the presidential suite, which the prince and his entourage were inhabiting, only once. The resort had reserved it for a retirement party for the CEO of the company. The suite took up the entire top floor of the Northern Lights Hotel and was posh in a way she hadn't even known existed.

Of course, you wore your best dress for that. To have dinner with a prince.

But then she recalled what he'd said about the gift she had given him of feeling normal.

Gratefully, with a sense of relief, Erin slid off the dress that suddenly made her feel like a child pretending to be a grown-up and threw on a pair of casual stretch jeans and a button-down shirt. She put on a hint of makeup and tucked her hair up into a messy bun.

Then she remembered his fingers taking the pins from that bun—it seemed like a lifetime ago—and the veritable avalanche that had unleashed. She took her hair back down and, before she could overthink it too much, tousled it with her fingers. She pulled on her jacket, picked up Harvey and zipped him inside, and headed out into the Touch-the-Clouds complex.

It was a beautiful star-studded evening and she was aware of it as if the night was alive around her.

But that wasn't quite it.

It wasn't the night that was alive. *She* was alive—tingling with a kind of nervous anticipation—in a way she had not been in a long, long time. If ever.

When she knocked on the door of his suite, she wasn't quite sure what to expect. Staff? What did she say? *I'm here to see the prince. I'm here to play Cinderella to his Prince Charming.*

But Valentino opened the door himself, welcomed her by kissing her, with some formality, on each cheek. The cat popped his head out and Valentino took him from her jacket, good-naturedly kissed both his cheeks, too—just to let her know she wasn't getting special treatment?—and then set him on the floor.

Harvey, blind as he was, ambled across the space and found the most expensive-looking, silk-covered chair in the opulent main living area that was right off the front door. He gathered himself and leaped with surprising prowess into it then curled into a contented ball.

"Apparently he considers himself suited to such a palatial lifestyle," Erin said. The suite was as she remembered; a gorgeous space where you were afraid to touch things. Evidently, Harvey did not share her intimidation.

"May I take your coat?"

She shrugged out of it and was instantly aware that Valentino did not normally take coats, because he stood there not quite knowing what to do with it.

She gently retrieved it from him, opened the coat cupboard and hung it.

"You look lovely," Valentino said.

It made her glad she had not worn the dress. He, too, was dressed casually in pressed jeans and a V-necked sweater over a collared shirt. He looked very much the ordinary guy— except for those luxurious dark curls and a handsomeness that would never allow him to be ordinary!

"Humph," she said, regarding him thoughtfully. "I thought, now that your secret is out, you might have had a prince outfit on."

He glanced down at himself. "What, exactly, would you imagine a *prince outfit* to be?"

"At the very least, a hat with a shiny brim, like army officers wear. I would think some medals. One of those wide ribbon things across your chest."

He was smiling. She enjoyed making him smile.

"You don't know any more about princes than I know about igloos."

"Or delivering babies," she reminded him. She snapped her fingers. "You should at least have a sword!"

He laughed, as she had hoped he would, and that tension she'd been holding since she had said yes to this invitation dissolved a little bit. This was her Valentino. The one she had chased through a snow-covered meadow.

Shared a bed with.

Not that she wanted to go there. But how was it not going to go there? The tension returned and intensified yet more as he led her through to the dining room. Like the main living area, this room was traditional and opulent. The long, polished, walnut table was set for two with beautiful china, both settings at one end. One at the head and one beside it. Valentino surprised her by holding out the head chair to her. Surely, that was his place at the table?

He took the other chair and reached for the bottle of wine that was sitting in a silver bucket.

"Note, it has already had the cork removed," he said with a grin. "And as an extra precaution, I'm decanting it. According to the sommelier, that lets any sediment drift to the bottom."

The grin, so familiar, tried to ease something in her, but the fact he had a sommelier at his disposal worked against that ease. Now that she was thinking about it, she could hear noises in the kitchen, which, if she recalled from the other time she had been here, was behind that swinging door. Delicious smells were wafting out of it. Unless she missed her guess, someone was preparing dinner for them.

Well, what had she thought? That he was going to order a pizza?

"I considered impressing you by uncorking it with a sword—"

Valentino, that man whom—in a complete break from her normal buttoned-down personality—Erin had loved shamelessly and spontaneously, was really a prince. And that prince wanted to impress her?

What strange fairy-tale world was this that she found herself in?

CHAPTER TEN

VALENTINO GRINNED AT Erin. It made him, dangerously, *her* Valentino and not a world figure of considerable fame and fortune.

"As I said, I considered uncorking the wine with a sword, but I couldn't find one on such short notice. Someone neglected to pack my ceremonial one."

That, all kidding aside, meant two things: someone packed for him and he actually *had* a ceremonial sword.

"All things considered, that is probably a good thing," she said solemnly and lifted the glass he had poured for her. "I propose a toast."

He lifted his glass.

To surprises, she thought. But out loud she said, "To keeping all your digits."

He wiggled his newly bandaged finger at her. And just like that, the laughter bubbled up between them as effervescent as the wine. Her discomfort eased, but then came back as the swinging door to the kitchen opened and a white-uniformed staff member came through. A royal crest had been tastefully embroidered in gold thread on the breast of his uniform. He was bearing platters of food.

"Your Highness," he said. "Miss."

As he set down the food, did he slide her a look that was ever so faintly disapproving? She shot Valentino a glance to see if he had noticed, but he did not appear to have. Surely, she was being overly sensitive and had imagined it?

"May I bring you anything else, sir?"

"No, Milo, thank you."

Did Milo give her another look before sliding silently from the room?

"I wanted you to have a taste of my country," Valentino said and served them both from the platters.

She took the snowy-white napkin from beside her setting and put it on her lap. She regarded the array of cutlery with a bit of hesitation. Her lifestyle had rarely required she knew which fork to use! In this new setting, the passionate, carefree, confident woman Valentino had coaxed to the surface mere hours ago seemed to be fading with alarming quickness.

Erin watched how Valentino addressed the feast that had been prepared for them, and she did what he did. She was aware that he was as much at home in this world of amazing food, impeccable manners and culinary rituals as she was a foreigner in it.

Her disquiet lessened when he shifted his chair over closer to hers. He plucked a tiny tomato out of a glorious salad with his fork.

He held the fork to her lips. "Try this."

Her lips closed over his fork and flavors exploded in her mouth, possibly made more intense by his closeness, by his fork being in her mouth.

"Delicious?" he asked her.

"Unbelievable." Did that kitchen door squeak open and then shut again? "Somehow I don't think you picked that up at the Snowbound Groceteria."

He laughed. "It was developed by our

palace horticulturalist. Its name translates to Tiny Tornado Tomato. We export them around the world now, to upscale markets."

"You travel with your own food?"

"My chef would never chance being able to find the quality or specialty ingredients he likes locally, I'm afraid. When we travel, he brings everything with him. He's snobby that way."

"Isn't it illegal to transport food into another country?" she asked. "My father once got off a plane in New Zealand with an apple they had given him on the flight—and he was charged a fine."

He contemplated that. "I have no idea, but I'm sure we would not do anything illegal. Probably we obtain permits or special permissions."

We. Meaning not him. She realized Valentino simply did not attend to the details of everyday life.

He moved on, making her taste the olives separately. They, too, were a specialty product of his kingdom, developed by the palace horticulturist. Taking great pride in the culinary accomplishments of his island home, Valentino explained each item on the menu to her. Every savory piece of food was evocative of a warm and colorful place.

Still, horticulturalists? Chefs preparing food? Sommeliers? Wait staff? People who quietly looked after permits and entry requirements? Protection staff?

"You must have been laughing when I called that salad at the cabin Mediterranean salad," she said. "Tasting this, it so obviously was not. You must have laughed about quite a bit of that meal. Steak that fell on the floor—"

"Licked by a cat," he told her, his eyes crinkling with merriment.

If she could just look at his eyes, maybe she could believe… "What? You never told me that part!"

"I protected you from it," he said, pleased.

"Oh." A prince protecting her. It stole words really.

"It was one of the best meals I have ever eaten," he said softly. "I would not change one thing about it. Except maybe the cork in the wine."

When the main meal was finished, Milo came out and prepared dessert at the table, two wedges of creamy cheesecake that he spooned a cherry topping onto. And then, with great flourish, he produced a torch, lit it and set it to the cherries. A blue flame danced over them briefly and died.

Milo looked so pleased with himself that Erin almost forgave him the subtle signs of disapproval he was giving off, especially now that Valentino had moved his chair so close to hers.

Valentino waited until Milo had left the room before he took his fork and fed her the stunningly delicious dessert.

She had a sudden memory of eating cake off his chest and felt embarrassed. She would have never done that, if she had known.

She would have probably never done any of it, if she had known.

Valentino seemed to sense her uncertainty. He picked up her hand and turned it, kissing the inside of her wrist.

"Let's talk about the future," he suggested, his voice low and sultry.

The future? Cinderella and Prince Charming belonged in fairy tales. As much as it felt like she had been dropped into one, she had to keep in mind that in real life, worlds that were so different collided, they didn't converge.

"What future?" she asked.

"I want you to come to Lorenzo del Toro. With me. Let me show it to you."

For a moment, she could almost feel the warmth on her skin, smell the scents. But she had to keep one foot in reality! She had to.

"Obviously, I can't. I can't just drop everything. I have a job."

"Surely, you get holidays?" he said persuasively. "Isn't the ski season nearly over?"

"We have a shoulder season." Not enough of one to bring them out of the red, but still, it kept the resort open and paid basic bills.

His eyes slid to her shoulders in a way that nearly melted her.

"I have a life," she insisted, hoping he would not ask for examples because, at the moment, a life—one without him in it—seemed particularly dreary.

"A cat," she added weakly.

"Harvey can come with you."

He really did not know anything about how real people lived!

"You don't just board a plane with your cat," she told him.

He looked confused, as if that had never occurred to him. But then he laughed. "Oh. Do you think I'm asking you to take a commercial flight?"

"Aren't you?"

"Of course not. We have a private plane. I would send it for you."

Erin was dumbfounded. *He would send a plane for her?* She had grown up with plenty of international traveling, but she had never been on a private jet.

She closed her eyes and let the seduction of the whole thing sweep over her. A vacation in an exotic place. With incredible food. Sunshine. Discovery. A private jet. An intriguing, gorgeous, sexy man.

Milo slid back through the door and stood

silently until Valentino acknowledged him with a look that clearly said *Not now.*

Milo, however, was not to be deterred.

"Your Highness…"

The formal address, the man's deference to Valentino, reminded Erin, again, how far apart their worlds really were. How she didn't really know Valentino at all.

He was not just the playful man who had given himself over to loving her, to playing with her in the snow…

But he was holding out an opportunity for her to get to know him better and on so many different levels. They had shared her world. Now he was inviting her to explore his.

She could feel herself leaning toward it…

Milo spoke. "Sir, the palace has just announced your engagement to Princess Angelica of Sorrento. I wanted to be the first to congratulate you."

Valentino gave the man a stunned look and then dismissed him quickly with an impatient wave of his hand.

Erin froze and let the words sink in. She

felt as though she had been slapped. In fact, she fought back the tears rising in her eyes.

Instead of letting him know her distress, she got up slowly, feeling as if she were in a dream. Even knowing better, even having grown up with her father, *still* she had fallen for Valentino's charm. Still, she had believed he'd wanted to show her his world.

"So," she said, tossing down the napkin, "apparently there are two things you neglected to tell me. One, that you're a prince. And two, you're a prince in a committed relationship."

His dark eyes were liquid. He looked at least as distressed as she felt. But she squeezed any sympathy she wanted to feel for him out of her heart. She tilted her chin proudly.

"Let me explain." His voice, his beautiful voice, was low and pleading.

"You had plenty of opportunity to explain," she snapped. "Any time up at the cabin might have been good. Before we were intimate comes to mind."

"Erin—"

"But maybe you don't have to follow the same rules as the rest of the world? Is that it?"

"That's not it. At all. If you would just listen to me—"

"To your explanation? Maybe you'd like to run this by your royal speech writer, but it's pretty hard to explain an engagement to someone else to the woman you have just invited to share time with you." Erin could hear an unnatural and very unflattering shrillness in her voice. She told herself to be quiet. But she couldn't. The words just kept spilling out of her, furious, outraged.

"When were you going to tell me that part? About the princess being your fiancée? Once I was there? When you were hiding me away somewhere like a tawdry little secret?"

Her mother's exact words to her father. *Your tawdry little secrets.*

"How were you going to keep your betrothed, Princess Whatever-Her-Name-Is, from knowing about me? Or is that kind of thing acceptable in your country?"

"Erin, it's not like that. I promise you, it's

not like that." He was getting up, easing toward her, gently, like one would ease toward a skittish colt that wanted nothing more than to bolt.

She *wanted* to hear it. She wanted his promises. She wanted his words to smooth it over so that it all made sense.

That's how stupid she was!

"No, I don't want to hear it," she lied, holding up her hand to him in the universal gesture of *Stop right there, buddy.* "I've heard enough explanations, thank you. You can put all the finery around it that you want. You can have your staff and your plane and your exotic food and people who light it on fire for you. It doesn't change the truth."

"The truth?" he asked.

"You, Your Royal Highness, are a complete ass."

Valentino watched, shocked, as Erin stormed from the room. The cat yowled in protest when she picked it up and a moment later the door slammed behind them.

He was tempted to go after her.

Not that he had much experience in these things, but instinct told him there were certain times that you would be taking your life in your hands trying to talk to a woman.

Besides, as he sank back down at the table, he allowed himself to feel the full insult of it. Erin *knew* him. She had to know him. It felt as if she was the only person who had ever truly seen him.

And she was so quick to believe the worst of him.

An *ass*?

No one had ever spoken to him like that before. He had never been called such an insulting name in such a scathing tone.

His indignation faded. Valentino felt a horrible sense of defeat. He resigned himself to the possibility that whatever had happened between them on that mountain was a moment of magic, somehow separate from time and space. It could not, it seemed, be recaptured here on earth.

Perhaps it had served its purpose, giving him the impetus to set Angelica free. For that dazzling moment in time, on the mountain with Erin, he had believed a different life waited for him, but now he was not so sure.

It was obvious to him that someone in his inner circle had reported his involvement with Erin went further than them stranded together in a snowstorm. That valentine stamped in the snow had been a dead give-away. The delivery of the dinner invitation to Erin's office this afternoon had probably cemented conclusions.

He had been reported, by someone, to his mother, the queen. Possibly, the palace even knew he was entertaining Erin tonight. Prob-ably, Milo had been instructed to make sure that Erin went home and had been given the ammunition to do that.

His family were pulling out all the stops. They were trying to drive him back into the fold, trying to force his hand, with the en-gagement announcement coming early.

It didn't really matter who had reported him. There was no point chastising them, or Milo, the server who had made the an-nouncement in front of Erin. His staff were loyal to him. But in the end, everyone in the kingdom, including himself, answered the commander in chief, who was his mother. His staff had probably all been ordered to do whatever they could to nip the romance with the Canadian girl in the bud.

Before it had a chance to become an embarrassment.

Or, more important, before it had a chance to persuade him to put his own happiness ahead of his sworn duty.

He had to return to his island immediately. He would announce his breakup with Angelica to his mother personally. There were going to be repercussions, but still, he had to make it clear that certain elements of his life would belong to him alone.

He looked at the remains of the dinner in front of him, his appetite gone. In fact, he felt quite ill.

Milo came through the door. He noticed the empty place and, for just a second, a look of carefully controlled sympathy crossed his face.

"Can I bring you anything else, sir?" he asked.

"No, thank you."

It was everything that Valentino had grown up with: a civil exchange. Emotion was swept under the carpet; the show must go on. Dignity and decorum. The public perception came first and foremost. Always. Control, and discipline, were everything.

He resisted, just barely, an urge to pick up a plate and throw it at the wall.

CHAPTER ELEVEN

ERIN WOKE UP the next morning to the sound of a helicopter lifting in the distance. The steady whomp of the blades slicing the air intensified the pounding in her head. She felt, for all the world, as if she'd had too much to drink, when she was pretty sure she had only had a few sips of that cork-free wine.

She told herself to ignore the noise, but she couldn't. She knew, in her heart, what the sound meant.

Valentino was leaving.

The helicopter would take him to wherever his private jet was parked. Did you park a jet? Was that the proper terminology? Moor it? Who cared? Stupid to waste time wondering about such things.

He was engaged.

Still, if she got up and went to her living room window, she could probably catch a glimpse of the aircraft that carried him. Away from her.

Forever.

Had she really thought, when he'd invited her for dinner, that something could ever come of it? Besides a fling?

She was hardly the kind of girl who inspired grand passions. She was not the kind of girl a prince would choose.

With those thoughts running through her head, Erin refused to let herself run to that window. Her pillow was damp with tears. The hangover she was feeling was an emotional one. Harvey, ever sensitive to her mood, was curled up, purring on the pillow right by her ear. It was reminiscent of the days of the childhood that she had been so determined to leave behind her.

Is that what she had clung to in her relationship with Paul? The fact that emotional turmoil had been happily absent?

But, come to think of it, strong emotion of any sort had been absent. Was that any way to conduct a romance?

Not that what she had experienced with

Valentino could qualify as a romance. A tryst, maybe. *A tawdry little secret.*

The prince was engaged.

It was shocking news, never mind that he had seemed as taken aback by Milo's announcement as she herself had been. The fact that Valentino had been romancing Erin—carrying on with her—when he was committed to another woman was despicable. Unforgivable.

It was just like her father. So sure of his charms. Gullible women falling all over themselves to be with him. Probably, women who didn't have a very good sense of themselves in the first place, so wanted to bask in the reflection of his glory.

"Yuck," she said out loud. The sounds of the helicopter had long since faded. She finally got up. As tempting as it was to call in sick, she knew herself too well. Moping helped nothing.

So she scrubbed her face and got herself and Harvey ready to go to work.

An hour later, she was crossing the village square, the snow crunching under her feet.

The main floor of the building she worked in housed a minimarket—the one she had teased Valentino about *not* shopping at—and she had to pass right by it to get to her office.

Any hope she had that there was some mistake about Valentino's engagement—that the surprise on his face meant something for the future he had talked about for them—was blown to smithereens.

The tabloids were out on a display rack in front of the building this morning. There were three different ones, but all had a variation of the same front-page headline and story.

Fairytale Romance:
Prince and Princess to Marry!

Someday My Prince Will Come:
Royal Engagement Announced!

Royal Romance:
Prince Valentino Proposes to
Princess Angelica!

Erin was not quite sure how Valentino had managed a proposal since he'd been having

dinner with her at the very time his engagement had been announced.

In his world, she thought, miffed, he probably had staff to look after the bothersome
little details of an engagement. The Royal
Proposer.

Naturally, she hoped Valentino's betrothed
was what he deserved, cold and unfeeling. A
horrible person. She hoped she had blotchy
skin.

But, no, Erin herself was the only one with
blotchy skin this morning. The pictures that
accompanied the headlines did not show an
ugly princess. The furthest thing from it, actually.

Angelica of Sorrento was, naturally—and
unfairly—gorgeous, right off the pages of
what the heroine of any a fairy tale should
look like. She had an abundance of wild,
dark curls, an amazing complexion, soft,
dark eyes, eyelashes as thick as Valentino's
own.

*They would make beautiful, curly-headed,
golden-complexioned babies together.*

In one of the pictures, the happy couple

had their heads together, nearly touching, laughing. The caption said it had been taken at a polo match the previous summer.

Of course! A polo match! Erin was surprised the prince wasn't playing in it! Who went to polo matches? Rich people. Sophisticated people. Who had jets.

And who had paramours tucked away in the far corners of the globe.

In another of the pictures, they were both on horses, riding a quiet forest trail, each looking completely comfortable in jodhpurs and riding helmets. Looking completely comfortable with each other. Looking exactly what they were: the most privileged, pampered people on the planet.

The third picture showed Angelica at the top of a curved marble staircase in a gorgeous gown, long gloves, a tasteful tiara. Every inch the princess. Valentino waited at the bottom of the stairs. Look at that! Dressed *exactly* like a prince, including the sword.

Erin, shocked at the level of her own anger, ungraciously hoped he would manage to chop off a finger while uncorking the wedding champagne.

She itched to buy one of the papers—to feed her desire to know everything there was to know about him—the jerk—but recognized it would do nothing but cause her more pain. So, with difficulty, she refused the urge.

Kelly was already in the office, at her desk. Any hope Erin had that she might have missed the tabloid headlines was lost when she stuffed one of the very papers Erin had just looked at in her desk drawer and gave Erin a look loaded with empathy.

Erin felt, horribly, like the unwanted sympathy might make her burst into tears. Hopefully, she had cried them all out last night. Hopefully, she did not have a single tear left to waste on Prince Valentino!

She hustled into her office, released Harvey from the carrier, and immersed herself in the world that had always been engrossing for her. She wished it brought more comfort. The storm yesterday had come too late. The season was now nearly over. If the snow held, they might have another month. Ticket sales were down nearly twenty-five percent over last year. She had heard several of the concession owners saying they were not having a good year, either.

She had nearly managed to block out everything but the numbers in front of her, when the office door squeaked open.

"Do you want to know the latest?" Kelly asked.

Erin, unfortunately, could not keep her curiosity at bay. She nodded reluctantly.

Kelly came across the floor to her desk and handed Erin her phone. It was open on the web edition of *Rags and Riches,* one of the most notorious of the tabloids.

Erin was stunned to see there was a new headline.

Royal Splitsville:
Prince Calls Off Engagement!

She read the story with an uneasy greediness to know what was going on in Valentino's life.

Only hours after it was announced, Prince Valentino of the island Kingdom of Lorenzo del Toro has called off his engagement to Princess Angelica of the neighboring island of Sorrento.

The prince himself is tight-lipped about the unfolding situation, but the royal family has issued a statement that they have every hope the couple, who have known each other since childhood, will reconcile. They ask for privacy at this time.

Neither the Sorrento royals nor the princess has released a statement, but sources close to her say she is devastated by the stunning callousness the prince has showed in breaking their engagement, which is now, humiliatingly, among the shortest in history.

After that, over the next few days, no matter how hard she tried, Erin couldn't avoid news of him, even if she wanted to.

The headlines had turned nasty. *Happily Never After!* one read.

News turned out to be a loosely applied term because there was really no news, not that that stopped the paparazzi feeding frenzy. Where there was no news, there was no lack of conjecture, no shortage of "sources close to" willing to give statements and expose the depths of heartbreak and misery the princess was experiencing.

Very powerful telephoto lenses, drones and helicopters were capturing pictures of both the prince and princess from a distance and through windows. The criteria for the photos seemed to be to catch Valentino looking grim-faced and cold—villainous and evil—and Angelica looking tear-stained, bewildered and broken—the fragile victim.

If Erin wasn't so angry—*spurned* was probably the correct word—she would have almost felt sorry for Valentino and the hounding he was enduring.

She did feel sorry for Angelica. Was she responsible, in some way, for that stranger's now so very publicly exposed misery? Responsible in the same way that those women her father had taken up with had been responsible for her mother's pain?

In her weaker moments, Erin asked a different question. What if she wasn't just the other woman? Wasn't one of many in a long string? What if Valentino had felt something in the time they had spent together that had made him realize he wanted more—that there could be more?

What if what had happened between them wasn't a sham at all, but was the most real thing that had ever happened to either of them?

What if what he had felt with her at the cabin was the reason for his broken engagement?

But those thoughts would be followed so quickly with *Who are you kidding? Who do you think you are?*

It was so confusing it made her head hurt. Erin felt as if she had a chronic headache. And then the worst possible thing happened.

A week into the tabloid feeding frenzy, Kelly came into her office and closed the curtains that covered the window that overlooked the village square.

"Don't look out there." Kelly passed Erin her phone.

Stunned, Erin saw a fuzzy picture of herself, looking quite frumpy, crossing the very resort square that Kelly had just closed the curtains on.

Under the terrible picture were the words *Prince's Secret Woman?*

Erin was dumbfounded. "How on earth?" she whispered.

"I think any number of people, both here on the mountain, and among his staff, know that the two of you were trapped together overnight. There was plenty of chatter about it in the main office. Then I heard lots of whispers around the resort that you'd had dinner with him. I'm sure that tidbits like these are worth a fortune to these kinds of rags."

She, Erin O'Rourke, girl least likely to create any kind of fuss, ever, was fueling this kind of gossip?

She thought of that toast she had made. *To surprises.* It occurred to her a toast like that required clarification: *Good* surprises.

"They're outside the window, aren't they?"

Kelly went and peeked out the closed curtains. "I'm afraid so. Clamoring, like sharks circling in anticipation of a gut bucket."

Did she have to be that graphic? Erin handed Kelly back her phone. Her coworker swiped to another screen and handed it silently back. There was an even more terrible picture of her, with Harvey creating a bulge under her jacket.

The papers had made the same mistake Valentino had made on their first meeting. The headline blared *Prince's Paramour Pregnant?*

Erin passed Kelly the phone back. "Don't show me any more," she pleaded. Her own phone started to buzz.

"I hope they don't have your number," Kelly said.

But it was Paul's name that came up. Considering, at least before she had met Valentino, that she had longed for this call—and the announcement he had come to his senses, that she was clearly the best thing that had ever happened to him—she looked at it with reluctance. Now? Really?

She hesitated and then, from long habit—

she'd always been so thrilled when he'd called her, found time for her—she answered.

"Paul," she said. She heard the total lack of enthusiasm in her own voice. She had been going to marry this man! Why would that make her feel like a loser? She could have had a nice unremarkable life, without any of the current chaos unfolding around her.

She was aware, just like that, she wouldn't take him back, no matter what. Was the current price she was paying worth that realization? She thought it probably was. And then some.

"And I thought you weren't exciting!" Paul said jovially. "A prince?"

He sounded oddly titillated, certainly as interested in her as he had ever been. He obviously was eager to have the inside scoop.

Erin was shocked by what came out of her mouth. "You're an ass, too."

Erin hung up the phone. Kelly giggled, shocked.

Erin's phone started to ring again, almost right away. The number was unknown. She stared at her phone in horror then quickly powered it off.

"Can you get a hold of Ricky for me?" she asked Kelly. "He's probably working the Lonesome lift today. Tell him I need to get up to the cabin, without anyone knowing."

"Done," Kelly said and then looked at her with such grave sympathy. "Oh, Erin, really? You? You are the least likely person to get caught up in something like this."

Almost the exact same message she had just gotten from Paul!

She was getting the same message, over and over, for one simple reason. It was true.

The ache she'd been nursing for days intensified until it felt as if her head were going to explode.

Ricky arrived within the hour and smuggled Erin and Harvey out a back door of her office building and onto a snowmobile. Even the drive up the mountain was good for her head. The further they got away from the chaos, and the more into the quiet sanctuary of high places, the better she felt.

By the time Ricky dropped her off at the

cabin, with a sat device, her headache had almost completely cleared.

"Don't use it unless it's an emergency," he said. "We don't know yet who's yakking to the press. But I'll tell you this—I wouldn't want to be them when I find out who it is."

"I wouldn't want to be them, either," Erin said, taking in the menacing look on his craggy old face. He looked very pleased with that assessment and, with a final wave, roared off back the way they had come.

"Family comes in so many different ways, doesn't it, Harvey?"

Just a short while ago, she had resigned herself to this. To her family being the people she worked with. Harvey.

It now, sadly, felt as if it would not be enough to fill the space left in the wake of Valentino.

The sound of the snowmobile engine grew more and more distant, and Erin regarded the cabin and the clearing. She could almost hear her and Valentino's laughter.

She needed to clean the slate, literally. After she deposited Harvey inside the door, she went and kicked snow over where she had stamped their names until the clearing was scrubbed clean. Well, except for the angels. She left the angels. She felt as if she needed all the help she could get.

She entered the cabin with a bit of trepidation. So much had unfolded here! She was going to have days to do nothing but relive memories and be with her tangled thoughts.

The best antidote to the thoughts that haunted her—the main one being *Who do you think you are?*—was to keep busy.

In the daytime, with Harvey happy in his baby carrier, she snowshoed and cross-country skied until she fell into bed at night exhausted.

The ache inside her dulled as she filled moments with busyness that shut off the chatter in her mind. The wood needed to be restocked, kindling always needed replenishing. She found some sandpaper and stripped down the kitchen set, ready for repainting. She had books and she had crossword puzzles.

On her third day in exile, Ricky arrived with groceries and an envelope.

"Are things settling down?" she asked.

"More vultures than ever camped out looking for you," he said.

"They're not letting it go?" It was easy to believe, up here without the internet or TV, papers or radio, that everything could be normal again.

"Um, I think there have been some new developments. I think Kelly put a newspaper in that envelope for you."

"Oh, dear," Erin said without enthusiasm.

"There's been this strange side benefit," Ricky said brightly, "the resort has been rediscovered."

"Rediscovered?"

"We couldn't buy this kind of publicity. The phone is ringing off the hook at the office. The website crashed. Twice. We're taking bookings for three years away. We've sold more season passes in the last week for next year than we did all this year."

This was what she needed to cling to, Erin thought as Ricky drove away. That there was sometimes a bigger picture. That good could come from bad.

She took her time getting to the envelope. Finally, she opened it.

She was stunned by what she saw.

It was a newspaper, folded in two. The half of the headline she could read.

Happily-Ever-The photo, also folded in two, showed half of a happy couple. The part of the picture Erin could see was of a joyous Princess Angelica.

Her fingers trembled. After all the kerfuffle, the engagement had been foregone. They had gone straight to the wedding. Angelica was an unbelievably beautiful bride. The dress was like something out of a dream. The white handmade lace of the veil against her dark curls was the picture of a perfect fairy-tale ending.

Angelica was the kind of girl who had happy endings. She had been born to them. Erin, the one who was not that kind of girl, couldn't bring herself, not just yet, to unfold that paper to see the other half of the happy couple.

CHAPTER TWELVE

VALENTINO STARED AT the photo of Angelica, radiating joy in her bridal finery. She had sent it to his phone yesterday, before releasing it to the press.

He recognized the groom only vaguely. A member of her protection team, a wholesome-looking young man who clearly would lay down his life for his new wife.

Valentino sighed. He had done his best to protect her. But, no, in the end, she wasn't having it.

She had called beforehand to tell him what she intended to do. He'd tried to talk her out of it and she had laughed.

"Oh, Valentino. I know you mean well, but you're being terribly old-fashioned. I don't need you to carry this burden for me, so that the press can have you as their villain."

"But now they'll make you the villain," he

warned her, aching for the misery she was leaving herself open to.

When she'd answered, her voice was strong. "It doesn't matter. I know who I am. It has nothing to do with the stories they tell. You know that. This is my choice to make. It is my right to choose." And then, softly, adding, "Antonio will protect me."

It was someone else's job to protect her. He hadn't realized how seriously he took that self-appointed responsibility until she'd said that, and he'd felt relief wash over him.

One less thing in his world that he was responsible for.

And so, against the express wishes of her parents, and her people, Angelica had run away—taking the beautiful dress and the heirloom veil that was probably intended for her marriage to Valentino—and married the man she'd chosen.

And then she had freed him, Valentino, by publicly releasing a few photos of the event. In those photos, she and her new husband's eyes shone with light, almost blinding, as they looked at each other.

There were going to be repercussions, and many of them, and Angelica and her new husband's faces said that love was worth it. That love made them strong enough for whatever came next.

So far, the paparazzi were indulging the pure romance of a runaway princess bride. But they were clamoring at Valentino's door more than ever. They wanted their story. They wanted to capture him sad and angry and betrayed. They wanted the spurious kind of elements to the story that sold papers.

This was the press: hero to zero and back again, in the blink of an eye.

Of course, his thoughts turned to Erin. He longed for her. Had she seen this? Would it change everything between them? Was there hope? For them? Was there a way, just as there had been a way for Angelica and Antonio?

Could he even, in good conscience, ask her that? He had planned to, that night everything had blown up in his face and she had declared him an *ass*. He had specifically invited her to see if they could discuss the future.

That had been impulsive. He had still been riding the wave of intensity that their time together had created.

Crazy. They barely knew each other. She had made it clear she didn't want to change that. She had made it clear what she thought of him.

Had she seen the news of Angelica's marriage? Surely, it would change her mind? What would he do if it did? If she contacted him?

He would ask her, again, to come here. To see if she could fit into this world, or more important, if she would want to.

But the days went by and there was no word from Erin. Could he blame her? Those horrible pictures that had been printed of her, the headlines, had no doubt given her a taste of the viciousness she might leave herself open to if she chose to pursue a relationship with him.

Valentino fought the urge to be the one to bridge the gap between them. No. If he really cared about her, he would not invite her into this life but protect her from it.

For the next few days, his course chosen, he threw himself into his duties. He did his best to forget her. They had been together in that cottage for less than twenty-four hours. How could he possibly be so changed by that? So obsessed with her? He longed for Erin with an ache that was physical.

He was barely eating and he wasn't sleeping. It might not be the best time to make a decision, but it was in that vulnerable state that he arrived at his conclusion.

This was his truth.

He had been born to power. He was a disciplined man. He had nearly always done what his station required of him.

So he was shocked by this awareness, this unfolding truth, that when it came to Erin, he was powerless. He *had* to see her. If she was not going to come to him, he had to go to her. He could not fight it.

There were pieces to set in place, naturally, so that the press would not be hot on his trail. He and Erin needed privacy. He would arrange a leaked story. Maybe even a decoy to send them in the wrong direction.

While he followed the direction his heart was leading him in.

It was nearly dark when Erin came back through the clearing. She had cut it close, but she was glad. She had snowshoed all day. She was exhausted. Hopefully, that meant tonight she would fall into bed too tired to even think *This is the bed we shared.*

She stopped short and frowned.

There was a light on in the cottage. The golden light from the gas lamps inside spilled out the windows and across the snow, warmly welcoming, like a painting on a Christmas card. She shrugged it off. She must have left them on this morning, but usually she was not careless with the gas lights. On the other hand, nothing about her seemed "usual" right now. Admittedly, she had been distracted.

As she got closer, she realized there was also a faint whiff of woodsmoke in the air. Surely that would not still be there from this morning's fire?

She felt a bit annoyed. Had some skiers or other mountain enthusiasts found her little sanctuary and made themselves at home? These mountain cabins were always left unlocked in case they were needed as emergency shelters, and she didn't begrudge anyone that, but she didn't feel up to company, either.

She had another thought. Maybe it was her father, taking a break from gallivanting around the globe, an aging playboy. Maybe, like the rest of the world, he was curious about her notoriety.

She felt as if she didn't have the energy to deal with him right now, either.

Making as much noise as possible, so much so that Harvey gave a little mewl of reprimand from inside his carrier, she took off the snowshoes, slammed them together and clumped up the steps to the porch. The door opened just as she put her hand to the latch. She braced herself, but nothing could have prepared her for—

Valentino.

"Hello," he said softly. His voice was like

a caress. His eyes were like a homecoming. She wanted nothing more than to fly into his arms.

But—

"Aren't you married?" she snapped.

"Married? Me?" He tilted his head at her. "How long have you been hiding up here?"

She didn't like it that he knew she was *hiding*. From the world. From her pain. From the insecurities that had, unfortunately, followed her.

Who do you think you are?

"Someone sent me the paper."

He quirked an eyebrow at her. Something was wrong with his eyebrows. They were white at the tips, and curling, as if he had cleaned a spider web with them. It was distracting.

"Of me? Married?" he asked, innocent, incredulous.

What kind of world was this he lived in? A celebrity world, obviously. One she could never belong in. Wouldn't want to! Engaged one day. Not engaged the next. Married one day…

Did those vows not mean anything to anyone anymore?

She stormed by him.

The paper lay where she had tossed it on the kitchen table. It was untouched, still folded. She grabbed it and thrust it at him, crossed her arms over her chest, waited for his *explanation*. Oh, how he loved to explain things!

Instead, he looked down at the paper. He looked up at her and had the nerve to smile.

"Sometimes," he said, "you just have to look at the world from a different angle."

He turned the paper over.

She saw the headline completed:

After!

And she saw the photo—the one she had been avoiding but could not quite bring herself to burn—of the groom looking adoringly at his new bride, Princess Angelica.

And that groom was not Valentino.

Her head shot up. She stared at him. Her mouth opened and then closed. She could feel tears filming her eyes.

"Come," he said, helping her out of her jacket, taking Harvey from her. "Sit down. I've made you hot chocolate."

She sat, stunned, while *the prince* brought her hot chocolate, sank beside her on the couch, watched her with that familiar warmth in his eyes. His eyebrows were still distracting.

She was dreaming, naturally. She took a sip of the hot chocolate while she contemplated his eyebrows. Scorched. Surely, in a dream, the hot chocolate would be perfect? And his eyebrows wouldn't look like that.

"Did you have some kind of incident lighting the stove?"

He cocked his head at her and looked a little sheepish. "And the lamps. How do you know that?"

The prince looking sheepish was too adorable to resist. She reached up and touched his eyebrows. "Your eyebrows have turned to ash."

"Better than ass," he said, straight-faced.

She giggled.

"I watched you light the stove and the

lamps several times. I might have had the sequence wrong. There was kind of a poof and a flash of fire and light. It was a little more excitement than I anticipated doing such a simple task."

The truth was that everything he did made simple things exciting. But she needed to remember there was a very thin line between excitement and disaster. That *poof* he described was about three seconds away from a cabin burned to the ground.

"Are you ready to let me explain? Ass that I am?"

She nodded. Her heart, that organ she had thought was dead inside her, was living again, thudding a tattoo inside her chest. "Yes, please tell me why you are here. What's going on. Why you didn't marry Angelica."

"Angelica and I have known each other since we were children. It was expected of us that we would marry. Love, of course, does not have anything to do with these kinds of arrangements in families like ours."

A man like Valentino—so passionate, so alive—condemned to a loveless life? It made her feel furious at the system he was bound to.

"To my shame, now, I didn't feel my marriage had to have love. She's beautiful. I respected her. And liked her. We're good friends, which I suppose is a love of sorts."

A love of sorts, yes, Erin thought, but not the kind you married. And yet, wasn't that *exactly* what she herself had been going to do? Marry Paul without passion?

"I actually felt as if I'd done fairly well in the arranged marriage department," Valentino continued. "Both kingdoms were in a frenzy of preparation for the engagement party."

Again, the parallel—she, too, had thought she had done fairly well in her relationship with Paul.

"But then she told me she didn't love me."

Just as Paul had told her. Not that he didn't love her, not exactly, but that something was missing.

"And I knew by the way she said it, that she already loved someone else. She said, of course, she would go through with our marriage. It was her duty. What she'd been born to.

"That's when I came to Touch-the-Clouds. I needed to think. There is something that cuts the legs out from under a man to hear a woman that you care for talk about marrying you as if it will be a trip to the gallows.

"I think I already knew in my heart what had to be done. But would I have had the courage to do it? Before I met you? Before I found out what I would be asking both her and I to miss? Maybe not. But, believe me, the first thing I did after I got down from the cabin that day after the storm was phone Angelica to tell her she was free.

"And then I was free. To ask you to dinner."

Erin was struck by the truth of it: they had both been on course to make a tremendous mistake. They had both willingly accepted less than they'd deserved from life.

She owed Paul a debt of gratitude that he had somehow seen that something was missing.

Valentino owed Angelica that same debt of gratitude that she had freed him.

They both owed it to the universe to embrace this second chance they had been given to get it right.

"Oh, Valentino," Erin whispered. "I called you an ass. I didn't even give you a chance."

"Well, given that my engagement was unexpectedly announced—equally surprising to me as to you—I can hardly blame you. Though I did at first. I blamed you. I was hurt.

"I thought you, of all people, should know who I was. My family—my mother, the queen—had gotten wind that I was with you. She rushed the announcement, thinking it would force my hand, force me back into the fold. She counted on me to be who I have always been. A man who put duty first.

"But when I left here, and I wasn't that man anymore, I couldn't put anything first, before what I had felt for you. So, I called it off. I tried to make it seem as if it had been my decision, hoping it would protect Angelica.

"Unfortunately, even having lived with the

media all my life, I could not have predicted the ensuing circus."

He smiled wryly. "Angelica let me know, in no uncertain terms, she did not need my protection. And that she would make her own choices.

"Which were to be true to herself and show the entire world she was not afraid to marry the man that she loved."

"I've been a complete idiot," Erin said softly. And not just about getting angry with him, jumping to conclusions, but about accepting so much less from life than it wanted to give her.

"Yes, you have been," he teased her.

She slugged him softly on the arm and he pretended hurt. "At least I didn't blow up my own eyebrows."

They laughed and the laughter made something inside Erin sing back to life. She realized she had not laughed since he had left.

"What now?" she asked him. "Where do we go from here?"

"Before," Valentino told her, "I wanted you to come to my kingdom. I wanted to see if we could have a future."

She registered the *before*. Her heart fell. She had, it seemed, missed her chance.

"But now?" she said. "Why are you here if I have thrown away my chance?"

"Thrown it away?" he asked, astounded. "That's not it, at all."

"Then what is *it*?"

"Traveling to the kingdom right now is out. The press are on me like hounds on the fox. If you showed up now, they would never leave us alone. We would have drones buzzing us every time we tried to step out. I couldn't ask you into that, and I needed to escape it.

"And then I thought, *I know the perfect place to escape.*"

"That's why you're here," she said. "To escape."

"Why are you so resistant to the truth?" he asked her softly.

"Which is?"

"Erin, I want to be with you. I was dying without you. Yes, I want to escape. I want to get lost in your eyes. I want to dive into them as if they were a cool pond on a hot summer day. I want to let what I see in them fold over me and soothe me, to heal all the parts of me that are wounded.

"I want to see where this all can go. I want to spend a week up here, intensely with you, and nothing else. How many places in the world would allow such an experience?"

That was true. She had never seen the cabin quite like that. A sanctuary. A love nest, hidden from the rest of the world.

"I want to see if the universe brought me to a ski hill in a storm so that I could change my destiny," Valentino told her softly. "So that I could know love instead of duty."

Love?

It seemed so wrong. It seemed too soon. It seemed so right. It seemed as if the rules of time were silly structures, not intended for them.

Destiny.

That is what this felt like. Destiny.

"Is it wrong to want to do so without the surprise of a drone shot of our most private moments being splattered all over the front pages? I admit I have sent the paparazzi on a bit of a wild-goose chase, worthy of their own devious devices, so that I could have time with you. Just you."

Erin carefully set down her hot chocolate.

And then she leaped into his lap, twined her arms around his neck and took his lips with her own. Homecoming.

"I plan to fit into your world," he informed her between kisses.

Didn't he know he already did? Wasn't it obvious?

"I brought books with me. So we don't get bored."

"I don't think there's much chance we are going to get bored," Erin told him. Still, if he'd brought books, she was hoping for the *Kama Sutra.*

Or maybe they could lie in bed and read Elizabeth Barrett Browning to each other.

"How do I love thee? Let me count the ways..."

"How to Build an Igloo," he announced, pleased.

CHAPTER THIRTEEN

As it turned out, Valentino discovered building an igloo, aside from needing perfect snow, required several elements that the book failed to mention.

For amateurs, building an igloo required a good sense of humor. It required puzzle-building ability. It required tenacity. Most of all, it required that he and Erin to work as a team.

If you wanted to get to know someone, he decided, building an igloo was nearly the perfect way to do that.

But that activity—and all else they did from cooking simple meals to making the bed together—was overshadowed by the awareness of each other that crowded out nearly everything else. Everything was complicated by it...and made better by it. His life had taken on a light that shone more brilliantly than the sun on snow around them.

Her laughter filled him.

Her touch healed him.

Her intelligence awed him.

Her strength complemented his strength.

Erin and Valentino had somehow happened on an activity that unveiled to them how, despite so many cultural differences, they were incredibly compatible.

And despite the fact they exhausted themselves on their project, they barely slept. Talking deep into the night, often falling asleep with the next word dying on their lips.

And yet they woke energetic, filled with excitement for another day spent together. Valentino had never felt so exquisitely and intensely connected to another human being in his entire life.

It filled a part of him that Valentino had not been aware was empty.

Finally, three days and six collapsed, abandoned, restarted, rethought, reconfigured igloos later, they stood staring, awed, at their completed project.

The polished snow blocks that formed the dome got their strength only from leaning on each other. There was no additional supporting structure.

There was a lesson about life here, Valentino thought.

"It's supposed to support the weight of a man standing on the roof, if we did it correctly," he announced.

Erin grinned impishly at him and crossed her fingers.

Like an ice climber, he scaled the rounded wall. On the top of it, he pulled himself to standing. It was a gorgeous, spring-come-early kind of day. He surveyed the clearing that had become his world: the cabin, smoke chugging out the chimney; the clearing still filled with the melting outlines of snow angels; closer, the cat in a basket they had brought for him, belly to the sun, paws pointed at the air, indifferent to their accomplishments.

Valentino crouched and held out his hand to Erin.

She giggled—that carefree, breathless

sound he had come to live for—and took his hand despite the fact she was protesting.

"Does the book say anything about it supporting the weight of two people?"

"Let's live dangerously," he suggested and pulled her up beside him on the dome. It was a perilous balance on the slippery curved surface, but they clung to each other, as interlocked as the snow blocks.

Isn't that exactly what they were doing? Living dangerously? Challenging every limitation others—and themselves—had tried to put on them?

The structure—their salute, really, to forging their own way in a world that wanted to tell them what to do—held.

He kissed her and let go of her hand. Erin slid on her bottom off the roof and he followed her, the crystal-clear air of the clearing ringing with their laughter.

He gathered supplies they had brought— a blanket, a candle, a thermos of tea—and crawled through the ice tunnel that led to the interior of their snow structure.

Given how bright it was outside, it was

fearsomely dark in there. He spread the blanket and lit the candle. Erin wiggled in, the cat in her jacket.

It was tinier than they had first envisioned, but that meant the candle they had brought in, plus their body warmth, heated the space, as the book had promised it would. There was just enough room to shrug out of their jackets.

"It's tight in here," Erin said.

"Cozy," he corrected her.

"Here's to cozy." Erin unscrewed the lid from the thermos, put it to her lips and then passed it to him.

He took a sip and offered his own toast. What had become *their* toast.

"Here's to surprises."

Four full days with her and she was still surprising him in the most delightful ways. He still loved his lips touching places her lips touched, like the rim of the thermos. Still lived for intimacy between them, small touches. Still was awed by the growing comfort, the heated looks, the moments of quiet contentment.

Harvey, on her lap, seemed quite crabby about the whole experiment. He glared back and forth between them, as if to say, *Uh, we have a perfectly good cabin...what nonsense is this?*

Nonsense of the best sort, Valentino thought.

And yet getting to know her better was an agony, too. Because, every day, his feeling that he could not live in a world without her intensified.

But this snowbound world was perfect. Here they could be private. And playful. Completely themselves.

Could he really expose her to the deep scrutiny that she would encounter in his world, a world completely alien to her?

Could what they had discovered about each other here stand up to the very unusual stresses of his life? At this moment, flushed with triumph and accomplishment, all his doubts fell away. In this moment, it felt as if what they had could stand up to anything.

"You have showed me your world," he told her.

She smiled. "That's not exactly true," she

said. "You have showed *me* my world. Opened my eyes to it. Showed me a way of looking at it, and a way of being in it, that I did not have four days ago."

She reached out and touched his cheek. Her eyes on his face held an expression that was everything a man could ever hope for.

Valentino felt *seen.*

He slipped his own hand up to cover hers, slid her fingers to his lips and tasted the now familiar taste of her.

If two people could use nothing more than their intention, their intelligence, their willingness to learn, to build a structure that could hold their weight out of something as flimsy, as insubstantial, as snow, couldn't they do anything?

"Come to my world," he whispered. "Let me show it to you. Everything will seem new. Please say yes."

She looked at him deeply.

Valentino was aware that everything Erin knew was here. This was her world. Over these days together, he had discovered, as she'd talked about her life, how safe she had made it, how the turmoil of her childhood had made her cling to routines, long for safety and security.

Did he have a right to do this? To ask this of her? It was too late for doubts. He had done it. He was aware he was holding his breath.

"Yes," she whispered.

And Valentino began to breathe again.

Erin could not believe what was happening to her life. Was this how you were rewarded for toasting the universe with *to surprises*?

She, Erin O'Rourke, Canadian account clerk whose only claim to fame was her father's skiing career, was on a private jet.

A royal jet.

The aircraft, staffed with uniformed people, had more opulent furnishings than most houses she had been in. It was more luxurious than the presidential suite that Valentino had inhabited at the Northern Lights Hotel.

There was even a bedroom, a master suite she had glimpsed on their way to the main cabin area. It was a beautiful space of many cushions, gray silks and deep walnuts. It made her heart hammer to think of doing some of the things they had done up here at thirty thousand feet. She was stunned by how the exoticness of that possibility stirred something in her that she had not known she possessed.

However, on their last night in the cabin in her world—the one that had become their world—Valentino had briefed her a bit on protocol.

How to address his mother when they met. How to handle salutes, attention, the press. Reluctantly, he had informed her, there was one area of their life they would have to put on hold as they entered his world.

Even if he had not told her, she would have known as soon as they got on the jet. She would have known by the way he avoided taking her hand, touching her, that they had entered a place where he had to be extraordinarily careful. Where they would both have to be extraordinarily careful if they did not want to earn the censure of the palace and the clamoring of the press.

It might have all been a little overwhelming except for the fact Harvey was in a basket in her lap, letting her know he was mightily unimpressed with his first trip in an airplane and overseas. He yawned and licked a paw.

And, of course, Valentino was at her side. It was slightly unsettling to see he was addressed, always, as Your Highness, or sir. It was slightly unsettling to think all of this was his.

His hand found hers and gave it a quick squeeze before letting it go again as they prepared for takeoff. She realized, when he let go, that the unabashed passion they had for each other at the cabin would not be appropriate here.

Obviously, because of his position, the very physical part of their relationship needed to be reined in for appearances' sake.

For some reason, that made her nearly breathless with wanting him. Erin took his hand, surreptitiously ran her thumb over his wrist, until he looked at her with such heat, she thought she would melt.

A staff member came to speak to them.

She slid her hand from his and looked out the window, smiling.

For all that he was a prince, Valentino was still the one who had given her a sense of discovering the new in her own world.

The one who was leading her now into this brand-new world. This was no time to be afraid. It was time to accept that life was an incredible adventure.

She had accepted the invitation.

She had to throw herself into it. There was no room here for that girl who harbored, always, the sense of not being good enough.

Indeed, it felt as if Valentino's attention to her had erased that part of her forever.

As soon as Erin stepped out the door of the plane, she knew she was in a magical place. The sun was warm but gentle on her face, like a kiss. The air held the mingled perfumes of spice and flowers.

From that first step, she entered the most extraordinary experience of her life determined to embrace every single thing about it.

A royal limousine met them and whisked them down narrow streets with whitewashed medieval buildings that seemed to lean over the streets, keeping the sun from reaching the cobblestones. Flowers cascaded out of the high window boxes that the sun touched. In places, colorful clotheslines, two stories up, spanned the street. Though the car was air-conditioned, Erin opened the windows to fully experience not just the sights but the sounds and smells of Valentino's home.

She could hear strains of music pouring out windows, laughter, a lovers' squabble, children shrieking, dogs barking. The air was redolent with scent: spicy cooking smells, exotic flowers, the sun on the white bricks.

It was fantastic.

The palace sat at the edge of those crooked streets, jumbled buildings, houses stacked up hillsides.

The cheerful chaos was left behind them as imposing wrought-iron gates swung open to lush expanses of lawn, gorgeous gardens, gurgling fountains. And at the end of a long, curving driveway, a palace.

It was not the typical "fairy-tale" palace, like Neuschwanstein Castle in Germany, but rather an imposing and majestic square. Constructed of huge white-marble blocks, the severity of the structure was diluted by the exquisitely carved detail around the doors and windows, the intricate designs on the caps that topped pillars, the lush vines that crawled up the walls, and the huge concrete vats of flowers that abounded.

Once inside the palace, Erin could not keep her mouth from popping open in astonishment. Though it was warm outside, the inside of the building was cool. As Valentino took her through to her suite, there was almost too much to take in: gorgeous gilt-framed paintings, chandeliers that dripped priceless crystals, hand-carved wainscoting, silk wallpapers, detailed tapestries and hand-knotted rugs.

Her suite was as ornate as the rest of the palace. She looked around, terrified to touch anything. It was his touch that grounded her.

By themselves, finally, he gathered her to him, covered her in kisses. Her ears, her eyelids, her neck, finally her lips.

"I've been longing to do that all day," he said huskily in her ear.

"Me, too," she said, taking his hand and pulling him toward the bedroom. "Should we—"

He backed away from her. "Sorceress," he said. "Sadly, there are no secrets in the palace. Your stay here will be a chaste one."

She looked at his lips and felt longing rip through her. Seeing him in this world—and their relationship being forbidden fruit—made her want to be exactly what he had called her. A sorceress, tempting him. She took a step toward him, but he laughed, shook his head and slipped out the door.

She found her way to her bedroom—a huge, carved four-poster was at the center of it. Tapestries hung on the walls.

Who does the dusting? She wondered practically.

There was a lovely pillowed bed for Harvey. The thought of a litterbox in this space made her wince, but still there was one, placed subtly in a closet.

She put Harvey on the bed. He sniffed it

and settled himself approvingly on what she was fairly certain was pure silk.

Her suitcase had arrived before her—it had not touched her hands once since she had packed it—and now it had been unpacked for her! It made her wish she'd had time to invest in new underwear! She hadn't been prepared for the fact people would be touching her things.

She went through to the adjoining bathroom. The tub, veined marble, was large enough to swim in. The fixtures were gold—and probably the real thing.

She suddenly felt overwhelmed. The plane, and now this. Plus, unspoken rules around being with the man she had become so comfortable with. She felt she was being plunged into a world where she could never belong.

And yet when Valentino came to collect her, her doubts were erased, again, by the look in his eyes. He stepped inside her room, took her face in both hands, and kissed her deeply and passionately.

"Don't do that and expect a chaste relationship," she warned him.

"You're right. It won't do to have you glowing with passion at the moment. Should we get meeting my mother over with?"

"Is it going to be horrible?" she asked.

"Of course," he said with a grin.

But it wasn't horrible. His mother was at a table in an ornate sitting room, which was a relief, since Erin thought she might be sitting on a throne with a crown on her head.

Instead, she was having tea, with a dog at her feet. She was also wearing a dress that might be called dowdy, if one dared to call the queen's dress dowdy, even in their own mind.

It was obvious where Valentino had gotten his good looks from.

They sat at the table with her, and a servant poured tea. Valentino introduced Erin as his friend. His mother, the queen, had obviously been putting people at ease her entire life and she was very, very gracious.

"I understand you love animals," she said, and Erin realized she had been *briefed*—given one detail about her—to make her feel welcomed. The queen was also good at not showing what she really felt. Though she was extremely charming, there was an impenetrable quality to her charm and her eyes were guarded.

They mostly discussed Harvey and the dog who snoozed at her feet.

"See?" Valentino teased her as they left the audience, "You survived."

"I feel kind of sorry for her," Erin admitted.

"For my mother?" he asked, incredulous.

"I get a sense of no one knowing her. Of deep loneliness. I—I'm sorry. I shouldn't have said that." There was probably a law against making observations about the queen!

But Valentino was looking at her, a small smile playing across his lips.

"You see, Erin? You see what others do not. They see her wealth, her power, her privilege, her station. Everyone wants something from her. It makes it impossible to trust, to be liked for herself alone. You see the heart she has never felt safe to show anyone."

His voice dropped. "It is the life you are saving me from."

After the audience with the queen, they seemed to be free, but with parameters. They had dinner that night in a small walled garden off her suite. Even though an exquisite meal had been left for them, and they were not interrupted, Erin was aware they were not really alone.

"Are there people everywhere?" she whispered to him. "Hovering in the shadows, waiting for you to need something?"

"I'm afraid so."

And so even after the delicious food, it felt as if they were starving. To touch each other. It was strangely tantalizing, their relationship suddenly fraught with suspense. Anticipation.

They got up from the table and Valentino led her to the darkest corner of the garden. He claimed, loudly, he wanted to show her a white flower that looked particularly stunning at night.

Instead, he pressed her up against the garden wall and ravaged her mouth, kissing her until they were both frantic with need.

Valentino yanked away from her when they heard the clink of dishware being cleared from the table in the garden. Erin giggled breathlessly. He ran a frustrated hand through the dark tangle of his curls.

"I thought my family left torture behind in the Dark Ages," he muttered.

The dishes clattered more loudly. They waited until the sounds stopped and then, like errant teenagers—and with all the same pent-up longing—went to their separate quarters.

As he showed her his country, they traveled in a three-car entourage. The first day they brought Harvey, but after that, to her shock, the cat agreed to tolerate Milo as his babysitter. She exchanged phone numbers, making Milo promise to call if there were any problems. She reminded herself—a little pathetically—of a nervous mother.

She had rarely been without the cat for over a year since his eyesight and hearing had started failing so badly, but she knew she was being silly. Milo had her phone number. She had his.

Valentino was an incredible tour guide, well versed in his country's colorful history, proud of its many accomplishments, passionate about the roads forward into the future. The country was amazing, but it was also amazing to see Valentino in this element. His element.

In the cabin, he had been exploring a new world. Eager, to be sure, but adorably inept at so many practical things.

Now, she saw the man that he truly was: confident, polished, comfortable with his position and power.

It heightened her already over-the-top awareness of him and a new tension sizzled between them. His hand reaching for hers nearly scorched her. Stolen kisses had the intensity of exploding rockets. His gaze resting on her could make her heart start beating so hard it felt as if it would break out of her chest.

After they had toured the ruins of one castle, they came out to find the road on both sides lined with people.

"Word must have got out that I was here," he said. "You don't mind if we stop, do you?"

"Of course not." Uncertainty hit her. "Do you want me to wait in the car?"

"No!"

She could tell his security team, who traveled in cars in front and behind them, especially Colonel Del Rento, hated this spontaneous stop as much as he loved it. It was evident he was admired and adored by the people of his country, and that he reciprocated those feelings.

He introduced her to the people as his friend. In some ways, it was not completely unfamiliar. At the height of her father's career, this is what it had been like traveling with him. People had recognized him, wanted his autograph, wanted to speak to him. Sometimes, quite a crush of people would form around him.

The big difference was that with her father, he had enjoyed the attention immensely because it had been all about *him*.

Erin noticed Valentino's utter and sincere interest in people. He smiled, clapped a shoulder, threw back his head and laughed. He would bend close to hear more clearly.

As with her father, when she sometimes had received reflected attention, mostly of the *Are you going to be a ski star, too?* variety, some people were very aware of her. Embarrassingly, one older lady curtsied. A little girl presented her with a hastily gathered bouquet of crushed flowers.

Her nose buried in those lovely flowers, Erin noticed Valentino being passed a baby boy. Something in her went very still as Valentino handled the baby with an ease that was unusual in a single man. He admired him and kissed his fat cheek before handing him back.

He, Erin thought, before she could stop herself, *is going to make a great father.*

The thought discombobulated her. He had made it clear, when he had come to the cabin, when he had brought her here, that he wanted to see what the future held for him.

He had introduced her to his mother.

Now, he was introducing her to his people.

Her future could be him. This land. His babies. A euphoria swept through her. It was quite unlike anything she had ever felt before.

It only grew as she watched him talk to one of the people in his entourage when they got back to the cars. Quietly, he was giving names and instructions: make sure we find out about crop insurance; send flowers to that woman, she's lost her husband; make sure that baby gets a teddy bear.

What she didn't like about traveling with him was the sense of constant surveillance—though it made those kisses stolen in that tiny cave at the base of the ruin even more sizzling—and the fact they were not free to be spontaneous. Erin longed to immerse herself in the noisy marketplaces, to have coffee and pastry at one of those outdoor cafés. But that was not his life.

Her favorite thing became the visit to the beach at the end of each day of sightseeing. While the front of the palace faced sweeping lawns and gardens, the back of it was perched on a rocky outcrop that overlooked the sea.

To Erin's delight, Valentino showed her a secret set of stairs cut into the granite that led to a gorgeous, private, white-sand beach.

Here, finally—save for Harvey, who had yowled his dismay when she had tried to leave him yet again—they were alone. They were children again—as playful on that beach as they had been at her cabin. They built sand-castles. They played in the turquoise waters, running, splashing each other. There were snorkels, and Valentino showed her the magical world that existed right below the surface of the sea. They stole kisses and touched sun-warmed skin.

Today, after a long day of sightseeing, Erin lay on a blanket. She was wearing a bikini that a few weeks ago she would not have worn. But a new her—a bolder her—was confident in herself and her body, that confidence born of the fire in Valentino's eyes when he saw her in bathing suits. She found she quite enjoyed tormenting him, pushing him to break out of the chaste prison his position put them both in.

The waves came up and he grabbed a surfboard.

"I'll show you how," he said.

For all the age-old beauty of his country, for all that she loved every minute together, how could she not love these moments best of all? Alone. Playing. Touching each other.

Standing on the surfboard was a lot harder than it looked. Soon, they were both soaked, gulping down water as they gurgled with laughter. Erin had finally just managed to stand when she saw a little gray head, bobbing toward her. Harvey had fallen in the water!

"Valentino! Save him!"

Valentino hurled himself through the water, but as she watched the rescue, she realized her crazy cat was paddling around, perfectly content.

She was laughing so hard, she had to hoist herself up on the surfboard. "Have you ever seen anything like that before?"

His laughter joined hers, and he made it to

the cat. He scooped Harvey, soaked, out of the water, came back and placed him in front of her on the surfboard she had straddled.

"Tigers swim," he told the cat. "You wonderful old warrior. You are part tiger, aren't you?"

Harvey preened.

And then Valentino put his hand on the back of Erin's neck and tugged her mouth to his. The kiss tasted of the sea. And of sand. Of the sun's warmth. Of things new. And of things ancient. The kiss tasted of promises.

It had a texture of its own: Erin could feel her future painting itself as his mouth claimed hers. The euphoria intensified until it was like a physical tingling inside her skin trying to get out.

They had been building to this moment for days, the anticipation of it razor-sharp between them. Now it was here, every physical longing, like too much water in a dam, suddenly bursting free.

She was hungry for him. Starving. And he was hungry for her. His mouth ravaged her willing mouth. He kissed the sun-warmed tops of her breasts, owning her, claiming her, letting his lips tell her *I need you. I can't live without you.*

It felt as if she could not live one more moment without the beautiful intimacy between them. She drew his head from her breast, claimed his lips, tasted him.

And then a drone came overhead and swooped down toward them, buzzing like a bothersome fly. She lost her balance and the surfboard tilted, sending her and Harvey into the water. She surfaced, sputtering and gasping.

Valentino rescued them both, one arm holding the cat, the other protectively around her shoulder as he got them back to the sand.

As he broke away from her, he sent a fearsome glare to the drone and then gave her a look, impotent and furious, at the pleasure denied them once again.

CHAPTER FOURTEEN

VALENTINO AWOKE AND was aware of an ache of need within him. His first thought was of Erin and how his need to touch her, to kiss her, to have her, had been thwarted.

That drone, yesterday afternoon. He sighed. The reality of the world. His world.

Mostly, though, he loved showing her that world.

Loved her wonder, her enthusiasm, her delight. He was experiencing his realm through her and it seemed as brand-new and as shiny as a bright copper penny.

But he missed waking to her in the morning, as if he had done it his whole life, not just for a few days in a cabin in the middle of nowhere.

It occurred to him he was edging closer.

Not edging, really. Barreling. He had seen the look in her eyes when he had held that baby. He wanted to spend the rest of his life with her. He wanted her to have his children. He wanted her to be his queen.

There was a soft rap at the door.

Milo came in bearing a tray with coffee and a selection of local morning papers. Valentino would take breakfast in the garden, later, with Erin. He was aware that he was eager to see her, as if the gold of her hair and the green of her eyes were as new to him as that bright penny.

Today, they would go to see the olive groves in the south. He hoped to get her on a horse. She had never ridden before, and there was no better way to see the groves. He couldn't wait to share this activity that he loved with her. He hoped she would take to it, that someday she would ride as wonderfully as she skied…

Finally, he came out of his thoughts and noticed Milo was still standing there, a funny look on his face.

"Is something the matter?"

"Sir, the papers—" Milo looked so distressed.

Valentino picked up the first paper.

He looked at the front-page picture. It was of him and Erin in the water, just after they had kissed. Even though they had missed him lowering his head to her breast, it was a shamelessly intrusive photo.

The press—still hoping to milk a little more from both his and Angelica's lives—tried to follow them every time they stepped out of the palace. Thankfully, the staff had become masters at distraction, sending them in the wrong direction, dispatching decoy cars so that Erin and Valentino weren't always on display. No drones were allowed in the air within a mile of his entourage.

But yesterday that one had slipped in from the other side of the island, coming over that cliff before he'd been able to protect Erin from it.

Valentino frowned as he saw that something had been circled in the picture, and that an arrow showed an inset picture with a blow-up of the circled item.

It was Harvey, soaked, looking like a

drowned rat, sitting between Erin's legs on the surfboard.

In his language, the headline blared *Crazy Cat Lady!*

There were several papers here, and he looked through them all. Each one had the same photo—sold, no doubt, to the highest bidders—and a variation of the crazy cat lady story.

It filled him with fury like nothing he had ever felt. How dare they miss her incredible beauty, her wonder at life, and expose something so banal? How dare they zero in on this minute detail about her, and blow it up cruelly and with such exclusive focus? Why wouldn't they see her love of an aging cat for what it was? Tender? Compassionate? *Good.*

His rage intensified when he realized he was powerless against it.

He looked at Milo. They had come a long, long way since that day when Milo had gleefully announced to Erin that Valentino was going to marry someone else.

Valentino was fairly certain that Milo was

nearly as enchanted with Erin as he himself was. He adored the cat!

Milo gave him a look of pure sympathy, understanding the prince's position, maybe before he, himself, fully got it.

Valentino loved her.

He loved Erin O'Rourke madly and beyond reason. He would do anything for her. He would die to protect her.

He was suddenly and sharply aware of the demands of holding a position in a royal household. Could he invite Erin, someone he cared about deeply—that he loved deeply—into the kind of life where the public pressures could be so cruel and unrelenting? Angelica had rejected it, and she had been born to it. How unfair would it be to ask someone who didn't know the full weight of it to share this life with him?

Share this life with him?

He had become too caught up in it all. The passion had swept away his ability to be rational. The joy he had felt in her presence had made him, selfishly, just want more and more and more.

Of laughter. Of conversation. Of *wanting* with an unholy need.

How could he even consider the possibility of her and him together—forever—when he would never be able to protect her from *this*? From her life being put under a microscope; for her eccentricities to be exposed to a mean-spirited world.

She had told him about withdrawing from ski racing because she was so sensitive to her father's criticism, the expectations placed on her by the press.

How much worse would this be? A collective critical spirit aimed right at her. The person she was—who had grown up in the sanctuary of those beautiful mountains—could be destroyed by this relentless attention, this cutting meanness, this desire to focus on fault.

It was a repeating story within royal families.

The outsider was brought in. Some fool thought love would be enough. And it never, ever, was.

It had already started. With the cat. Then

it would be her hair, or a dress she chose, or an extra pound put on, or a gaffe at a royal function. They would tear away at her like vultures on carrion, making her smaller and smaller...

He could not stand the pain of what he was seeing as her possible future if he brought her into his world. He threw down the paper and gave Milo a look.

"How can you love someone and do this to them?" Valentino asked, his voice hoarse with pain. "Ask this of them?"

He supposed he hoped Milo would have an answer, would hold out hope, would help him see things from a different perspective.

Instead, the man looked absolutely crushed—as if he had just seen a place of complete light turn dark—as he turned and left the room.

Erin looked at the note from Valentino. He had canceled their plans for today. She had been so looking forward to the olive groves. He had been going to show her how to ride. The thought was terrifying. And exciting.

That was exactly what her feelings were of late: terrified and excited.

Every single thing they did together shone with a light.

He said he would be busy today, that something unexpected had come up, but if she would join him for dinner in the garden, he would be honored.

She had a lovely day. Despite being shadowed by security, she finally was able to go to a market. She had a rich and chocolatey cup of coffee and a sumptuous pastry at a local café. No one paid the least attention to her.

She felt as if she was absorbing Valentino's country through her pores. What she noticed was the softness of it, in stark contrast to her own home of harsh climates and landscapes.

Here, everything was soft: the light, the heat, the rolling landscapes, the flavors. She was falling in love with Valentino's beautiful island nation every bit as much as she was falling in love with him.

That truth warmed her, as rich and delightful as the drink she was sipping.

She loved him. Loved him. Loved him. Loved him.

The phrase was still repeating in her mind on an endless delicious loop as she entered the garden just as dusk was falling. The perfume of flowers was heavy in the air. A table had been set on the lawn. It was romantic, with a beautiful linen tablecloth, flickering candles, places already set. The stars winked like diamonds in the black-velvet sky above the garden.

Obviously, Valentino had planned a romantic dinner for two.

Her heart stopped as she saw him pacing back and forth near the back wall. He seemed nervous, and it was so unlike him. Her eyes went from him to the beautiful table setting.

He was going to propose.

He saw her and stopped. For a moment, she saw something in his face that terrified her—a sadness so acute, she wondered if someone had died.

"No Harvey tonight?" he said as he came and greeted her with the traditional kiss on each cheek.

"Milo is quite taken with him. The feeling seems to be mutual."

He glanced toward the sky. "Let's hope for some privacy," he said. "If a drone comes, we'll move inside."

The thought of the drone seemed to upset him, added to an almost agitated air about him. Something she was not accustomed to.

They sat and he poured wine. He drank his too fast, in two gigantic gulps. A feast had been put before them. It sometimes seemed as if the kitchen staff were trying to outdo themselves in their efforts to show her the wonders of their island cuisine. It was so endearing. She had made a point of going to the kitchen after every meal and discussing it with them. Thanking the chef.

Why was Valentino so not himself? Was he going to propose? Somehow, she would not have imagined it like this.

Had she imagined it? Him proposing?

Of course she had! She had imagined him on one knee, his eyes—those oh-so-familiar deep brown eyes—resting on her face, filled with tenderness and hope.

Will you...?

Yet tonight his expression was anything but tender.

Finally, she could not get on with the pretense of enjoying dinner any longer. She set down her fork.

"What is wrong?" she asked.

He hesitated. He looked anywhere but at her. But then he did look at her, drew in a deep breath, set his shoulders.

"We've made a mistake."

Her mouth fell open. This was so far from what she'd expected.

"I'm sorry," she stammered. "What?"

"Not we. Me. I'm sorry. It's unfolded too quickly."

She stared at him, not believing what she was hearing. This was the same man who had trailed his fingers across the heated surface of her skin. Insatiable. Who had stood on top of an igloo with her. Who had swam, laughing in the sea with her just yesterday, splashing her, chasing her around through the waves. Who had stolen kisses as if he could not get enough of her.

The man who had held that baby and filled her with the most terrifying thing of all... hope.

"I don't understand," she said. His face was so remote, the Valentino she thought she knew replaced with the suave and distant stranger.

She said she didn't understand. But she was beginning to, she just didn't want to.

Her life was playing out in a constant, nauseating loop: she expected one thing and the exact opposite happened.

Twice now, she had expected a proposal and gotten this instead.

Why was she so surprised? Had she really thought she was a girl who could hold a man like Valentino's interest?

Even Paul, the most ordinary of guys, had seen her for what she was.

Beyond ordinary.

Boring.

Valentino wouldn't even look at her. He looked at his hand. He was grasping the stem of his wineglass so tight, it looked as if he might snap it.

He said, "Erin, there's someone else."

She heard shame in his voice. And defeat.

Love turned to hate in the blink of an eye. The euphoria that she had been floating on since she had arrived at Valentino's home hissed out of her, air out of a pricked balloon. She could feel everything inside her collapsing—as if a bomb had been dropped—into the space that had been filled with wonder, with discovery, with bravery, with a sense of adventure.

How could he do this to her?

How could he bring her all the way here to cut the legs out from under her like this?

The awful truth hit her. She had never known him. Not at all. She had believed what she'd wanted to believe, built a fairy tale around him.

The only part of the fairy tale that was true was that he was a prince.

She should have obeyed her instincts. They had warned her he was an ass. She would not give him the satisfaction of spitting those furious words at him, of letting him know how deeply she was wounded.

She got up carefully from the table. With her spine ramrod-straight, she walked away from him. She did not look back.

Valentino watched her go. Shored up by some innate dignity, by a strength she might not have even been aware she possessed, it struck him that Erin O'Rourke moved like a queen.

He turned away from the sight, from her absolute bravery in the face of his betrayal. He was afraid if he watched any longer, he would scream *No, I didn't mean it. It was all lies. Come back.*

He shouldn't have said the last part. The most awful lie of all, about there being some-one else.

But he needed Erin not just to go but to never look back. He needed what had flashed through her eyes for him: pure and primal disgust. Maybe even hatred.

He needed those things because, if she looked back, he was not sure he would be strong enough to do what he had to do.

He needed to save her. And that meant letting her go.

If he loved her, truly, he needed to send her back to her old life before it was too late, before she was so notorious that—because of him—there could never be an old life to go back to.

CHAPTER FIFTEEN

ERIN WAS NOT even sure how she and Harvey got home. The journey was a blur. Somehow she had been back on that jet. Valentino must have arranged that in his eagerness to erase his *mistake,* to get rid of her.

For days after arriving at the resort, she felt as if she was in a fog. She could not bring herself to go to the cabin, to see if anything remained of their igloo and angels.

She went over the day before his horrible announcement with a fine-tooth comb. What had she said? What had she done that was so wrong? Why had he pulled the plug so suddenly? How could there be someone else when they had spent every waking moment together?

It must be someone from his past. Someone who had come forward after they had heard about his split from Angelica. It had to be someone more suited than her.

Erin also tried to figure out how she could be feeling one thing—she loved him, loved him, loved him—and he quite another. How was that possible without her awareness? And yet it was an awful, awful repeat of what had happened with Paul.

During the day, she was able to turn her mind to work, to other things, but in her dreams, she was with him, laughing. She would awake to a sense of grief.

Still, Erin surprised herself, too. She did not retreat from life. She did not hide out in her apartment going over things endlessly.

She found an almost shocking core of strength.

Each day Erin felt a little more certainty, a quiet confidence, that that she had never felt before. Increasingly, she was aware she might not be sure who Valentino really was, and in fact, it was quite likely she was never going to unravel the mystery of him.

But she was sure who she was.

Ironically, it was the time she had spent

with him that had awakened this new confidence in her, a quiet sense of herself.

She became aware that her insecurities were rooted in her father's criticisms. She had developed a sense of not being good enough.

When he and her mother had split, she had taken on bits of that, too. What could she have done to save her family? If she had been a different person, a better person—if she had kept skiing competitively—would it all have turned out differently?

That is why she had accepted Paul, forgiving his slights, his insults, his lack of enthusiasm for her and their relationship. Because she had felt that was all she deserved. She had accepted what she thought she could get.

Despite the bad ending with Valentino, she had *grown* in the context of loving him. She had become *more* than she was before.

Even Kelly noticed the changes in her. "You're different," she said.

Erin didn't even have to ask her how. She could *feel* some basic difference in herself, born of shared laughter, of quiet talks, of heated looks and touches. Born of being with a person where she had become more completely herself than she had ever been before: silly, strong, adventurous, bold, shy.

And despite her new strength, she indulged one weakness. Erin scoured the tabloids, online and paper copies, looking for some news of him, a glimpse of him, a look at his new lover.

But each day passed with nothing.

How was that possible? He had done everything in his power to try to keep their budding relationship away from prying eyes and he had not been successful.

In fact, just this morning, there had been a text. It was the first she had heard from anyone from her days with the prince. Milo had her phone number because he had cared for the cat.

She'd been terrified—and hopeful—when his name popped up.

Terrified that he was sending bad news about Valentino. Or a picture of the new love that she told herself she could handle seeing.

When she looked at the photo—no text,

no message—she was not sure why he had sent it.

It was a photograph of the front of a newspaper, from when she'd been there. That day that Harvey had swam with them. She vaguely remembered a drone coming over.

She wasn't able to read the headline—it was in their language. But looking at that picture, at both of them laughing, of Harvey perched on the surfboard, Erin felt exactly as she did when she first woke up every morning.

Grief-stricken.

She had closed the picture right away, feeling it robbing her hard-earned strength, feeling angry at Milo for sending it.

Partway through the day, it nagged at her. Why had Milo sent the newspaper article? It wasn't as if she could understand it.

Still, on her lunch hour, she felt compelled to open it again. She stared at the picture. Such love! How could it—

She looked at the headline. Surely, in this day and age, she could translate what it said?

Sure enough, she found an app on her phone and carefully typed in the exact lettering.

That didn't seem right.

The translation must be wrong.

Crazy Cat Lady!

Erin went very still. She got it. She got it completely.

The papers were making fun of her.

Valentino didn't have a new love interest.

He was doing what he perceived he needed to do to protect her. Just as with Angelica, he was willing to be the one who took it, who paid the price, who made the sacrifice.

For her.

To keep her safe.

She thought of his mother and the wariness in her; the loneliness she had seen in the cool shadows of the queen's eyes.

That was what Valentino was sentencing himself to. That was what he was prepared to do *for her.* That is what he thought love was.

And that was what he thought of her. That she wasn't strong enough. That he had to take it for her.

She saw Milo's sending the picture for exactly what it was.

A challenge to be more than she had ever been before: braver, stronger, more certain.

She saw it for its purpose.

To intervene like this, Milo must be extraordinarily worried about Valentino.

Erin knew what she had to do. She had to gamble that she was right. She had to trust that what had unfolded between them was real.

The most real thing that she had ever experienced.

She had to act more fearlessly than she ever had before.

Valentino was putting himself in a lonely prison because he thought she needed rescuing.

Oh, the irony. It was not her who needed rescuing! It was him.

She had to rescue the prince.

"Sir, there's someone here to see you."

"I'm not receiving today." Valentino saw

the distress on Milo's face. It had been growing for days.

Valentino, on those odd days when he glanced at himself in the mirror, could see why. He looked awful. He was losing weight alarmingly. He was unshaven. There were dark circles under his eyes. His dreams were the dreams of a man tormented by what he had lost.

He knew he had done what he'd had to do.

But he had not expected to be haunted so completely by the look on Erin's face when he had betrayed her.

Surely, he could have done it differently? Surely, he could have made her see reason without hurting her so badly?

Milo left the room, shutting the door quietly behind him, and Valentino wandered over to his window. His beautiful land had been stripped of its color. He was blind to beauty now.

He should have just told her he was dying. It felt more true than what he had said.

He heard the door whisper open.

"Milo! Leave me! I don't want anything."

Especially not him hovering with *that* look on his face.

Milo didn't answer and he turned to glare at him.

His world stopped. As he drank her in— the shining waterfall of her hair, the green of her eyes, the pale rose of her lips—he was aware of seeing color for the first time in weeks.

He could feel the weakness in him, as if he were a man drowning and a life ring was within reach. But what if you had to sacrifice someone else to save your own life?

He did not think he had any strength left. Not one ounce.

Yet he found just enough to lift an eyebrow at her, to strip the sigh within him from his voice. "How did you get here?"

"I flew. I had to bring my broom since I didn't have the private jet at my disposal."

Her words transported him back to the very beginning when he had teased her about her fairy-tale cottage minus the child-eating witch.

This was not the time for jokes. Though,

when she said it, her voice so light, like music, he could feel himself leaning toward her, leaning toward the memory of their shared laughter, leaning toward a quiet strength in her eyes.

How was it she looked so much better than she ever had, when he was so much worse?

Really, just confirmation he had done the right thing.

"I had to leave Harvey," she said. "I couldn't figure out the intricacies of traveling with him. Kelly is looking after him."

"You left Harvey?" A strange panic welled up in him. She'd only leave Harvey if it was an emergency. What if she had come to give him some awful news?

"I know. Your tabloids will be disappointed when they find out. Crazy Cat Lady with no cat."

"That was cruel of them," he said. "I'm sorry you had to see it."

She looked at him gravely then came and touched his arm. Her touch on his arm made him close his eyes and just drink in the way her closeness felt.

When he finally opened his eyes again, she was looking at him with an unsettling *knowing*. *A*s if the gig was up. As if she knew everything.

"It's okay," she said soothingly. "I'm okay."

He heard the truth in that. And wondered again at the unfairness of it. How could she be okay when he was not?

"This time," he growled at her. "What about next time? What about when they are tearing into you about your clothes, or your accent, or the fact you used the wrong fork at a state dinner? What then?"

She didn't seem to get the seriousness of this at all. She was smiling at him, ever so tenderly.

"Is that why you lied to me?" she asked.

He stiffened. "What makes you think I lied?"

"To protect me."

He made one last effort. He gathered all his strength. He said, "No! There is some-one else."

"Uh-huh," she said with aggravating and patent disbelief.

"Don't you know who I am?" he said. "People believe me."

"Maybe people who don't know you."

Every moment they had ever spent together seemed to flash before his eyes. It was true. She knew him like no one else ever had. Or ever would again.

"Valentino," she said firmly, "there is no one else."

"How do you know?" he demanded with what was left of his strength.

She cocked her head at him. "Okay. Tell me the color of her hair."

But he could not think of any hair color except the sun-on-wheat color right in front of him.

"Eyes?" she prodded him.

Green. It was the only color he could think of.

"What do you feel like when she kisses you?"

His eyes fastened on her lips and the memories seared through him white-hot.

"That's what I thought," she said. "There is no one else. I know. I know by looking at you. I should have known right away that it was a lie."

What could he say? He couldn't very well produce evidence it wasn't a lie.

"I had to make you go," he whispered.

"Because of the story," she concluded. "You thought I would be hurt by the story, by being called names."

"It wasn't just that story. It was all the stories that would come. It would be watching, helpless, as they pecked away at you. It was what a life with me would steal from you."

"You understand what you're saying, don't you?"

"Completely," he said.

"That you love me. You love me so much, you would sacrifice your own chance at happiness to protect me."

He was silent. She was so smart. Why had he thought he could fool her for any length of time?

"The irony is, Valentino, that to be the woman worthy of that love, I have to be willing to risk the arrows. I have to be strong. I can't let you protect me. I can't let you sacrifice yourself for what you perceive as my well-being.

"I don't think a life with you could steal anything of value from me. It would just give and give and give.

"Love and love and more love.

"And I'm not leaving you. No matter what you say or do, I can see your truth in your face. I can see it in how you've suffered— look at you—to protect me.

"Here's where you have it all wrong—you are not a prince riding in to rescue me. You will always be to me, first and foremost, a man not a prince.

"You will always be, to me, the one I would risk everything to rescue."

Her words poured over him like a warm balm over a raw wound. "You're turning the fairy tales on their head," he finally said.

She smiled at him. "I know, Valentino. I know."

And he could resist no longer. He reached for the life ring she had thrown him. He allowed himself to be rescued by her love. He went into her arms and laid his head on her shoulder, the warrior home from the war.

"Erin," he whispered, his voice hoarse and raw, the warrior's surrender complete, "I love you. I will love you forever."

Valentino watched Erin come across the meadow toward him. Summer had come to the mountains and the clearing, once filled with snow angels, was now filled with wildflowers. She wore a ring of them in the hair, which flowed freely onto her shoulders, bare to the sun.

She was wearing a white dress, though he was not sure he would have called it a bridal gown. She carried a basket, Harvey lolling in it contentedly, as if he, not she, was the star of today's show.

Valentino wondered: did all grooms feel this way as their bride came toward them? On top of the world? Like the luckiest man alive? Anointed by a mysterious force? Made strong and whole, not by their own power, but by love?

Erin could have had the wedding of the

century. She could have worn a gown encrusted with jewels and a priceless lace veil that had been passed down for centuries. She could have had her wedding in a cathedral with a full children's choir, with a carriage waiting outside the door to carry them through the streets of the country that had come to adore her during the short days of their courtship.

Indeed, that wedding Erin had rejected, was what his mother had wanted. And her father, Enrique, would have been beside himself with delight if the wedding had been conducted with pomp and circumstance.

But this was Erin's day and she knew exactly what she wanted.

In the last few months, she had come into herself in ways that were as unexpected as they were wonderful. She *shone* with life. She had a unique ability to embrace the unexpected. The love flowed out of her and embraced everyone that she touched, which was why she had become so beloved to his people in such a short time.

But she had held firm about today.

She wanted to celebrate, not who they were publicly but what this cottage and this meadow had given them.

Whenever they were here, they were just two people and it was love that crowned them, love that lent them its glory.

In light of how difficult it was to keep a secret, to keep things private, it was something of a miracle that they had managed to have only a few other people here: Milo, Kelly, Ricky and an officiant.

In a short while, a helicopter would whisk the visitors away.

And they would be home.

Not in this meadow, as much as they loved it, and not in the cottage.

Home was where they were, together.

Forever.

EPILOGUE

THIS, VALENTINO THOUGHT, was possibly one of the hardest things he had ever done. He held the cat in his arms, wrapped in a hand-made blanket that had been a gift to Harvey from Milo.

Milo, who never stopped—even though more than a year had passed—trying to make it up to his princess, to Erin, that he had been the one who had delivered the cruel news of Valentino's engagement to Angelica.

Erin was at Valentino's side, the baby due any day, tears streaming down her face, as they made their way to the small walled garden where they still made time for each other every single day and shared romantic meals.

Even now it occurred to him how Harvey had protected Erin right until the end. Except for his increasing blindness and inability to hear, there had been no long illness, no injuries, no loss of appetite or interest in life.

They had just woken up this morning and Harvey had looked for all the world as if he was asleep in his basket next to their bed. In fact, they had gone out and had breakfast before noticing he had not joined them, as he usually would at the first sniff of food.

The cat had not been asleep.

Valentino had notified the gardener, who had dug a small hole and now waited beside it, head bowed, shovel in hand.

The gardener must have told others because staff were now streaming into the garden, silent and respectful as Valentino knelt and laid Harvey in the tiny grave.

Valentino touched the blanket and said out loud, "Your work here is done, old warrior. You truly had the heart of a tiger. But it's my job now. You rest in peace, knowing I will make her feel safe. Cherished. Listened to."

If it was hard for Erin, in her condition, to get down, it didn't seem like it. She knelt by the grave, touched her fingers to her lips and then to that blanket.

"Thank you," she whispered. "My friend."

In her new language she whispered, *"Beloved."*

Valentino drew her to her feet and put his arm around her shoulders. She turned her face into him and cried as the gardener silently shoveled.

When he was done, Valentino lifted her chin and nodded over his shoulder to direct her attention to what was happening.

They were coming forward, the palace staff, one by one. Each of them held a single flower, which they laid on that small heap of rich, newly turned black soil until it was blanketed with bright blossoms.

Harvey had become quite famous. Rather than shirking the *Crazy Cat Lady* title the press had so maliciously branded her with in those first public days of their relationship, Erin had embraced it. Soon, Harvey had his own social media accounts and his own channel on the streaming service. At first, it was only the people of Canada and Lorenzo del Toro who embraced Harvey.

But then he had become a media sensation

with millions of followers and millions of views of his videos, which were sometimes nothing more than him snoring softly on top of Milo's blanket in his basket. In the fall, they had allowed a charity to make a calendar of him and the sales had been through the roof.

The cat, according to experts in such things, had made the Royal family "relatable." The cat, and Erin, with her natural athletic grace, her easy way, her intelligence, her charm, her instinct for how to do the right thing, had brought his family out of the Dark Ages.

She had done it so gently, and with such humor and compassion, that it had not been a painful transition.

It seemed the last flower had been laid, when the garden gate swung open. Milo came through it, though you could barely tell it was him for the size of the giant spray of yellow flowers he carried. He was weeping noisily as he walked. He knelt before the grave, set his flowers on it.

This is who Erin was. Hugely pregnant, she didn't even hesitate to get back on her knees. She knelt beside Milo, put her arm around him and leaned her head against his shaking shoulder.

She was putting away her own pain to bring him comfort.

The staff—Milo—were here for the cat, of course. But it was really for her, to acknowledge the gift she had brought to this island and to his household. Humanity.

These people were not her staff.

They were the family she had always wanted. And they knew it.

Valentino knew it. He was her family. Soon, they would welcome a baby. Despite pressure to reveal the sex, the truth was they lived by their motto—*to surprises*—and did not themselves know whether the child would be a boy or a girl.

He looked at the two people kneeling by the small grave. This was life then: one day you said hello and one day you said goodbye.

He could feel them rising to the challenge, dancing with the timeless, glorious, endless cycle of death and birth.

And love. That incredible force that Valentino had come to know.

That power that transcended it all.

* * * * *

00219845   ✔ KU-517-662

THE P   OF WALF   RARY

ROYAL HISTORICAL SOCIETY
STUDIES IN HISTORY

JOHN BURNS

JOHN BURNS

Kenneth D. Brown
Lecturer in Economic History
The Queen's University of Belfast

THE POLYTECHNIC OF WALES LIBRARY TREFOREST

LONDON
ROYAL HISTORICAL SOCIETY
1977

941·08230924
bUR BRO

© Kenneth D. Brown 1977

ISBN 0 901050 34 2

The Society records its gratitude to the following, whose generosity made possible the initiation of this series: The British Academy; The Pilgrim Trust; The Twenty-Seven Foundation; The United States Embassy's Bicentennial funds; The Wolfson Trust; several private donors.

Printed in England
by Swift Printers Ltd
London, E.C.1.

219845

CONTENTS

ACKNOWLEDGEMENTS

This book has been several years in the making and I have incurred numerous debts of gratitude. The Twenty-Seven Foundation provided a generous grant to facilitate most of the research on which chapters six to eight are based. The staffs of the several libraries mentioned in the bibliography were unfailingly helpful and courteous. Dr Joyce Bellamy kindly placed at my disposal material on John Burns which she had collected for the *Dictionary of Labour Biography*. Professor Gordon Cherry of Birmingham University offered helpful guidance on the difficult subject of early housing and town planning legislation. Rather different but equally welcome assistance was given by my brother, Dennis Brown, and uncle, Norman Pratt, both of whom provided hospitality on the numerous occasions I found myself in London. Mrs Louise Porter typed the manuscript with all her usual speed and accuracy.

I am grateful to the British Library of Political and Economic Science, the British Library Board and to Lord Gainford for permission to quote respectively from the Passfield, Burns, and Gainford Papers. If I have failed to contact any other copyright holders I sincerely apologise to them.

My friend and former colleague, Chris Wrigley, read each chapter as it was written and did much to shape the book in its early stages. Dr Kenneth O. Morgan of The Queen's College, Oxford, and my colleague, Alun Davies, both read the manuscript in draft form. To all three I am particularly grateful for helping me to clarify obscure passages, improve others, and to eliminate many errors of fact and interpretation. The imperfections which remain are, of course, entirely my own responsibility.

This book is dedicated to my wife who must by now feel that she has lived with John Burns for long enough.

The Queen's University of Belfast   Kenneth D. Brown

INTRODUCTION

John Burns was born in 1858, the year of London's 'Great Stink', and many of his early associates must have later been tempted to take the popularly coined name for the foul odours then emanating from the River Thames and apply it as well to Battersea's famous agitator and politician. For Burns was the first major British labour leader to reject the demands for doctrinal loyalty and consistency made by newly emerging working-class and socialist political parties, a rejection for which he has never been forgiven. In the mythology of the labour movement Burns's name has become synonymous with betrayal. Indeed, a sometime colleague in the revolutionary Social Democratic Federation, Joseph Burgess, wrote a biography of Burns in 1911 with the sole intention of warning others against the danger of following him on the downward path to Liberalism, and he succeeded in portraying his subject as a blend of Titus Oates, Judas Iscariot, and Peter the Painter.[1] In his preface to the book the Federation's founder, H.M. Hyndman, expressed surprise that anyone should think it worthwhile to write about Burns at all. 'The record of a turncoat from his class, who has done all he can in office to thwart any improvement being made in the condition of those whose cause he formerly pretended to champion, is not very pleasant to read.[2] Will Thorne, another leading Social Democrat, claimed that men like Burns 'only come into our movement for what personal aggrandizement they can get out of it'.[3] Equally jaundiced were the comments made by F.D. Summers in his pamphlet, *John Burns the Battersea Liar,* and later leftwing writers have continued in similar vein. One communist author, for instance, while paying tribute to Burns's early work, goes on to deplore the fact that his ambition finally overcame his earlier idealism.[4]

On a different tack Burns's performance as President of the Local Government Board in Liberal administrations between 1906 and 1914 has also been much criticised. Here, too, his name has become a byword,

[1] This was Robert Blatchford's verdict when he reviewed the book in the *Clarion,* 19 May 1911.

[2] J. Burgess, *John Burns, the Rise and Progress of a Right Honourable* (Glasgow, 1911), vii.

[3] W. Thorne, *My Life's Battles* (1925), 119.

[4] *London's Struggle for Socialism,* ed. G. Armstrong (1948), 53.

epitomising ministerial paralysis in the face of sycophantic and over-bearing civil servants. Beatrice Webb noted in her diary that she was initially against the Labour Party taking office in 1923, 'instinctively fearing the "John Burns's attitude" on the part of the Labour leaders when once they are face to face with officials'.[1] Bernard Shaw suggested such a weakness in his play, *The Apple Cart,* in which Burns appears thinly (or perhaps rotundly) disguised as Boanerges, a bluff, proletarian minister, easily deceived into believing that he was the manipulator when in fact he was the manipulated. Most recent writers have dismissed Burns's ministerial career as singularly inept, 'administrative feebleness' characterising a man who was 'out of his depth'.[2] D.C. Somervell dismisses Burns's resignation from the cabinet in 1914 as unimportant on the grounds that he should have been put out long before.[3] Nor does Burns emerge any more favourably from J.A.M. Caldwell's detailed study which presents him as a self satisfied political climber, a reactionary administrator, an incompetent parliamentary performer, and a legislative bankrupt.[4] But nearly all these modern verdicts have followed the interpretation originally placed upon events by Sidney and Beatrice Webb and those who shared their ambitious schemes of social reform before 1914. The Webbs, however, were hardly dis-passionate witnesses, for Burns dominated those areas of domestic policy in which they were so interested; indeed, he was the obstacle on which their plans foundered.

An air of mystery surrounds Burns's political eclipse after 1914. On the outbreak of war he resigned from the Board of Trade where he had gone in January 1914 after his eight year stint at the Local Government Board, and walked not only out of the government but also out of history. He never publicly explained the reasons for his resignation, nor why he subsequently quit politics altogether in 1918. Around both omissions myths inevitably accumulated, fed by his own love of the mystique thus created. Small wonder that a former cabinet colleague, Charles Masterman, could refer to him in 1927 as 'the greatest enigma of modern politics'.[5] As recently as 1970 a Battersea parliamentary candidate, commenting on an article about Burns in the

1 *Beatrice Webb's Diaries, 1912-1924,* ed. M. Cole (1952), 255.

2 Judgements made respectively by L.C.B. Seaman, *Post-Victorian Britain, 1902-1951* (1966), 28; and P. Rowland, *The Last Liberal Governments: the Promised Land, 1905-1910* (1968), 42.

3 D.C. Somervell, *British Politics Since 1900* (1950), 99.

4 J.A.M. Caldwell, 'The Genesis of the Ministry of Labour', *Public Administration* 37 (1959), 367-89.

5 *Sunday Express,* 2 January 1927. The *News Chronicle,* 25 January 1943 also referred to Burns in this way.

local press, suggested that it 'revealed the lack of authoritative documentation of Burns' career by recent historians, which is probably why so many myths have grown up about him'.[1]

On none of these matters, however, have Burns's biographers been very helpful. Summers and Burgess saw him through rose, if not red, coloured spectacles and wrote with all the moral indignation reserved by the faithful for the heretic. On the other hand, A.P. Grubb, sometime assistant editor of the *Methodist Times,* produced a hagiography, surprising in one sense because of Burns's noted lack of sympathy with most forms of organised religion.[2] It may lack the political bias of Summers and Burgess but it is shot through with elementary factual errors. More accurate and with some aspirations to objectivity was G.H. Knott's study in the Bijou biography series.[3] Published in 1901, however, it obviously has nothing to say about Burns's role as a minister. Neither do the brief contributions made by A.G. Gardiner and Justin McCarthy, both of whom really presented little more than pen portraits.[4] In similar vein was an article written at the time of Burns's entry into the Campbell-Bannerman government, although it does throw some interesting light on the attitudes which he was to bring to bear on his work at the Local Government Board.[5] Inevitably, as befitted the first working man to reach cabinet rank. Burns attracted some attention from foreign writers, but Jacques Bardoux's essays are clearly derived mainly from English sources and have almost nothing to say about his ministerial career.[6] It was not until 1943, the year of Burns's death, that G.D.H. Cole produced anything approaching a scholarly account.[7] But to some extent Cole was still grinding the Fabian axe. His pamphlet was short and not based on any detailed study in private papers and records. This latter privilege was reserved for William Kent who spent long hours in discussion with Burns during the early part of the second world war. By then, however, Burns was in his eighties, his memory hazy, or perhaps deliberately fanciful as he recalled the events

1 H. Smallbone in *South Western Star,* 25 September 1970. The article on which she was commenting was C.J. Wrigley, 'The Myth and the Facts in the Life of Honest John', ibid. 4 September 1970.

2 A.P. Grubb, *From Candle Factory to British Cabinet. The Life Story of the Right Hon. John Burns* (1908).

3 G.H. Knott, *Mr John Burns M.P.* (1901).

4 A.G. Gardiner, *Prophets, Priests and Kings* (1908), 170-8; J. McCarthy, *British Political Portraits* (1903), 179-201.

5 R. Donald, 'Mr John Burns the Workman Minister', *Nineteenth Century* (February 1906), 191-204.

6 J. Bardoux, *Silhouettes d'Outre-Manche* (Paris, 1909), 1-34.

7 G.D.H. Cole, *John Burns* (1943).

of years before. The result was a book that rambles through his life in an unstructured way, the only organising theme being that of time.[1] Its lack of perspective is further heightened by Kent's eye for a good anecdote, with the result that the real insights which the book undoubtedly contains are often obscured by a welter of stories, frequently blown up out of all proportion to their true significance. Only when his manuscript was complete did the author get access to Burns's invaluable diaries, although in fairness it must be conceded that they often serve to confirm the picture built up from other sources.

It is adequate testimony to Burns's importance that so many biographical studies of him have been produced, most of them while he was still active in public life. Since 1950, however, he has flitted fitfully across the pages of a score of works on the early British labour movement but no substantially new work on him has been undertaken.[2] He remains essentially as Burgess and the Webbs cast him, a monumental egoist who betrayed for his own ends the class on whose backs he had risen to power, and who was a total failure in government office. But much new evidence has come to light since Burns died, not least in the opening of government records and the private papers of nearly all his important political contemporaries. On the basis of this it seems time to take a fresh look at 'labour's lost leader'.

[1] W. Kent, *John Burns. Labour's Lost Leader* (1950).

[2] There are short but useful accounts of particular aspects of Burns's career in S. Pierson, *Marxism and the Origins of British Socialism: The Struggle for a New Consciousness* (1973), 190-4; and A.E. Duffy, 'Differing Policies and Personal Rivalries in the Origins of the Independent Labour Party', *Victorian Studies* 6 (1962), 43-65.

1

BATTERSEA TO NOTTINGHAM, 1858-1885

At the mid point of the nineteenth century London was the largest city in the world. In order to traverse it fully it was necessary, as the Frenchman H.A. Taine noted, 'to spend several days in succession in a cab, driving out north, south, east and west, for a whole morning, as far as those vague limits where houses grow scarcer and the country has no room to begin'.[1] In three decades after the ending of the Napoleonic Wars the city's population doubled and by 1851 roughly three million people lived in the administrative county of London. The scale and speed of this massive increase presented innumerable social problems to an antiquated system of government which embraced some 300 different bodies deriving powers from about 250 acts of parliament. Public health facilities, such as they were, crumbled beneath the unprecedented pressure. Periodically, therefore, London was racked with cholera epidemics as the rivers filled up, reeking of what Disraeli called 'ineffable and intolerable horrors'.[2] Housing was naturally at a premium. The capital's stock of dwellings had been inadequate anyway, but the supply was further reduced by the demolition necessary for the construction of railways, docks, and new government buildings. Paradoxically, even street clearance and urban improvement schemes had the same effect, as local administrators cleared away the worst slums but frequently omitted to build anything in their place.[3] Crime and vice flourished. In 1859 London had about 3,000 brothels and eight and a half thousand prostitutes.[4] Most were concentrated in the east end and the older waterside districts south of the river, but the west end too had its houses of ill-repute — for the fashionable.

Yet notwithstanding these unsavoury aspects of daily life, people continued to pour into London. Much of the population increase was made up of migrants — one estimate suggests well over 300,000 in the decade after 1841 — from other parts of Britain where traditional employment opportunities were being distorted by the impact of industrialisation.[5] Not that the capital necessarily offered better

---

1 Quoted in A. Briggs, *Victorian Cities* (1968 ed.), 86.

2 Quoted in F. Sheppard, *London, 1808-1870: the Infernal Wen* (1971), 283.

3 Ibid. 288.

4 Ibid. 367. Clearly there were many more. These figures refer only to those known to the police.

5 H.A. Shannon, 'Migration and the Growth of London, 1841-1891; a Statistical Note', *Economic History Review* 5 (1935), 81.

prospects of work, for some of her older major industries were beginning to feel the effect of provincial competition and were falling behind. But London's port facilities expanded as foreign trade boomed and the city retained its importance as an administrative centre. Not surprisingly, therefore, it was in the service industries that the bulk of the workforce was employed. In 1861 the Greater London area contained 469,000 workers engaged in manufacturing industry as against 903,000 in the service sector, administration, and the professions.[1] Manufacturing industry in the capital comprised two main groups. First, there were the light industries producing a range of highly finished goods such as clothing, furniture, and jewellery. These usually long-established trades were concentrated in a ring which stretched from Clerkenwell through Westminster to Southwark, Stepney, and the east end. Engineering, the other main sector and one which had enjoyed great prestige in the first half of the century, bulked large on the south bank of the Thames in Southwark and Lambeth. This district was the obvious area to which an engineer, newly arrived in London, would gravitate and it was here that Alexander Burns settled in the mid 1850s.

The son of an evicted Ayrshire peasant, Burns had come south along with many other Scots and for some time had worked for Mather and Platts the great Lancashire textile engineers, before finally settling in Lambeth. It was here that John Elliott Burns was born on 20 October 1858.[2] This latest addition to his family must have come as something of a mixed blessing to Alexander Burns, for he appears to have found it difficult to provide adequately for his wife Barbara and their large family and several of the children died in infancy. Others relieved their father's burden by leaving home or taking jobs in order to supplement the family income. Mrs Burns herself took in laundry and once he was old enough John began to work after school for a local greengrocer. When he was about nine or ten the whole family moved to Battersea, one of the fastest growing urban areas in the whole of London. The population of 1831, some 5,000, was then well on the way to reaching

1 Sheppard, *London,* 159.

2 There is some confusion about the actual date of Burns's birth. He sometimes celebrated his birthday in November and an article in the *Labour Elector,* 12 October 1889, gives November as do his apprenticeship indentures. His birth certificate shows, however, that he was registered about a month after his birth and it was probably this date that he remembered. Though it has proved impossible to trace his ancestry very far and Kent (*Burns,* 1), says that he denied any connection with Robert Burns, John Burns was not above claiming the poet as a forbear when it suited him. There is also a tradition in the village of Bedwyn, Wilts. that Burns was the illegitimate son of a lady-in-waiting and David Herbert Llewellyn, a son of the Earl of Pembroke who paid the Burns to take the child into their own family. There is no reputable historical evidence to support this.

the 100,000 it was to become by 1881. Financial hardship seems the best explanation of this move, for the family moved into a basement and the constant struggle to make ends meet was already leaving its mark on a mind that was both impressionable and alert. When he contested his first parliamentary election in 1885 Burns was to recall that he had been 'brought up under the adverse conditions peculiar to children of artisans who have a precarious existence'.[1] Soon he was compelled to leave St Mary's National School in Battersea because his father could not afford the weekly penny to keep him there, and he took a number of short-term jobs, including spells as a page boy in Hampstead and at an underground bakery in Battersea's main thoroughfare, Lavender Hill. In June 1870 he began work at Price's Patent Candle Company in Battersea Park Road, probably putting wicks in night lights. But his schooling, however brief, had stimulated his mind. He had won prizes for his work and there had been inculcated in him a love of books that was never to diminish. At a weekly wage of about four shillings he could not have had much spare cash, yet what there was apparently went on books. Two years later he moved to Wilson's in Wandsworth as a trainee rivetter. By dint of assiduous attendance at night school and supplementing his income by working as a Sunday pot boy at the Winstanley Arms he finally saved enough to become an apprentice engineer. It was perhaps indicative of his determination to better himself that he should take a job in a public house though he had decided as early as the age of eleven to be an abstainer. It was indicative of another side of the developing character that he was soon dismissed from Wilson's after an argument with his foreman.[2] Late in 1873 he was indentured as an apprentice to Messrs Horn, an engineering firm situated at Millbank. He later recalled that while at Horns he ate his lunchtime 'piece' in the cloisters of Westminster Abbey, and it was probably here that his great love of London and its architectural heritage was born.[3]

His indentures to Horn's gave him a weekly wage of five shillings, rising to fourteen in his sixth and final year. His father contracted to provide him with meat, drink, and clothing and for his part the aspiring engineer agreed, ironically as it turned out, 'to behave himself

1 Burns Papers. Battersea Collection (Hereafter B.C.) Notebook. The book contains biographical notes prepared for a speech or an election leaflet used during the 1885 general election.

2 This account of Burns's early life differs in some small detail from Kent who did not meet Burns until he was old and his memory hazy. I have used from Kent what fits in with Burns's own much earlier accounts in the *Labour Elector*, 12 October 1889, and the potted biography in the Battersea Collection notebook.

3 Burns Papers. G.L.C. Collection. Undated note in Burns's writing in box labelled 'Photographs and Invitations'.

towards his Master as a good and faithful servant ought'.[1] Alexander Burns, however, did not live to complete his part of the agreement as he died in June 1876. Burns himself also failed to get through his time at Horn's. He was already reading advanced radical literature, avidly absorbing Robert Owen, Tom Paine, Cobbett, Ruskin, and Carlyle. All of these writers evoked sympathetic responses in the mind of an adolescent who had already shown himself unwilling to accept authority without question. He later claimed that it was Owen who first gave him a 'glimpse of the millennial vision of what might be if co-operative brotherhood succeeded cut-throat competition as the principle of the social organism'.[2] But his attempts to share this vision with his fellow employees did not strike Messrs Horn as conduct becoming of a good and faithful servant and his indentures were once more cancelled. Fortunately he was able to complete his apprenticeship at Mowlem's. He also found there the man who was to show him that the ideas which had grown out of his own experience and been refined by his reading, particularly of Carlyle and Ruskin who were his favourites, were 'not a dream but a scientific theory of the evolution of industry and society'.[3] That man was Victor Delahaye, one of the numerous French exiles who had fled to London after the collapse of the Paris commune.[4] Delahaye, who had settled in Lambeth, soon took the newcomer under his wing and there were plenty of opportunities for the two to talk, as Mowlem's sent them on contract works all over the south-east. Delahaye became, as Burns later acknowledged, 'one of the formative influences of my own life' and 'a centre of inspiration to all around him'.[5] In 1872 Delahaye had helped to form in London a French Marxist group called the Comité Revolutionnaire du Prolétariat. Together this committee's *Status* and its 1874 manifesto, *A la classe ouvrière*, provide a useful guide to the sort of ideas that Burns might have picked up from Delahaye, especially as the latter was a member of the propaganda sub-committee responsible for producing the manifesto.

The C.R.P. started from the initial premise that the working class was in bondage to capitalism and that the ultimate aim of political action was the abolition of class in order to ensure equality for all and the

---

1 There is a copy of his indentures, dated 25 February 1874 in Burns Papers. B.L. Add. MSS 46288, f. 5.

2 'The Labour Party and the Books that Helped to Make It', *Review of Reviews* 33 (1906), 570.

3 Burns's own phrase used in the *Labour Elector*, 12 October 1889. S. and B. Webb, *History of Trade Unionism* (1920), 385, n.2, are wrong in asserting that Burns met Delahaye after his return from Africa in 1881.

4 See S. Hutchins, 'The Communard Exiles in Britain', *Marxism Today* 15 (1971), 90-2; 117-20; 180-6.

5 Quoted in Grubb, *Candle Factory to British Cabinet*, 32.

collective ownership of the land and means of production. To achieve working class freedom it was clearly necessary, the manifesto continued, to secure political power. 'Le pouvoir politique est indispensable pour imposer les réformes économiques exigées par les travailleurs: en conséquence, la question politique et la question sociale sont indissolublement unies et ne sont que la double face d'une seule et même question'.[1] Even more significantly, as far as the development of Burns's own views were concerned, political power was to be acquired by means of the ballot box. 'Nous répétons à nos frères en travail ce que nous disions en '71: L'abstention politique est le pire de tous les moyens, quand, à défaut d'un fusil, nous n'avons d'autre moyen de lutte que le bulletin de vote. Il faut voter'.[2] The manifesto then went on to stress that it was vital to vote only for workers, as the working class had been duped for too long by 'charlatans qui après avoir sollicité notre concours et notre appui, ne pensent plus le lendemain qu'à défendre les privilèges de la classe bourgeoise'.[3] Imbibing ideas like these, matching them against his reading and childhood experience, Burns soon found himself clashing with authority again. This time it was for asserting the right of free speech in defiance of a ban on public speaking on Clapham Common imposed by the Metropolitan Board of Works. For this misdemeanour, committed in 1878, he was arrested but acquitted. Some years later, however, when he was again in the hands of the police and for a much more serious offence, he claimed that from the age of sixteen or seventeen he had always expected that one day he would be 'brought face to face with the authorities for vindicating the class to which I belonged'.[4] Yet the incident on Clapham Common had one happier outcome, for amongst the audience were a Battersea shipwright named Gale, and his daughter, Martha, who together led the public protests against Burns's arrest. This was the beginning of a friendship that soon deepened into love.

In 1879 Burns at last completed his apprenticeship and joined the West London branch of the Amalgamated Society of Engineers, his first formal contact with the organised working-class movement. He promptly fell out with his employer who refused him the wages of a

1 'Political power is vital in order to secure the economic reforms desired by the workers; consequently the political and social questions are inextricably linked and are merely two sides of the same problem'. Comité Revolutionnaire du Prolétariat, *A La Classe Ouvrière* (1874), 15.

2 'We repeat to our comrades what we said in '71; political abstention is the worst of all methods when, in the absence of arms, we have no other way to fight except through voting. We must vote'. Ibid. 8.

3 The charlatans who, having solicited our help and support, can only think the next day of defending the privileges of the bourgeoisie'. Ibid. 15.

4 Quoted in Kent, *Burns*, 10.

skilled man to which he was now entitled, and in consequence he applied successfully for a post as an engineer foreman with the United Africa Company. How his decision to go to Africa was received at home is a matter of conjecture. Except for his mother and two younger brothers, David and Alexander, Burns appears to have had very little to do with the rest of his family, suggestive perhaps of that egocentricity which characterised him as he matured. Certainly Martha must have missed him and he certainly missed her, but he needed a job and clearly wished to travel. At any rate, an undated manuscript in his papers headed 'Trip to the Niger' begins by asserting that he was 'out of work. In love and adventurous'.[1]

The physical activity for which some of the Burns family showed a marked capacity — brother Alex was an amateur boxer of some local note and Burns himself enjoyed cricket and skating and played football for Wandsworth Clarence Rovers — found plenty of outlets in Akassa on the West African coast. As soon as Burns arrived he was met by another company employee, John Parkin, and together they 'commenced to work. Felled trees, built factory, enginehouses etc'.[2] For nearly two years Burns worked in Akassa, moving steadily towards the conclusion that poverty was a product of capitalist economic organisation, for as he told a friend later, there was far more poverty, slavery, and human misery in the slum areas of London than there was in Africa.[3] The first speech he ever delivered under the aegis of the Social Democratic Federation was larded with references to his African experiences, all used to justify his demand for socialism. Africa also provided living proof of the evils of imperialism. 'The natives', he observed after one lengthy trip into the interior, 'lived very happy till the white man comes . . . All the rows caused either by missionaries or agents provoking the natives'.[4] When in 1885 Khartoum fell and General Gordon was killed Burns spoke at Socialist League meetings condemning the war in the Sudan as a venture inspired by capitalists on the lookout for fresh markets, shades again of his period in Africa. Apart from work, however, there was little in Akassa to occupy a man who did not drink and whose love was half a world away. So he filled his spare time with travel and reading. It was now that he read Mill's *Political Economy,* the book that made him into a socialist.

it seemed to me that if this was the worst that the ablest writer

1 Undated manuscript headed 'Trip to the Niger', Burns Papers. B.L. Add. MSS 46308, f. 10.
2 Ibid. f. 15.
3 Quoted in Grubb, *Candle Factory to British Cabinet,* 42.
4 'Trip to the Niger', ff. 17-18.

could allege against it [socialism], the case was proved. I had, of course, Socialist leanings before this but I had hesitated. I 'lingered trembling on the brink, and feared to launch away'. But when I had read all that could be said against it, I saw I had no further reason to shrink from taking the plunge. I became a Socialist. [1]

In 1881 Burns returned to England and claimed his sweetheart, marrying her in July 1882, at St Philip's church in Battersea. But his desire for travel seems to have been greater than his desire for his new wife, for after a one day honeymoon he departed, alone, for a continental tour. At a time when most new husbands would have been embracing their wives Burns was busy embracing the proletariat of France, Germany, and Austria, in the process exhausting the last of the savings he had accumulated in Africa. The experience was good practice for Martha, however, who was often to find herself alone in the future as her husband's political career blossomed but on this occasion at least she had good cause to wonder at his sense of priorities. The tour over, however, the wanderer returned, found himself a job as a journeyman engineer at Brotherhoods, and threw himself energetically into the capital's political life.

London had always been a centre of radical belief and activity, much of it chanelled through the various political clubs which have been rightly described as the artisans' universities. [2] By and large, the dominant political ethos of the clubs was radical-republican-secularist. but the late 1870s saw the development of a strong Marxist and socialist trend within the secularist movement. Apart from a few copies of the *Communist Manifesto* most of the writings of Marx and Engels were not available in English but Marxist ideas were circulating in England and especially in London through various continental socialists, like Delahaye, who had settled there to escape persecution. [3] The London link between the English artisans and the continental socialists was provided by the Manhood Suffrage League, founded in 1874 and based in Soho. In its early days meetings were attended by prominent trade unionists such as George Shipton and George Odger, and it was one of the most important constituents of the Democratic Federation founded in 1881.

The upsurge of radical and socialist activity which took place in England at the beginning of the 1880s focused very much on the issue of free speech, a cause for which Burns had already been arrested in

1 Quoted in Grubb, *Candle Factory to British Cabinet*, 31.

2 S. Shipley, 'Club Life and Socialism in Mid-Victorian London', *History Workshop Pamphlets* 5 (1972), 27.

3 *Wage Labour and Capital* was translated into English in 1886, *Capital* in 1887. Engels's main works were not widely available until the 1890s.

1878. It was in the course of his continuing struggle for this principle that he first came into contact with the S.D.F. By January 1884 he was one of several people who were each subscribing one shilling a week to keep *Justice,* the Federation's ailing newspaper, alive. In April of that year he delivered his first speech, at Borough Road, as an official member of the organisation. It was evidently a successful meeting, for he won over fifteen converts, sufficient to start a new branch. A month later, *Justice* was noting that he had made an 'eloquent speech' at a Battersea Park Road meeting and it was this eloquence that made him such an asset to the Federation.[1] Membership was small, the executive dominated by middle-class intellectuals, and working-class recruits were eagerly being sought. Now there came an engineer from solid working-class stock with a tremendous voice and a mastery of the apt phrase. Hyndman later claimed that when Burns first joined he was 'as ignorant and uncouth a recruit as ever came among us' and that all his speeches and articles were written for him.[2] This can be dismissed as nothing more·than sour grapes, however, for Burns was neither ignorant nor uncouth. His early reading is adequate testimony to this and in addition his diary shows that he was fond of the theatre. Notwithstanding his strictures Hyndman still had to admit that Burns was 'the best stump orator I ever heard'.[3] Others, equally hostile, made the same grudging admission. Burgess claimed that the S.D.F. used him as a sort of giant gramophone.[4] Joseph Clayton suggested that he 'surpassed all his colleagues and contemporaries . . . In his speeches the epigram and irony were racy, of the soil, they belonged to the London streets whence he had been raised. . . His phrases were sharp and bit the attention of the hearers as they were meant to do'.[5]

Clearly, the views which Burns was putting over with such verve and colour were not always very acceptable to his audiences, and yet he showed no lack of courage in the face of large and often hostile crowds. Moral courage he had already exhibited in courting the displeasure of various employers by advocating views of which they did not approve. Nor was he short of physical courage. In Africa he had jumped into the sea from a steamer to rescue the ship's drowning cook, and on another occasion he had made repeated forays into shark infested waters to

---

1 *Justice,* 31 May 1884.

2 H.M. Hyndman, *The Record of An Adventurous Life* (1911), 339.

3 Ibid. 342.

4 Burgess, *Burns,* xiv.

5 J. Clayton, *The Rise and Decline of Socialism in Great Britain, 1884-1924* (1926), 61.

recover the steamer's lost propeller.[1] Now both types of courage were pressed into service for the socialist cause. In July 1884 the London Trades Council organised a meeting in Hyde Park to protest against the action of the House of Lords in rejecting the third Reform Bill. Always keen to jump on any likely band-waggon of popular discontent the S.D.F. decided to set up a stall in the park. From this platform H.H. Champion, Hyndman, and finally Burns addressed the crowds. By the time Burns rose, some four or five thousand people had gathered. He 'began very well', wrote William Morris to Andreas Scheu, 'and was a good deal cheered till in an unlucky moment he began to abuse J. Bright whom of course our Franchise friends had been worshipping all day'. Burns dared to refer to the Liberal hero as a 'silver tongued hypocrite', whereupon, continued Morris, the crowd

> fell to hooting and howling, but Burns stuck to it. . . some fellows seemed to be going for Burns, and there was a rush that way and I was afraid he might be hurt. . . at the bottom of the hill we managed to make a ring again and Burns began again and spoke for 3 or 4 minutes: but. . . there was another ugly rush which broke up our ring. . . I heard say that they were for putting Burns in the Serpentine, but it didn't come to that, for the police had been sent for and they took charge of B.[2]

It seems likely in any case that Burns would have put up a vigorous fight against a ducking. Although he was only short in stature he was strongly built and more than useful with his fists.

But, thus saved from the irate crowd and nothing deterred, Burns continued with his evangelising oratory for the S.D.F. Often leaving home at three or four in the morning he addressed workers at factory gates, street corners, and in public parks before beginning his own daily work at eight. At the weekends he was frequently in the provinces talking to strikers, or giving public speeches, all in the hope of winning more converts. This devoted if rather thankless activity absorbed nearly all his spare time, but he did find opportunity to skate and also to play cricket, an unlikely game perhaps for a man of his background, but one which he thoroughly enjoyed for many years.[3] His money, too, went to the cause. Much of it he spent on the books and pamphlets necessary to provide ammunition for his speeches. Edouard Bernstein mentions at least one occasion when he met Burns in a restaurant and the latter

---

1 See the account given by one of Burns's fellow-employees, 'Stories of the Niger', *Blackpool Times*, 15 March 1889. Cuttings survive in Burns Papers. G.L.C. Collection. Box labelled 'Photos and character of John Burns'.

2 W. Morris to A. Scheu, 26 July 1884. *The Letters of William Morris to His Family and Friends*, ed. P. Henderson (1950), 209.

3 Perhaps it was not so unlikely. Other leading socialists like Keir Hardie and Bob Smillie also played.

14

ordered neither food nor drink because he had no money with which to pay for them.[1] Perhaps in recognition of his self-sacrifice Burns found himself elected to the Federation executive at the annual meeting held in August 1884.

The executive met in a stuffy basement room in Westminster. The only illumination was provided by a couple of candles stuck in cheap tin candlesticks which must have added atmosphere, if little light, to the counsels of the would-be-revolutionaries. Certainly there was more heat than light being generated at executive meetings by the time Burns was elected, and far more friction than fraternity, for his elevation coincided with the flaring up of the first of the major rows that were to dog the S.D.F. throughout its history. Conflict had been simmering beneath the surface for some time over a wide range of issues. Primarily, there was a division between the Hyndmanites who believed in the need for some sort of parliamentary action in order to achieve socialism and a second group, crystallising around Scheu and Morris, which felt that the way to revolution lay through social agitation and derided parliamentary effort. This split between right and left (though such terms were not then used) was further widened when French Guesdists proposed that an international socialist conference be held in London in 1885. The ideological position of the Guesdists was akin to that of the Scheu-Morris group, and when more moderate Belgian socialists suggested that the conference be held instead in Antwerp the left resisted fiercely. Hyndman favoured the Belgian suggestion because he detected behind both the Scheu-Morris group and the Guesdists 'the authoritative domination of a clique, a family circle in international socialism'.[2] The family circle to which he referred was the Marx-Engels group, represented directly in the S.D.F. by Eleanor Marx and her lover, Edward Aveling, and backed by Morris. Over and above the ideological splits between the two groups were superimposed clashes of temperament and personality. Hyndman's moral sensibilities were outraged by the fact that Aveling and Eleanor Marx lived openly together, while Aveling was doubly suspect because he had been accused of stealing funds from the National Secular Society. Hyndman in turn had antagonised the Marx-Engels group, firstly by expounding without acknowledgement Marx's ideas in his own *England for all,* and then by refusing to speak at Marx's graveside in 1884. More sinister from the Marx-Engels viewpoint, however, were Hyndman's dictatorial tendencies, particularly his refusal to allow the whole executive to have a say in the running of *Justice.*

1 E. Bernstein, *My Years of Exile. Reminiscences of a Socialist,* trans. B. Miall (1921), 208.
2 *Justice,* 27 December 1884.

This was the situation when Burns joined the executive in the summer of 1884. By the autumn, the atmosphere at council meetings was electric. Engels told Karl Kautsky that at one meeting in October the executive members had quarreled so vehemently about some trifle that the words 'damned liars' were freely scattered about.[1] Burns himself seems to have been too busy with the work of the newly established strike committee to take much active part in the dispute at this stage but when the rupture came he sided firmly with Hyndman. On 16 December 1884, Hyndman attempted to have expelled from the executive a member who had made charges of self-seeking against him. Burns, along with Champion, Harry Quelch, Jack Williams, J. Murray, and Herbert Burrows voted for Hyndman but to no avail, as the expulsion motion was lost by nine votes to seven. A few days later the Marx-Engels group successfully moved a resolution of no confidence in Hyndman and then, strangely, resigned and set up the Socialist League on 30 December. On the same day the remainder of the Federation executive, including Burns, issued a statement denying the charges which had been laid against Hyndman, and calling a general meeting for January 1885. At this meeting Burns affirmed in no uncertain terms his support for his leader. The whole thing, he claimed, had been an organised attack by a small clique. Hyndman, he continued, had at least shown his sincerity by preaching socialism at street corners for sixty-six consecutive Sundays. [2]

William Morris, with whom Burns remained on very good terms, believed that those who supported Hyndman did so honestly but that they had been fooled. Certainly in later years Burns was to make virtually identical charges of self-seeking and dictatorship against the S.D.F. leader, and Hyndman's opponents of 1884 were subsequently much kinder in their recollections of Burns than was Hyndman himself.[3] But Burns's support for Hyndman in 1884-5 was not due to political innocence. It sprang directly from the fact that he shared his leader's belief in the efficacy of parliamentary action as a means of securing political change. For some time he had been a member of the local parliamentary debating society in Battersea, and in 1885 he moved a resolution at an A.S.E. delegate meeting in favour of running

---

1 Quoted in E.P. Thompson, *William Morris. Romantic to Revolutionary* (1955), 401.

2 *Justice*, 31 January 1885.

3 For example, see Bernstein, *Years of Exile*, 208; E.B. Bax, *Reminiscences and Reflexions of a Mid and Late Victorian* (1918), 106. Frank Harris is hardly a reliable source of historical information but there is some truth in his claim that Hyndman alienated most of the able men with whom he worked and was eventually left alone 'with his arms about Jack Williams' neck'. F. Harris, *Latest Contemporary Portraits* (1927), 322.

independent parliamentary candidates. If any further proof were
needed of his commitment to parliamentary action it is provided by
his acceptence of an invitation to stand as a socialist in the general
election of November 1885.

In the course of 1884 Burns had been to Nottingham as a
delegate at the annual A.S.E. conference and while there had addressed
meetings on behalf of a local S.D.F. branch. At the beginning of 1885
he had attended the Industrial Remuneration Conference in London as
an S.D.F. representative and his intemperate remarks there had earned
him some notoriety, albeit brief, and Nottingham socialists, led by
Tom Proctor, also an A.S.E. official, decided to capitalise on this by
inviting him to fight an election in their city.[1] After a mass meeting in
the market square Burns accepted their nomination and thereafter
spent much of his time addressing election meetings in working-class
districts of Nottingham West, one of the three single member constituencies created under the Redistribution Act. Nottingham was an
old radical stronghold which had been much affected by the socialist
revival of the 1880s and by the beginning of 1885 it had three branches
of the S.D.F. In addition Burns's compaign benefitted from the fact
that Nottingham, like many industrial towns, had suffered heavily
from unemployment in the winter of 1884-5, the city fathers
spending some £7,000 on relief works.[2] His main opponent was the
Liberal, Colonel Charles Seely, and it seems that the local Liberals were
sufficiently alarmed to try and buy Burns off. Conservative organisation
in the constituency was in a bad way. The original choice of candidate
had been Charles Powell, a London trade unionist and secretary of the
Church of England Working Men's Society. But on the day that Burns's
candidature was announced by *The Times,* Powell withdrew, his rather
lame excuse being that he did not wish to involve the Anglican church
society in politics — a consideration which he had evidently ignored
when he first accepted nomination.[3] At very short notice, therefore,
the Conservatives put up Edward Cope, a local lace manufacturer.

At the beginning of October Burns launched his campaign by issuing
a ten-point manifesto. It was a fairly standard socialist-cum-radical

1 The Industrial Remuneration Conference had been organised by members of
the Statistical Society and a committee appointed to discharge the terms of a
bequest for inquiring into whether the existing distribution of industrial products
was satisfactory. It was chaired by Sir Charles Dilke, then President of the Board
of Trade. The third day was given over to the advocates of 'extreme views'.
Burns was one of the S.D.F. representatives.

2 R. Church, *Economic and Social Change in a Midland Town; Victorian
Nottingham, 1815-1900* (1966), 250.

3 *The Times,* 7 September 1885.

document, giving high priority to free education, an eight-hour day, and adult suffrage. Burns also advocated, as he continued to do for the rest of his political life, legislative independence for Ireland and the abolition of hereditary authorities like the House of Lords. He also demanded the nationalisation of land, mines, banks, and railways. Although he had the backing of a short-lived newspaper, the *Nottingham Operative* (edited by Joseph Burgess) publicity for this programme depended almost entirely on the efforts of the local comrades and his own powerful voice. On the sidelines *Justice* cheered lustily. Burns, the editor declared, was making a splendid fight which would be crowned with success. But this was prophecy born of enthusiasm rather than realism, as indeed the paper almost seemed to admit, for it went on to suggest that the 'unscrupulous capitalist' Seely should retire and leave the field to Burns who was clearly the popular candidate.[1] But popularity did not win elections in late nineteenth-century Britain and the odds were stacked heavily against the socialist candidate. Some at least of the men who might have supported him did not qualify to vote or were not on the electoral register. Many working-class radicals were suspicious of him, particularly after his well publicised onslaught on John Bright, and the local trades council did not support him. The antipathy of some local working men, noted Harry Snell, another of his election workers, was 'almost unbelievable'.[2] The local press was unanimous in its condemnation of his programme and the Liberal papers utilised to the full rumours that Burns was involved in the so called 'Tory gold' scandal.

Anxious that the S.D.F. make as creditable a showing as possible in its first major parliamentary contests (Jack Williams was standing at Hampstead and John Fielding at Kennington) Hyndman and Champion had accepted an offer of financial assistance from a former Marxist, Maltman Barry, and some £340 was transferred to Federation funds.[3] It transpired that Barry was now working for the Conservative Party which had put up the money in the hope that S.D.F. candidates would split the anti-Conservative vote. Rumours that such a transaction had taken place were rife and certainly damaged beyond repair the prospects of Williams and Fielding. Burns could certainly have done with some financial aid. His extremist remarks at the Industrial Remuneration Conference had, not for the first time in his life, offended his employer who had promptly sacked him.[4] Election expenses were considerable,

---

1 *Justice*, 21 November 1885.

2 H. Snell, *Men, Movements and Myself* (1936), 63.

3 H. Pelling, *The Origins of the Labour Party, 1880-1900* (Oxford, 1965), 40.

4 Years later when he was a cabinet minister, Burns was asked by George V to

18

particularly for a man who had been living on unemployment benefit from his union and who arrived to begin his compaign with just £2 in his pocket. But none of the Tory gold went to Burns. Snell was very emphatic on this point long after any assertion to the contrary would have mattered very much.[1] In fact, most of Burns's money came in dribs and drabs, some from leading radical figures such as Annie Besant, more from innumerable individuals, trade union and socialist organisations from all over the country. The only substantial individual donation came from a wealthy Fabian soap manufacturer, R. Hudson, who was a personal friend of Champion's.[2]

All in all, therefore, it came as no surprise when Burns finished bottom of the poll, picking up a mere 598 votes against the 3,797 given to Cope and 6,609 for Seely. Although the actual campaign had been marred by a few incidents of rowdyism, polling itself passed off quietly enough. But trouble did break out, however, when the ballot boxes began to arrive at the Exchange Building for counting. The authorities had already strengthened the local police with detachments from neighbouring areas and when a mob began stoning these reinforcements, Alderman Gripper, locally known as 'King Agrippa', read the Riot Act. Without any prior warning the police, some of whom an official inquiry later revealed to have been drunk, then made a baton charge into the crowd, injuring some 150 people in the process. Burns reacted characteristically. Pushing his wife into a nearby fried fish shop for safety he joined the crowd and began digging up cobble stones to throw at the police.[3] But on the whole, given the drawbacks that he was not a local man nor, except within certain limited circles, very well known, Burns did quite well. Certainly his 598 votes looked enormous when compared with the derisory totals raised at Hampstead and Kennington — respectively 27 and 32. He had been well beaten, but he had demonstrated his ability to capture the imagination and support of at least some of the working class.

show a party of visiting German dignitaries round London's engineering shops. Burns included Brotherhoods in the tour and noted gleefully that his former employer had bowed and scraped to his guests. 'Revenge is sweet', Burns commented. Burns Papers. B.L. Add. MSS 46308, f. 50. n.d.

1 Snell, *Men*, 63.

2 Burns Papers, B.C. Notebook. Hudson gave £25.0s.-6d. Other contributions came from places as far apart as Sheffield, Dublin, Hull, Belfast, and Newport.

3 This account is based on Masterman's article in the *Sunday Express*, 2 January 1927; A.C. Wood, 'Nottingham Parliamentary Election, 1869-1900', *Transactions of the Thoroton Society* (1956), 58-60; P. Wyncoll, 'The Early Socialists in Nottingham', *Marxism Today* 17 (1973), 238-46.

2

THE RUPTURE WITH THE SOCIAL DEMOCRATS, 1886–1888

By the beginning of 1886 the outlook for the S.D.F. was gloomy in the extreme. Echoes of the 'Tory gold' scandal were still reverberating within the movement, and a great deal of criticism was being directed at Champion and Hyndman, much of it in public.[1] The eventual result was yet another schism, C.L. Fitzgerald breaking away with a couple of branches in Nottingham and Bristol to form the short-lived Socialist Union. Financially, too, the Federation was in a parlous state and *Justice* was only kept afloat by dint of a drastic reduction in its size. Nor could Burns's own prospects have seemed any brighter. After several years of almost ceaseless crusading he had little to show for his efforts, other than a slight increase in Federation membership, a few hundred votes in a general election, and some premature greying of his beard. He was again out of work and the prospects of finding employment, even for a skilled engineer, were poor. For some years trade had been in an indifferent state and parts of the economy were in the depth of a severe cyclical depression. Unemployment had risen steadily and 1886 was destined to see an official unemployment level of 10 per cent.[2] This official figure told only part of the story, however, for it was based on returns made by unions that paid unemployment benefit to their members. Other trade unionists, and the majority of the labour force who were, of course, not unionised, were ignored, so the actual situation in the labour market was probably much worse than the official statistics suggested. Building activity was slack while the metal and engineering trades were also particularly hard hit. In the latter two trades unemployment in 1885 ran at half as much again as the national figure.

Although this prolonged industrial depression had some beneficial aspects in that the prices of imported foodstuffs fell, it also pushed many people into chronic unemployment with which neither personal savings nor charity, the traditional private remedies, could cope. At the same time the Local Government Board, in the interests of both principle and economy, was trying to tighten up on the administration

1   See the letter from J. Hunter Watts in the *Pall Mall Gazette*, 4 December 1885. As S.D.F. treasurer Watts was unaware of the 'Tory gold' transaction. See also the letter from a council member, C.L. Fitzgerald in *Democrat*, 12 December 1885.
2   B.R. Mitchell and P. Deane, *Abstract of British Historical Statistics* (Cambridge, 1971), 64.

of the state's remedy, out-door relief given under the poor law. There thus arose during the 1880s a situation in which rising unemployment coincided with an increasingly restrictive attitude to relief and an erosion of the traditional 'self-help' resources of the working class. As Engels pointed out, each winter was raising 'afresh the great question "what to do with the unemployed" '. He added that nobody really knew the answer but that it was almost possible to 'calculate the moment when the unemployed, losing patience, will take their fate into their own hands'.[1] In fact it was the S.D.F. that tried to take the unemployed in hand, hoping that it would reap some benefit in the form of new recruits. It was this undertaking that was destined to push John Burns from the relative obscurity of Battersea onto the national stage.

The S.D.F. had been trying since 1884 to capitalise on the misfortunes of some of London's worst-hit workers, those in the east end, most of whom were unskilled. Several other pressure groups, among them the Fair Trade League, had also seen the possibilities of using the unemployed as a stick with which to beat the government in their own particular interests. Formed in 1881 to press for the imposition of preferential tariffs on foreign manufactured imports, the League had set up the East End Sugar Workers Committee in 1885 to stir up the unemployed on behalf of protection. When the League arranged a public demonstration for Trafalgar Square on 8 February 1886, S.D.F. leaders decided to take advantage of this opportunity to preach socialism at what was expected to be a large crowd. Shortly before the Fair Traders began their meeting, therefore, Hyndman, Williams, Champion and Burns set up their own platform in the Square and soon had the attention of a good number of people. Hyndman began by delivering what *The Times* later called a 'violent harangue'.[2] Burns was even more outspoken The House of Commons, he thundered, 'was composed of capitalists who had fattened on the labour of the working man . . . to hang these . . . would be to waste good rope . . . there must be a revolution to alter the state of things. The next time they met it would be to go and sack the bakers' shops in the west of London. They had better die fighting than die starving'.[3] He delivered this stirring message in his usual rumbustious style all the while clinging precariously to the foot of Nelson's Column. But the police had only permitted him to speak from this platform on condition that he would do his best to get the crowd to disperse

1 Quoted in J. Harris, *Unemployment and Politics, 1886-1914* (Oxford, 1972), 54.
2 *The Times*, 9 February 1886.
3 Ibid.

peacefully and the end of his oration, therefore, was rather lame. The Federation, he concluded, wanted peaceful change if possible but would not shrink from using violence. At the moment they were too weak to cope with armed force but, he cried, 'when we give the signal will you rise . . . Then go home quietly and the signal will be given if the government does not act'.[1] The general tenor of his remarks, however, had been sufficient to inflame the crowd greatly and it was perhaps in recognition of his hold over the masses that the police then asked Burns to lead the demonstrators down Pall Mall to Hyde Park where they might more easily disperse. Burns readily agreed and tying a red handkerchief onto a stick so as to be more readily identifiable in the crush, he set off at the head of the vast crowd. The strange and noisy procession winding its way through the heart of London's clubland provoked a good deal of excited comment and some members of the Carlton Club began to jeer and staff threw down crusts of bread.[2] This was too much for men who in many cases had been out of work for months and who had been roused by the Federation leaders. The detachment of police supposed to be in Pall Mall had been misdirected to the Mall and in their absence stones were thrown, windows smashed, and a riot quickly developed causing some £11,000 worth of damage. It was not for some time that the crowd eventually surged into Hyde Park and broke up as darkness began to fall.

The incident outraged middle-class opinion. For some time past the monthly press had been exercising itself about the poverty stricken east enders and the potential threat which they presented. One writer, for instance, had warned that 'this seething mass of human misery will shake the social fabric unless we grapple more earnestly with it . . . the proletariat will strangle us'.[3] To many the riot seemed to bring this threat even nearer, appearing as a first predatory flexing of the proletariat's muscles and the reaction was frightened and strong. *The Times* demanded that the leaders of the outrage should immediately be arrested and stressed that no fear of making them into martyrs should be allowed to stand in the way of their most severe punishment.[4] The Queen wrote angrily to Gladstone expressing in no uncertain terms her *'indignation at the monstrous riot . . . a momentary triumph of socialism and a disgrace to the capital. If steps, and very strong ones, are not speedily*

1   *Democrat*, 13 February 1886.
2   This account is based on *The Times*, 9 February 1886; Burns's own account in his papers, B.L.Add. MSS 46308, ff. 40-1; and S. Childers, *The Life and Correspondence of H.C.E. Childers* (1901), II, 238-44.
3   S. Smith, 'The Industrial Training of Destitute Children', *Contemporary Review* 47 (1885), 108-10.
4   *The Times*, 9 February 1886.

taken to put these proceedings down with a high hand, to punish *severely* the REAL ringleaders . . . the Government will suffer severely'.[1]

For three days Londoners were beset by panic and wild rumour. On the 11 February dense fog added to the general air of uncertainty in the capital and rumours of fresh riots were so rife that many shops remained shut throughout the day. By two in the afternoon the capital had all the appearance of a Sunday. In the early evening *The Times* received a panic-stricken telegram announcing that 30,000 roughs were marching on Trafalgar Square and urging that the police and army be called out to save the city.[2] The government, meantime, was in something of a quandry. Clearly public anger had to be assuaged and yet some of the responsibility for the trouble could be laid firmly at the feet of the Home Secretary, Hugh Childers. Several papers demanded that he resign for his mishandling of the affair. Yet Childers had only taken up office on the very day that the riot took place and he had been assured by his predecessor that all necessary steps had been taken to deal with the demonstration. The first indication he received of any trouble came in a telegram from his wife, announcing the death of an uncle and adding, somewhat cryptically, that "Our windows have escaped but those of our neighbours have suffered. Puzzled by this obtuse reference to the rioting going on in the city, Childers promptly dispatched a secretary to discover the precise meaning of this – the delay entailed allowing the situation in Pall Mall to deteriorate still further. Communications were limited too, for individual police stations were not yet connected by telegraph or telephone though Childers himself had advocated such a system as early as 1880. But wherever responsibility for the mix up lay, both the police and the Home Office had been publicly discredited. To offset criticism, therefore, it was decided to hold an inquiry into the police's role, and also to bring charges against the ringleaders.

Burns meanwhile, had found himself a job as a fitter in the press erecting department at Hoe's engineering shops. He had barely begun when he was arrested by Inspector Littlechild of the Metropolitan Police on a charge of riot. Williams, Champion, and Hyndman were also picked up and all four remanded on bail. The police kept a watchful eye on their subsequent movements. Irrepressible as ever Burns commenced his regular Saturday speech on 20 February by addressing

1 Queen Victoria to W.E. Gladstone, 11 February 1886. *The Letters of Queen Victoria*, ed. G.E. Buckle (3rd series, 1930), I, 52.
2 *The Times*, 11 February 1886.
3 Childers, *Life and Correspondence*, II, 238.

it to 'friends, fellow workmen, and detectives'.[1] The riot seems to have raised his hopes, for he went on to claim that a bloody revolution was in the making and that if the upper and middle classes did not make peaceful change possible then they would have to bear the responsibility for the death and destruction that would inevitably follow. But despite his undaunted militancy and the hysterical demands of *The Times* Burns actually emerged quite creditably from the magistrates' hearing which began at Bow Street at the end of the month. Several witnesses confirmed that he had done his best to prevent mob violence. The Hon. Guy Downing identified Burns and his brother Alex as the two who had helped him evade a gang of roughs intent on stealing his watch. Others asserted that both Burns and Williams had tried to prevent the stone throwing and that Burns had forcibly restrained at least one pickpocket. Inspector Dunlop of *A* Division confirmed that Burns had kept his part of the agreement about speaking from the base of Nelson's Column and had tried to get the crowd to disperse peaceably.

Nevertheless the magistrates, sensitive perhaps to public opinion rather than the weight of the evidence, decided that there was a case to be answered and committed the four for trial. Thus it was that in April Burns found himself in the dock at the Old Bailey charged with uttering seditious words and of conspiracy with his comrades to utter such words. The case for the crown was presented by the Attorney General, Sir Charles Russell, and centred on whether or not Burns had used the phrase 'bread or lead' and other similarly inflammatory words. Burn's defending counsel, W.M. Thompson, argued in reply that the S.D.F. manifesto was quite clearly committed to peaceful social change and that while Burns's words had certainly been rough, they had not been seditious. His suggestion that hanging was too good a fate for M.P's was merely an oratorical exaggeration, and he reminded the court that the eminently respectable Joseph Chamberlain had once employed a similar phrase about Foullon (a government official in Paris at the time of the French Revolution) being hung on a lampost with grass stuffed in his mouth. When Burns himself finally addressed the court on the third and final day of the trial his speech was an eloquent defence of his action and provides a useful indication of his views at this time. Since the age of sixteen, he said, he had done all he could to publicise the plight of the poor in a peaceful way and yet the middle and upper classes had remained totally disinterested. He would not retract anything he had said in Trafalgar Square, but he did object to being saddled with phrases that he had never used. He had not used the

---

1 *The Times*, 22 February 1886.

words 'bread or lead' but he was deeply moved by the plight of the poor and wished to find some 'means by which a peaceful change of all that inequality might be effected'.[1] This powerful advocacy was reinforced by a judge's summing up favourable to the defence, for Justice Cave confessed that he could see no evidence to suggest that the riot was a direct outcome of the speeches made by the Federation leaders, nor that the accused had made any prior agreement to utter seditious words. He also drew attention to the efforts that Burns and Williams had made to prevent the worst excesses of mob violence. In view of this summing up and of Sir Charles Russell's inability, which he freely admitted, to establish exactly what sedition meant, the jury had little alternative but to bring in verdicts of 'not guilty' on all four defendants, though it did add a rider to the effect that Burns and Champion had used highly inflammatory language. *The Times* was disgusted and the S.D.F. leaders certainly got off more lightly than the Commissioner of Police, Sir Edmund Henderson, who resigned as a result of the findings of the inquiry into the police role in the incident.

The case brought the Federation valuable publicity. So, too, did the fact that shortly after the riot Joseph Chamberlain, the President of the Local Government Board, issued a circular urging local authorities to schedule necessary public works for periods of depression. The demand for a public works approach to unemployment relief was by no means confined to the S.D.F. but the timing of the circular enabled socialists to claim the main credit for its appearance. Throughout the remainder of 1886 therefore, the struggle for the unemployed was maintained with some vigour. In November plans were made to follow the Lord Mayor of London's annual procession with a parade of the unemployed, a move which was promptly banned by the City Police Commissioner, Sir James Fraser. The ban caused Burns some amusement. They would hardly have planned a revolution, he told an audience in Battersea, and then given the authorities six weeks notice in order to prepare for the butchery which some would like to see.[2] Subsequently when the Federation decided to test the legality of the ban by holding its proposed demonstration Burns went bail for John Ward who was arrested. In the new year, the S.D.F. turned to leading unemployed marchers into the main London churches. Burns took an active part in this too. In January he headed a march to Battersea Old Church

---

1   Ibid. 10 April 1886. The words 'bread or lead' had not appeared in the paper's account of the riot but its reporter, John White, said this was because he had not wished to alarm his readers unnecessarily. For Burns's speech see also his pamphlet, *The Man with the Red Flag* (1886).
2   *The Times,* 1 November 1886.

where he delivered a stringent attack on the royal family. The following month he appeared at St Paul's Cathedral to disrupt a sermon in which Dr Gifford was arguing that there would always be rich and poor. Some weeks later he told a crowd that he regretted the failure of recent assassination attempts on the Czar of Russia, asking those who deprecated the use of force 'if they did not like the idea of Joseph Chamberlain following the Czar and Lord Salisbury to heaven by means of a chemical parcel post, to join hands with those who were trying to remove the causes which made political assassination necessary'.[1] It was indicative both of his courage and his commitment that he continued to voice such sentiments in the face of growing difficulties in getting work. In the summer of 1886 Mr Hoe dispensed with his services and there followed intermittent periods of work and unemployment. At the beginning of 1887 he was working at the London Hospital but in the summer he finally found an employer sympathetic to his views. He began work in the Westminster workshop of an electrical engineer named Lorraine, who was also a member of the Democratic Club.

As the autumn gave way to winter there were signs that the unemployment figures were at last improving but the S.D.F. was determined to sustain its agitation in the centre of London. Almost every day ragged armies of unemployed converged on the city from the east end, much to the annoyance of local interests. Nearly 6,000 traders and residents from the Trafalgar Square area presented a petition to Home Secretary Matthews protesting against the loss of business and amenity caused by the marches. The manager of one hotel in the area claimed that since the Federation campaign had begun in October over a thousand bookings at his hotel had been cancelled. The parades were also placing some strain on the police, and the Metropolitan Police Commissioner, Sir Charles Warren, was inclined to take a strong line. On 18 October one march was forcibly broken up and some twenty people apprehended. A second march broke up in disarray when its leaders were arrested for using inflammatory language. But the marchers continued undeterred with their daily pilgrimages and at the end of October Warren issued an order threatening police action against mobs which attempted to molest passers by. On 9 November he went even further and, after consultation with Matthews, he imposed a ban on all public meetings in Trafalgar Square. In agreeing to this ban Matthews was running a risk which his predecessor at the Home Office had not been prepared to countenance. After the 1886 riot Queen Victoria herself had suggested that the Square should be closed to public meetings but Childers had

1 *South Western Star*, 16 April 1887. Quoted in Kent, *Burns*, 27.

replied that 'to withdraw a permission, granted or recognised by successive Governments, would be a very grave step'.[1] Yet it was precisely this step that Matthews was now agreeing to take, and in so doing he trod very hard upon the toes of Irish Home Rulers.

Opinion in Britain was divided over the issue of whether or not Ireland should be given control of its own destiny and made independent. In July 1886 Gladstone had resigned as prime minister after his Home Rule Bill was defeated and the Conservatives, resolutely opposed to the idea of home rule, triumphed at the subsequent election and took office under Lord Salisbury. The feelings of Irish Nationalists and their radical supporters in Britain were thus running high, and when a Nationalist M.P., William O'Brien, publicly denounced British rule as the cause of most of Ireland's miseries, he was arrested and jailed. In protest O'Brien refused to wear prison uniform, whereupon the prison authorities took away his trousers. The chilly but defiant O'Brien, sitting in his cell and wrapped in blankets, provided an immediate if unlikely rallying cry for home rulers, and indirectly served to bring Burns back into the limelight even though he had been showing some signs of discontent with the S.D.F. as a vehicle of social change. At any rate he had taken little part in the current unemployed campaign and according to one source he was by now in favour of trying to establish a much broader base for working-class action.[2] For some time he had been involved in the Metropolitan Radical Federation, an umbrella organisation for the capital's radical and socialist groups. The Radical Federation had planned to hold a meeting in Trafalgar Square in order to publicise O'Brien's plight, a move with which Burns heartily concurred as he was a strong proponent of home rule. But Warren's action in banning meetings with effect from 8 November cut right across this arrangement and in this way the matter of O'Brien's trousers and the unemployed fused into what were for many much more fundamental issues over the rights of free speech and assembly, a matter on which Burns also felt strongly.[3] The stage was thus set for conflict between the M.R.F. and home rulers on the one hand, and the forces of law and order on the other. Matthews made things worse by refusing to receive a deputation from the M.R.F., and violence was being

---

1   H. Childers to Sir H. Ponsonby, 14 February 1886. *Letters of Queen Victoria*, ed. Buckle, 54, n.2.
2   F. Engels to L. Lafargue, 21 May 1887. *Engels and Lafargue Correspondence*, trans. Y.Kapp (Moscow, 1960), II, 44.
3   Writing to A.F. Tschiffely in the 1930s Burns still maintained that Warren had had no legal right to ban the meeting and that in doing so he committed a serious legal blunder. A.F. Tschiffely, *Don Roberto, Being the Account of the Life and Works of R.B. Cunninghame Graham, 1852-1936* (1937), 214.

freely predicted. The radical M.P., R.B. Cunninghame Graham, who had headed the deputation, made arrangements against the arrest which he expected.[1] Mrs Besant thought that so many people would turn up to assert their right of assembly in the Square that one good push would be enough to break through any police cordon. Edward Aveling said that he was quite prepared to use violence to get access to the Square if necessary.

Warren's measures to prevent the meeting were thorough. Well before dawn on the morning of the 13th, a Sunday, a small body of police moved into the Square and by ten o'clock their numbers had risen to 2,000 men. Other police patrolled the streets around the Square, watched by excited bystanders. More men were stationed at strategic points along the routes leading to Trafalgar Square. All Metropolitan policemen not actually positioned in or near the Square, or otherwise on duty, were being held in readiness at nearby police stations. Warren knew that the main processions would come from the districts south of the river and he therefore placed large bodies of police on those bridges nearest the Square. Just in case the civil authorities proved unable to cope a battalion of Grenadier Guards was on stand by at St George's Barracks, and a regiment of Life Guards drawn up in Horse Guards Parade. Soon after one o'clock mounted police began to move among the growing crowd, keeping it on the move and breaking up any large groups.

The demonstrators themselves, however, were taking things at a much more leisurely pace. The main processions were still gathering at assembly points in different parts of the capital. At Clerkenwell Green, for instance, crowds began to gather well before the start of a widely advertised public meeting there and promptly at two o'clock a brake drew up and disgorged several of London's best known radicals, including Mrs Besant and William Morris. By half-past three the procession, by now augmented with marchers from other parts of London, had moved off in the direction of Trafalgar Square. The inscriptions carried by some of the marchers were indicative of the general mood. 'Put your trust in God and keep your powder dry' exhorted one.[2] Others contented themselves with carrying plain red flags. Warren's objective in placing police detachments along the expected route had been to prevent any body of people reaching the Square as a procession. When the Clerkenwell contingent reached the Holborn end of St Martin's Lane the police moved in to disperse it. Even *The Times's* correspondent

1 For Graham see ibid; also J. Meyers, 'The Genius of Failure: R.B. Cunninghame Graham', *London Magazine* 15 (1975), 54-73.
2 *The Times*, 14 November 1887.

was alarmed by the apparent freedom with which the police wielded their batons, 'striking indiscriminately in all directions . . . the spectacle was a sickening one'.[1]

A similar clash was taking place on Westminster bridge. There, however, the police were heavily outnumbered and many of the demonstrators seem to have been well prepared with supplies of sticks, bricks, and even knives, for two of the seventy-three policemen injured had stab wounds. In the end, however, police discipline told and the marchers, like their comrades from Clerkenwell, were broken up, and they were allowed over the bridge in dribs and drabs, although thirty of them went not to Trafalgar Square but to nearby St Thomas's Hospital for medical attention. Similar battles took place in other parts of London and in each case the police were successful in destroying the processions. In the Square itself the police had been continuing their efforts to prevent the build up of large crowds, hampered by growing numbers both of demonstrators and spectators. In the midst of it all buses and trams passed and repassed through the Square, bulging at the seams with curious sight-seers. They added greatly to the general confusion, though their presence must have aided the police in that their constant movement made it dangerous for large numbers of people to congregate in one place. Just before four o'clock the crowd suddenly swelled and all the remaining space around the Square filled up as the dispersed marchers pressed in. It was at this stage that Burns appeared on the scene. He had been billed as one of the main speakers at the demonstration and had arranged to meet M.R.F. leaders at Charing Cross station. In the confusion, however, the only one he could find was Cunninghame Graham and after a short consultation the engineer and the M.P. linked arms and led a concerted rush at the police cordon around the Square. For a moment the cordon sagged as the wave of demonstrators beat against it but the timely addition of some reserves prevented any breakthrough. After a couple of minutes of confused struggle the wave receded in disarray, leaving Burns and Graham however, firmly in the hands of the police.

By now it was evident that the meeting was not going to be held. But the crowd showed little inclination to break up and the police were wearied by their long stint of duty. As dusk fell, therefore, the army was called in. Two squadrons of life guards clattered up from Whitehall led by a magistrate who read the Riot Act and ordered the crowd to disperse. At the same time 400 footguards marched in, bayonets fixed and each man carrying twenty rounds of ball cartridge. In their midst — perhaps for effect — marched the regimental surgeon attended by his

1 Ibid.

bandage and splint bearers. Thus reinforced the police were able to move in greater strength against the crowd and by half-past five the area was almost clear. By seven o'clock the troops were back in their barracks and Bloody Sunday was over. Burns and Graham, however, spent the night at Bow Street in a police cell, and Burns entertained his gaolers with snatches from 'The Mikado' in which he had performed at an S.D.F. concert earlier in the year.

But if some sort of uneasy calm reigned in London's streets during the night of 13 November, a storm of anger broke the next day. Outrage manifested itself in several ways. Shop keepers arriving to open their establishments protested angrily about their broken windows, although the surprising thing is really that there was not a great deal more damage done to property. There seems to have been almost none until the final police charge and even then the first window broke under the impact of a misdirected police baton rather than a plunderer's fist. *The Times* inevitably clamoured for penal sentences on those who had been arrested.

> It was no enthusiasm for free speech, no reasoned belief in the innocence of Mr O'Brien, no serious conviction of any kind, and no honest purpose that animated these howling toughs. It was simple love of disorder, hope of plunder . . . it may be hoped that the magistrates will not fail to pass exemplary sentences upon those now in custody [who] . . . have laboured to the best of their ability to convert an English Sunday into a carnival of blood. [1]

On the Stock Exchange grateful investors established a fund for the police in recognition of their sterling services. The authorities took immediate action to strengthen their hand against any further attempts to hold meetings in Trafalgar Square and over the next few days thousands of special constables were sworn in. The buses which the Metropolitan police service had acquired for rapid transportation were maintained at a constant state of readiness, and six thousand batons were borrowed from the Liverpool Watch Committee. Even more dramatically, the government placed an order at the Woolwich Arsenal for a supply of buckshot. Fresh regulations were issued banning all meetings within the Square and prohibitiing all processions from approaching it.

There was a great deal of activity on the radical front too. Resolutions condemning police brutality poured into the Home Secretary's office from radical clubs all over the capital. A Law and Liberty League was set up to defend all the people accused of crimes in connection with the defence of free speech. Of the 300 or so that had been arrested,

[1] Ibid.

forty were charged the following Monday, including Burns and Cunning-hame Graham. For some days, too, sporadic clashes took place round Trafalgar Square where heavy police guards were still posted and in one of these the protestors got their first martyr, Alfred Linnell, who died as a result of injuries received in a fight with the police at the end of November. But although the tough action of the police had disturbed many people and the Radical Federation had failed to establish its point, few seemed to have had the stomach for another major confrontation. When the S.D.F. tried to arrange a meeting in Trafalgar Square at the beginning of December, only a few hardy souls turned up, despite extensive advertising. The authorities, too, appear by now to have overcome their worst fears, for only about thirty policemen were on duty round the Square and they were withdrawn when it began to rain.

With feelings thus dying down somewhat, it was felt safe to bring on the trial of Cunninghame Graham and Burns, both of whom had been remanded on bail. The case opened at the Old Bailey on 16 January 1888, Burns defending himself, Graham having the services of a future Liberal prime minister, Herbert Asquith. Nine charges were levelled but Burns spent most of his time trying to prove – successfully – that he had not assaulted P.C.s Martell and Blundell during the affray, and he concluded with a characteristic political oration. The unemployed were being discriminated against, he claimed, because they were poor and if the situation was not improved, he warned darkly, then Britain would reap the same lamentable harvest as other European countries. His passion, however, failed to move the jury, for in the course of his speech Burns had omitted any reference to the salient facts of the case, an omission which the prosecuting Attorney General did not fail to pick up. It took the jury little more than half an hour to find both men guilty on the charge of unlawful assembly, for which they were both sentenced to six weeks without hard labour, a much more satisfying outcome in the opinion of those who had been upset by the judge's leniency in the trial of April 1886. As the *Western Mail* put it. 'The sentences will have an excellent effect . . . in teaching people of this kind that . . . they cannot be allowed to get up their own whims in opposition to the legal edicts and proclamations of properly constituted authority'. The *Echo* was equally pleased but sounded a note of caution, wondering if perhaps the sentences might not have the effect of turning the accused into political martyrs.[1]

But the crown of martyrdom must have rested somewhat uneasily on Burns's head. Whereas Cunninghame Graham had no financial worries, Burns's very attendance at the trial had cost him a week's pay and he

[1] Both quoted in *Justice*, 28 January 1888.

had been unable to pay his rent. Now he faced the prospects of six
weeks imprisonment, having at the same time to maintain both his wife
and his elderly mother who lived with them. But his comrades were
rallying round. Champion had already promised that Martha would
share 'any crusts that may still be extractable . . . I am not yet I think
so poor as to be unable to promise to see her through any period of
detention you are likely to get'.[1] Mrs Besant was also raising funds
through the medium of the Socialist Defence League and the S.D.F.
launched an appeal in the columns of *Justice,* from which Martha
received a guinea shortly after her husband began his sentence and then
three subsequent payments each of thirty shillings.[2]

Superficially the riot left Burns in a very optimistic mood. In
December he wrote that 'a revolutionary epoch has commenced . . .
the middle class, with their characteristic greed and ignorance, will not
yield till force, the only arbiter, makes them'.[3] Nor was he deterred by
his imprisonment, despite the rigours of a regime that permitted him
only six ounces of bread a day and, apart from a brief period of
exercise, left him with nothing to do but read the bible provided in his
cell, hardly a very congenial book for a man of his outlook. While he
was serving his sentence the first anniversary of the 1886 riot occurred
and he celebrated in defiant fashion, singing the 'Marseillaise' and in-
scribing 'Long live socialism' on his cell wall.[4] When he was released —
early for good conduct — he urged the audience at a celebratory meeting
to make Trafalgar Square their revolutionary square and then to go on
to tear down the English bastille at Pentonville, 'the embodiment of all
that was bad in the worst possible forms of government and the system
of society'.[5]

In view of the militancy behind these remarks it is surprising that
Dona Torr could later claim that the riot of 1887 and its relatively
easy suppression ended for Burns (among others) 'the illusion that the
revolution was just round the corner . . . the futility of playing at
insurrection (was) accepted . . . Burns . . . had desired seriously organised
physical force'.[6] In one sense this statement is true, for there can be no
doubt that Burns left prison much disillusioned with his fellow workers.

1 H.Champion to J.Burns, 17 January 1888. Burns Papers. B.L.Add. MSS 46288,
ff. 68-9.
2 H.W. Lee to M. Burns, 20 January 1888; 2, 9, 16 February 1888. Ibid. ff. 76,
90, 91, 94.
3 *Justice,* 3 December 1887.
4 Burns Diary, 8 February 1888. B.L.Add. MSS 46310.
5 Quoted in Kent, *Burns,* 33.
6 *Tom Mann and His Times,* ed. D. Torr (1956), 265.

Yet Torr's statement must not be taken to mean that the riot changed John Burns from an advocate of violence to a disciple of peaceful parliamentary action. His views were never so clear cut, despite the claims made later by former comrades in the S.D.F. who in any case had every reason to exaggerate the extremity of his early views in order to magnify still further the enormity of his subsequent betrayal. Certainly he was fully committed to the struggle to bring about social change. 'The causes of the social degredation of the masses must and shall be swept away', he wrote on one occasion;[1] on another, 'the industrial life of today is such as to necessitate a complete revolution'.[2] Change was being resisted by other classes and it followed, therefore, that it could only come about through successful prosecution of a class war and Burns was very scornful of those who did not believe in the existence of the class struggle. His was probably the inspiration behind a manifesto issued at the end of 1884 to trade unionists which attacked the refusal of T.U.C. leaders to accept the concept. At about the same time he was suggesting that the T.U.C. should measure its contribution to the workers' cause 'not by the compliments bestowed on its decisions by landlords and capitalists, but, on the contrary, by the amount of disapprobation that their resolutions receive from their worst enemies'.[3] At the Industrial Remuneration Conference he had mocked speakers who had suggested that industrial conflict could be resolved by moralising capital. 'You might as well try', he had sneered, 'to moralise the lion who is about to devour the lamb. You might as well attempt to moralise the boa constrictor that has his coils around the body of his victims'.[4]

This reflected his deep-seated dislike of industrial capitalism and privilege, a theme which ran through much of his early writing. He once likened miners to profit-making machines whose masters luxuriated on the shores of the Mediterranean or passed their time 'gliding up the Bosphorous on a steam yacht'.[5] He also despised social privilege. The demand for the abolition of hereditary authority always found a place in his election manifestos, and he told an audience of unemployed at Old Battersea Church in 1884 that though they had been asked that day to pray for the royal family, in his opinion they were already sufficiently well blessed — mainly at other peoples' expense.[6] This attitude was at the core of John Burns's socialism. Socialism for him meant the ending

---

1   *Justice,* 12 September 1885.
2   Ibid. 24 January 1885.
3   Ibid. 13 September 1884.
4   Industrial Remuneration Conference, *Report* (1885), 484
5   *Justice,* 12 July 1884.
6   Quoted in Kent, *Burns,* 27.

of all monopoly power and privilege and the granting to the people of their share of the wealth they helped to create. Toryism and Liberalism, he suggested on one occasion, were only successful 'in so far as their promises are Socialistic and attack vested interests and monopoly'. [1]

Burns's support, then, for social change was unequivocal. But it is important to remember that he was an agitator and an orator, not a political theorist or logician. His views did not possess the order or coherence that many later writers imply, and there was a marked ambivalence in his thought when it came to considering exactly *how* social change was to be secured. It is true that he often used the word 'revolution' with all its connotations of violence, and he frequently revelled in conjuring up for his audiences quite specific visions of the carnage that might be involved in bringing change about. But it must be stressed that all reports of his speeches are, of course, second-hand and the journalist with an eye to good copy was always likely to remember best the exciting phrase or pithy epithet, perhaps in the process giving it a prominence which it did not deserve. Nor was it easy for a reporter always to be sure of who was saying what in the course of a noisy demonstration – witness the dispute over whether Burns had used the phrase 'bread or lead' in Trafalgar Square. In addition there is good reason to believe that he often went further than he intended because he found that the more exciting his language the more the crowd responded and he enjoyed the adulation of the masses. George Bernard Shaw recalled at least one occasion when he over-reached himself in this way. Burns was once giving a public speech on the position of women. 'He would', said Shaw, 'sometimes inadvisedly climb a height of rhetoric without any provision for getting down again. He was picturing in a peroration the time when woman would at long last have her rights – 'and then', he said, 'we shall see her exfoliate as – as – as – as we should all wish to see her exfoliate'. [2]

The main period of Burns's most inflammatory speaking and writing came in the years 1886 and 1887, a time when several British socialists, encouraged perhaps by over-reaction on the part of the public, believed that a revolutionary situation existed. [3] It is worth remembering here that the manifesto of the Comité Revolutionaire du Prolétariat had advocated parliamentary action 'à défaut d'un fusil', and perhaps briefly

1 Draft of a letter to the press, November 1887. Burns Papers. B.M.Add. MSS 46288, ff. 43-4.
2 E. Marsh, *A Number of People. A Book of Reminiscences* (New York, 1939), 216.
3 Both Aveling and Morris, for example, thought that the 1886 riot constituted 'the first skirmish of the revolution'. *Commonweal*, March 1886.

in 1886 and 1887 Burns may have thought that that deficiency was about to be made good.[1] It was at this time that he attacked Tom Mann for advocating an eight-hour day at a meeting of the S.D.F.'s Battersea branch. Leaping to his feet in protest he cried out that the time was past for such trivial reforms. 'The capitalist system was on its last legs and it . . . was our duty to prepare at once to seize the whole of the means of production and wipe out the capitalists'.[2] It was now that he made his remarks about sending Joseph Chamberlain and Lord Salisbury to heaven by chemical parcel post. When Mrs Besant asked a meeting of Fabians in the autumn of 1886 how accumulated wealth could be nationalized, Burns was one of two members of the audience who advocated the use of force.[3]

Yet only a month before Burns had also supported a resolution moved by Mrs Besant at another Fabian meeting in favour of parliamentary action and there can be no doubt that, in Burns's political thought, revolutionary and constitutional action co-existed as means to bring about the desired transformation of society.[4] At the same time as he was making violent public speeches he was writing a paper on revolution, and he concluded by expressing the hope that 'the inevitable revolution' would be 'anticipated by the concession to the people of those powers springing from property now enjoyed by the privileged classes. In England stage by stage the people will acquire what in other countries force alone may secure'.[5] Burns had tried to stop mob violence in 1886, and he had stressed in his address to the jury his preference for peaceable change. Within a month of his release from Pentonville he was telling delegates to an international trade union conference in London that the time had come now for the workers' battle to be transferred to 'the floor of the House of Commons'.[6] Even in his most violent utterances, violence seems to have been held out only as a sort of ultimate threat. After his comments on the Czar, for example, he went on to suggest that those who deprecated the use of force should join with those who, like himself, were trying to remove the causes that made political assassination necessary. In another picturesque metaphor he argued similarly that the blind

See above p.9.

B. Tillett, *Memories and Reflections* (1931) 43-4.

Practical Socialist, October 1886.

This ambiguity was inherent in the whole political position of the S.D.F. See H. Collins, 'The Marxism of the Social Democratic Federation', *Essays in Labour History, 1886-1923,* ed. A. Briggs and J. Saville (1971), 47-69.

Undated but pre-1888 manuscript headed 'Revolution'. Burns Papers. B.L. Add. MSS 46308, f. 5.

Undated manuscript headed 'Trade Unions'. Ibid. 46309, f. 20.

Samson of labour had his hands on the pillars of wealth and would tear them down *unless* given the right to live in decent conditions, eat properly, and rear his children adequately.[1]

What the riot of 1887 did to John Burns's political outlook, therefore, was not to convert him from one form of political action to another, as Dona Torr's statement might be taken to imply. Rather, it resolved once and for all the ambivalence in his understanding of how change could be secured. He had seen that some of the working class at least were ill-prepared to work for constructive social change, even preferring looting and violence for their own sake, and he was not the only socialist coming to this conclusion. Champion had been disgusted by the mob violence of 1886 and said later that if he had had a gun he would have used it against the looters.[2] Shaw pointed out that the people wanted food and work, not revolution.[3] Burns himself had no interest in revolution *per se,* only in ameliorating social conditions, and after his release from prison he confessed to being 'ashamed and disgusted with his own class. They were not educated as they ought to be, and a great deal of that was owing to their own apathy and indifference'.[4] In May, having spoken to a meeting in Hyde Park he lamented the fact that the audience had been 'inclined to rowdyism . . . they seem more intent on a row than anything that benefits them'.[5] It was now that there began to creep into his speeches that moralising tone that was to dominate them increasingly as time went on. Appeals to the class war disappeared, to be replaced by exhortations to self help. It is instructive that only eighteen months or so after his release from prison he could write that 'there is no "strike" in the loafer. It is a fool's mission to preach revolt to *him*.'[6] Instead he turned to those workers who did show signs of interest in organising themselves for social change, trade unionists.

Whatever was later said about Burns's conduct, there can be no doubt of the sincerity of his desire to achieve something positive for the working classes. This was why he was so disgusted at their apparent apathy. It was this same desire that lay behind his move towards a broader political base than that provided by the S.D.F. Even before the riot of 1887 he had welcomed the way in which socialists and radicals

1   *The Times,* 22 November 1886. My italics. See another speech in similar vein given in Bermondsey and reported in the *South London Press,* 20 February 1886.
2   *Pall Mall Gazette,* 9 February 1886.
3   Ibid. 11 February 1886.
4   Quoted in Kent, *Burns,* 32.
5   Burns Diary, 13 May 1888. B.L. Add. MSS 46310.
6   J. Burns, 'The Great Strike', *New Review* I (1889), 414.

had been finding common ground, while of course it had been the London radicals who had taken the initiative in organising the challenge to the government ban on meetings in Trafalgar Square. It was symbolic perhaps that before leading the crowd against the police Burns, the socialist, had linked arms with Cunninghame Grahame, the radical. Burns received very sympathetic treatment in the *Star*, the paper run by the Irish Nationalist, T.P. O'Connor, who was hoping to revitalise London Liberalism by bringing together local Liberal organisations, radicals and, where possible, socialists. Clearly he saw in Burns a useful figure in this strategy. Burns's private papers are full of resolutions of sympathy from radical and liberal groups, again attesting to the way in which the events of 1887 brought him still closer to the radicals.

But the corollary of this move towards a broader political base was a shift away from the narrow sectarianism of the S.D.F. which, he was coming to believe, was too limited in its outlook ever to achieve anything very concrete. Any doubts he may have had about its bigotry were resolved at the meeting arranged by the Law and Liberty League to celebrate his release from jail. The meeting was chaired by Jacob Bright M.P., brother of John Bright whom Burns had so roundly abused in 1884, and many other radicals were on the platform. But Hyndman chose the occasion to launch a totally unprovoked attack on the radicals, much to Burns's disgust. In May he wrote dispiritedly in his diary that he 'felt very depressed about the immediate future of the movement. Am convinced that we have dissipated nearly all our energy in the wrong direction and upon the wrong man'.[1] His suspicions were confirmed by his friend, Tom Mann, who was working with very little success as an S.D.F. organiser in Lancashire. 'Do you think', Mann asked in March, 'the S.D.F. as an organisation will ever develop to considerable proportions? I confess it looks horribly slow work. I can't see much headway that's been made the last eighteen months as an organisation.'[2] Three months later he was even gloomier, telling Burns that he was not going to the party's annual conference and that he had 'lost hope as regards the S.D.F.'[3] Burns himself did attend the conference but it served only to confirm his fears. Attendance was poor and income had fallen. 'The S.D.F. as a national body', he noted, 'must be remodelled not to say merged with other bodies ere it does good work'.[4]

But any hopes he had in that direction were destroyed by the constant internecine bickering going on within the organization. 'In the face

1 Burns Diary, 10 May 1888. B.L. Add. MSS 46310.
2 T. Mann to J. Burns, 16 March 1888. Burns Papers. B.L. Add. MSS 46285, f.6.
3 T. Mann to J. Burns, 25 June 1888. Ibid. f. 7.
4 Burns Diary, 6 August 1888. B.L. Add. MSS 46310.

of a common foe', he wrote just before Christmas 1887, 'We cannot afford to waste our energy by idle useless quarrels'.[1] Yet this was precisely what was happening within the Federation. In the early summer of 1887 Champion had quietly dropped out of active S.D.F. work to advocate a more constructive policy. It took the form of supporting independent working class candidates for parliament. In June 1888 he launched a new paper, the *Labour Elector,* to publicise his policy and to give support to the T.U.C.'s Labour Electoral Association, formed with just such an object in view as Champion had in his own mind. Division with the Federation leaders came, however, over what policy was to be followed by a successful candidate. Hyndman wanted him to wage ceaseless class warfare on the floor of the House of Commons. Champion wanted something more positive. Around this issue the Federation once more began to crack and Burns took Champion's side. At the annual conference Hyndman tried to strengthen his hand by proposing to replace the delegate council with a revived executive. Burns led the opposition to this, arguing fiercely that it would allow the rise of despotism and cliqueism, virtually the same charges, it will be noted, that the founders of the Socialist League had made. Hyndman did not take very kindly to the criticism but Burns did not care very much, for once the conference was over he had escaped from politics altogether, taking Martha to Margate for a holiday recommended by his doctor.

Burns's health had been poor since the beginning of the year. Despite the bold front he had put on while in prison, he had been unwell and spent part of the time in the prison hospital. Visiting him, William Morris noted that the famous stentorian voice was weak and that Burns himself seemed a good deal pulled down.[2] In March Burns had commented in his diary on the adverse affects of his constant propagandising and 'resolved to work less after work is done in the factory and rest more'.[3] Yet he did not keep his resolve and the spring and early summer of 1888 saw him as busy as ever in public speaking. Work was not as congenial as it might have been either, for his foreman, a man named Holden, hated the views for which Burns stood, and spent most of his time trying to get him dismissed. He finally succeeded just before the S.D.F. conference and Lorraine's sacked him.

Once his brief holiday at Margate was over Burns returned, feeling

1 *Justice,* 3 December 1887.
2 W. Morris to J.A. Morris, 19 February 1888. *Letters of William Morris,* ed. Henderson, 279.
3 Burns Diary, 12 March 1888. B.L. Add. MSS 46310.

refreshed, to begin again the all-too-familiar search for work. It took only four days but he was barely settled in when he was again thrust into the Federation's bickerings. Hyndman made a bitter attack on Champion and his policy at a council meeting. Burns defended Champion, confiding afterwards to his diary that Hyndman had been motivated solely by egotism and jealousy. [1] A few weeks later at a Battersea branch meeting Burns again spoke up for Champion's policy, damning Hyndman as a skunk. [2] 'Leaders', he wrote at the end of the month, 'are those who lead. When a man lacks the moral qualities essential for leadership and resorts to tactics to supply what he morally lacks then the end of his leadership is not far off'. [3]

From this point on Burns and Hyndman diverged more and more, even though the local branch which Burns had founded continued to offer him support and he was still much in demand as a speaker. For his part Hyndman never forgave Burns for what he regarded as his apostasy, rooted, he believed, in his egotism and self seeking. It is an aphorism, but nonetheless true, that all men can see in others the faults which they themselves possess. While Hyndman was by no means the last person to accuse Burns of personal ambition and egotism it is worth noting that a common factor in nearly all the rifts which periodically split the S.D.F. was the charge that Hyndman himself suffered from these same character defects. Burgess suggested that it was Martha's ambition that really lay behind the break with Hyndman. 'She is exceedingly ambitious . . . I don't think Mrs Burns cares very very much for what you call the movement'. [4] Yet Martha Burns only met her husband because of her interest in free speech, and in 1884 she had been contributing sixpence a week from her housekeeping money to keep *Justice* afloat. [5] Nor is there any evidence to suggest that Martha was the driving force behind Burns, but rather that she was very much a background figure in his public life. It was not her ambition that produced the rupture between her husband and Hyndman. Its roots lay partly in the clash of two similar and strong personalities, partly in Burns's lack of interest in doctrinal purity, and mainly in his passionate desire to do something practical for his class.

He was finding much encouragement in the way the trade union movement was changing. He shared Champion's enthusiasm for the T.U.C.'s Labour Electoral Association. Again like Champion, he gave

1   Ibid. 2 October 1888.
2   Ibid. 26 October 1888.
3   Ibid. 30 October 1888.
4   Burgess, *Burns,* 89-90.
5   *Justice,* 2 August 1884.

public support to suitably independent parliamentary candidates, including Keir Hardie at Mid-Lanark in April 1888. Reading the reports of the annual T.U.C. conference in 1888 he noted with pleasure that its proceedings were becoming more socialistic every year. He added, significantly, that 'when policy and party exigencies drive Labour candidates into Socialism it is time I gave up the position of agitator, became a 'respectable' workman'.[1] In one sense he had already refused one chance to do just that, when he turned down invitations to stand as assistant secretary of the A.S.E. But what Burns had his eye on by this time was a place on a new body that parliament was currently in the processing of creating, the London County Council.

1   Burns Diary, 4 September 1888. B.L. Add. MSS 46310.

3

COUNTY COUNCIL AND DOCK STRIKE, 1889-1891

The establishment of the London County Council represented the most recent and, as it turned out, the most successful attempt by parliament to tackle the apparently intractable problem of administering the undisciplined sprawl that London had become by the end of the nineteenth century. Except in the City of London itself there had been no central administration in the capital until 1854 when the Metropolitan Board of Works had been created and the existing confusion of vestries, commissioners, and trusts had been subjected to a certain degree of rationalisation. Although the board achieved more than it was sometimes credited with, rival groups interested in the question of London government continued to press either for a central controlling authority or alternatively for some system of municipalisation. In 1888 the advocates of centralisation achieved some measure of success when Salisbury's government passed the Local Government Act which set up a triennially elected London County Council of 118 members. Elections were to be held in each of London's parliamentary constituencies and Battersea, therefore, qualified for two councillors.

The initial impetus behind Burns's candidature appears to have come from the local branch of the S.D.F. Between Burns and the Federation's national leaders relations were by now severely strained but he had quite a strong following within the local branch. He had after all been its founder, and the Sidney Hall was always packed and the collecting boxes fuller than usual whenever he took the platform. Further, some at least of the local members agreed with the policies Burns and Champion had been putting up against Hyndman; indeed, the matter caused divisions so deep that the comrades were frequently 'prone to lose touch with the spirit of fraternity'.[1] It was a local S.D.F. man, W.S. Sanders, who headed Burns's election committee and organised his campaign, although 'campaign' is perhaps too precise a word, as no systematic canvassing was carried out and the whole effort was run on an income of slightly more than £36.0.0.[2] Its main thrust depended almost entirely on the personal efforts of the candidate who took a week and a half off work and delivered speech after speech in which his oratory rose to new heights. His great knowledge of London and its history was combined with his instinctive feel for its people to paint a

---

1 W.S. Sanders, *Early Socialist Days* (1927), 26.
2 The accounts were published in the *Labour Elector*, 9 March 1889.

picture that glowed with colour, life, and appeal. Long after he had left politics, Burns was still able to recall with excitement his first council election compaign. Always, he told an interviewer from the *Star* in March 1939, he had kept before himself and the electors the vision of 'a dignified, beautiful London, free from poverty, and uncontrolled by selfish interests'.[1] He rather overdid the picture by asserting that alone of the candidates he had the necessary experience, energy and determination to deal adequately with the sort of problems to which the new council would address itself, but the electors of Battersea apparently agreed with him. He was returned at the top of the poll on 17 January with 3,071 votes, his running partner, James Tims, being the other successful candidate. The result was not really as surprising as some journalists tried to make out. Certainly Burns had stood as an avowed socialist yet this was probably of less import than the fact that in a predominantly working-class constituency he was a well known champion of working-class interests and his victory rested in part at least on his personal popularity.[2] He was also an active trade unionist in an area which by the standards of the late 1880s was quite highly unionised. At a time when the organised workers of Battersea were beginning to show considerable interest in securing political representatives from their own class Burns, the working engineer, could point to his long advocacy of just such a policy. He had represented labour in the local parliamentary debating society and had devoted a great deal of time to encouraging working-class participation in the affairs of the local vestry. In short, as has been suggested, he was 'a remarkably appropriate person to be the focus of the desires for working class representation at this time'.[3]

Perhaps even more important in his success was the fact that the election took place at a time when advanced thinkers of many varieties were trying to forge a progressive, anti-conservative alliance. In Battersea itself a Progressive Society had been established in the early 1880s and in 1888 local radicals and socialists had fought a common and successful campaign in the vestry elections. Burns had shown himself willing to break free of the S.D.F.'s doctrinal straitjacket in the interests of practical reform and his council manifesto was that same judicious blend of principle and practical policy that he and Champion had been advocating in the *Labour Elector*. It demanded the abolition

1 *Star*, 21 March 1939.

2 This at least was Morris's opinion. See W. Morris to J.A. Morris, 21 January 1889. *Letters of William Morris*, ed. Henderson, 307.

3 C.J. Wrigley, 'Liberals and the Desire for Working Class Representatives in Battersea, 1886-1922', *Essays in Anti-Labour History*, ed. Kenneth D. Brown (1974), 132.

of the privileges enjoyed by the City of London, the cumulative rating of land values, and that the council should undertake industrial and distributive enterprise. It further advocated a concerted attack on river pollution, the establishment of trade union rates and conditions for all council employees, and a council take-over of public utilities. This was exactly the sort of programme which appealed to advanced radicals and one of the most influential, T.P. O'Connor, gave Burns strong backing in his widely circulating paper, the *Star*, and tried to secure him a straight fight.[1] Annie Besant was another to whom this programme appealed. She had first tried to bring radical thinkers together under the aegis of the Law and Liberty League founded with Burns's help and initially for his benefit.[2] Mainly at the instigation of Mrs Besant's journal, the *Link*, the revitalised Metropolitan Radical Federation had organised a successful anti-Conservative campaign in the London school board elections of 1888 and it, too, backed progressive candidates in the L.C.C. elections.[3] Burns's success in Battersea must be seen, therefore not only as a triumph for his own ebullient personality and a vindication of his past work, but also as part of this wider current that was drawing together different shades of progressive thought in the common cause of radical but non-doctriniare social reform, and which swept seventy progressive candidates into the new council.

The council began its work on the last day of January 1889. Even though the first few sessions were mainly taken up with procedural and organisational matters Burns gave immediate notice of his intention to ensure that it was to be an advanced and democratic body, totally above any suspicion of corruption. Almost his first act was to oppose the election of Lord Rosebery to the chair on the grounds that his lordship had links with financial interests which might be involved in negotiations with the council. Then he gave his backing to unsuccessful motions to have meetings begin in the early evening (instead of the scheduled 3.00 p.m.) and to allow all meetings, including those of the nineteen committees which were established, to be open to the public. Although he hotly denied it, there was probably an element of truth in the suggestion made by a Moderate councillor that both resolutions, if carried, would have allowed Burns to play more effectively to the gallery. Naturally it took some time to complete the process of taking over from the old Board of Works and thus it was not really until the spring that the council was ready to get down to any practical work. It

1 *Star*, 7, 10, 16 January 1889.

2 See above p.29.

3 D. Rubinstein, 'Annie Besant and Stewart Headlam; the London School Board Election of 1888', *East London Papers* (1970), 3-24.

had barely got under way when Burns's attentions were diverted, briefly, but significantly, to the great labour struggle that was brewing in the capital's docks.

London's dockland contained a good proportion of the thirty or so per cent of the capital's population found later by Charles Booth to be living on or below the margin of subsistence. The basic problem was chronic under-employment, as the demand for labour in the docks could vary considerably from day to day. In the West Ham docks, for instance, the daily requirement fluctuated between 2½ − 5,000 men and thus on any given day thousands of riverside workers had no work and no income.[1] The means of recruitment was degrading in the extreme, men being 'called on' at various times throughout the day, foremen choosing the fortunate few from the clamouring mass.

> We are driven into a shed, iron-barred from end to end, outside of which a foreman or contractor walks up and down with the air of a dealer in a cattlemarket, picking and choosing from a crowd of men, who, in their eagerness to obtain employment, trample each other under foot, and where like beasts they fight for the chances of a day's work.[2]

Not surprisingly, trade union organisation had made little headway in this unfavourable environment. A Labour Protection League had been established in the early 1870s mainly though not exclusively for dockers but it had crumbled away into insignificance by the 1880s, leaving only the stevedores and lightermen strongly organised. The rest were in almost total disarray, though Ben Tillett, an ex-sailor, had been trying since 1887 to enlist port workers into his Tea Operatives and General Labourers Association. But he met with little success. Membership oscillated greatly, rarely exceeding 800, and the casual nature of port employment made it almost impossible to build up funds. Predictably, Tillett's attempt to lead a strike at Tilbury in 1888 had failed abysmally. But for some years the port employers had been experiencing financial difficulties, mainly because their surplus handling capacity had pushed prices down to rock bottom. In 1888 the East and West India Dock Company had gone bankrupt and wage reductions had been imposed on a wide range of dock workers. The following year and for similar reasons of financial expediency the India Company made a downward revision in the scale of the 'plus' bonus, the extra payment calculated on a tonnage basis and added to the basic rate of five pence an hour. The company had never revealed the precise basis on which the 'plus' was calculated but the men suspected that they were being cheated

1 E.G. Howarth and M. Wilson, *West Ham* (1907), 229.
2 B. Tillett, *A Brief History of the Dockers Union* (1910), 9.

and it was a dispute over such a payment that ignited the accumulated debris of years of bad feeling between men and masters in the London docks.

Tillett took up the matter of the disputed 'plus' with the employers on 7 August but they ignored his letter. He then found himself under some pressure to adopt a strong line, for a new union, founded by a bargeman named Harris, had appeared in the Victoria and Albert Dock and was attempting to recruit in the South Dock where Tillett's own efforts had been concentrated. This new union contained a fair sprinkling of gas workers who usually sought refuge in the docks when the summer decline in the demand for gas resulted in their being laid off. These gas workers were in jubilant mood, for the previous March Will Thorne had successfully launched the National Union of Gas Workers and General Labourers which had grown to an astonishing size in a very short time. After some procrastination, therefore, Tillett, fearing that this leavening of militant gas workers might soon swallow up the Tea Operatives, finally agreed to call a strike. Ostensibly the issue was about the disputed 'plus' bonus. In fact the areas of disagreement were many and Tillett presented a comprehensive set of demands to the employers, including a claim for a wage increase to six pence an hour with overtime at eight pence, a guaranteed minimum of four hours work once a man was called on, and the abolition of piecework and the contract system which operated in some docks. The companies declined to consider these demands on the grounds that they were too costly, and in any case they probably believed that the men were too weakly organised to back their demands with effective action. But three days after the South Dock men stopped work, the two powerful stevedores unions, the Amalgamated and the United, struck as well. On 19 August the Victoria and Albert, London, and St Katherine's men all stopped work and an exodus began at Milwall and Tilbury. Two day's later the lightermen joined in. By 22 August the stoppage was port wide and, despite the initial confidence of the employers, the strike was to last for more than a month and came to occupy an honoured place in labour's battle roll.

For years the dock gates had been among Burns's favourite campaigning grounds. Often he had left home at four o'clock in the morning to address dockers assembling for call on, a system he personally found so distasteful that he compared it to people tussling in the passages of a burning theatre.[1] Always his message had been the same. Improvement could only come through greater solidarity and more organisation. 'The notion of combination. . .' he wrote 'had been hard to drive into

---

[1] Burns, 'The Great Strike', 415.

him [the docker]. But we had warmed them up now, and they knew that it was a question of combination or nothing'.[1] Not only was Burns well known in the docks because of his reputation and frequent appearances at the gates but he had himself worked briefly in the docks in 1887. Further, he was also known to many of the gas workers, for he had taken the initiative in forming a branch of Thorne's union at Vauxhall and it is indicative of his general interest that he had been the main speaker at the meeting which had launched Harris's union in the Victoria and Albert Dock.

He had already been much encouraged by signs that unskilled workers were at last beginning to appreciate the message of organisation and he threw himself into the strike with all his usual energy and enthusiasm. Since his election to the council, he had given up his job and been paid from a specially created local wages fund so he had no worries about devoting time to the fight. So avidly did he work that he was rarely in bed before three o'clock in the morning and he lost a stone in weight. Martha, too, was fully occupied, assisting Eleanor Marx with the general secretarial work involved in the strike. Burns acted as secretary of the committee appointed by the Tea Operatives to oversee financial affairs and later he served on the United Strike committee formed when the Tea Operatives and other unions involved decided to pool their resources. 'Only those who were in the thick of the strife', commented one report later, 'could know the amount of drudgery, organising and routine work ... which he undertook'.[2]

Perhaps more importantly, Burns acted in conjunction with Tom Mann and Tillett as a negotiator on behalf of the strikers, much to the annoyance of the dock companies who at one time threatened to deal only with men in their employ. It was Burns who was mainly responsible for clinching a settlement with the wharfingers, giving their employees sixpence a day, and eightpence for overtime. The alliance between the wharfingers and dock companies had been an uneasy one and this settlement represented the men's first success. Subsequently Burns went on in company with Tillett to represent the strikers at the meetings convened when Cardinal Manning intervened and secured a final settlement in the middle of September. Under its terms the dockers got their wage claim, a minimum of four hours guaranteed work, and regular call on times. Later meetings were to be held to consider alternatives to the 'plus' bonus and the contract system. This was Burns's first major experience of formal industrial negotiation and

1 Ibid. 416-17.
2 *The Legal Eight Hours Demonstration in London: A Brief History of the Movement* (1891), 22.

46

occasionally his inexperience showed up. At the end of August, for example, with funds running low and little prospect of a settlement in sight, he supported a proposal to call out all other London workers in a general strike. A 'No work' manifesto was issued, only to be almost immediately withdrawn, partly because it was evident that it would alienate public sympathy, partly because unexpected financial assistance arrived from the Brisbane Wharf Labourers Union. Contemporary historians of the strike also suggested that sometimes Burns was too easily swayed, instancing the occasion when on 7 September he and Tillett seemed to accept an offer from the employers, only to reject it later after a meeting of the strike committee. 'Burns', they suggested, 'could not resist the fascination of Cardinal Manning while in his presence; he was equally open to counter pursuasion when amid the uncompromising surroundings of the Wade's Arms'.[1] This should not be exaggerated. When a settlement was finally reached Burns had to go over its terms three times with the men in the West India Dock before they agreed to it, there being strong objection to the fact that all blacklegs were to remain unmolested. On the whole, considering his relative lack of experience, he handled the negotiations well. The terms were probably as favourable as the men could have expected, especially as there were signs that the public sympathy which had so assisted them was running a little thin as the strike dragged on. Throughout, Burns had encouraged the committee to resist arbitration proposals from interested outside parties and had insisted that all the men involved should be satisfied before any return to work was countenanced. 'All unions must defeat to benefit one', he told Mann.[2]

But above all Burns brought to the strike his golden voice. In the process he transformed an industrial dispute into something akin to a religious revival. During the first three days of the struggle he made thirty-six speeches all over dockland. Marching round the docks with other demonstrators he would appear looming over walls and gates, denouncing men who were still at work and calling on them in thunderous tones to join the stoppage. It was he who addressed the vital meeting of stevedores who were by no means at one in their decision to join in, and yet whose experience was vital to the strike's success. The fact that the struggle lasted for four weeks was in no small part due to his ability to maintain the morale of the strikers. After the failure of the proposals made on 7 September the atmosphere among the dockers was gloomy and the usual daily march to Hyde Park was much down in numbers. Yet Burns roused them in a spirited

1 J.L. Smith and V. Nash, *The Story of the Dockers' Strike* (1889), 147.
2 J. Burns to T. Mann, n.d. Burns Papers. B.L. Add MSS 46285, f.4.

speech rejecting compromise. The following day with another £1,000 in the strike fund from Australia he made one of his finest speeches. 'This lads', he cried' 'is the Lucknow of Labour, and I myself, looking to the horizon, can see a silver gleam, not of bayonets to be imbrued in a brother's blood, but the gleam of the full round orb of the docker's tanner'.[1] Small wonder that the Lord Mayor, frustrated in his efforts to negotiate a compromise turned bitterly to Tillett and said, 'you and Burns are the strike'.[2] At almost daily conferences in the strikers' press room Burns, aided by Champion, delivered good copy to the assembled newsmen, using his mastery of metaphor and simile to portray a gallant David struggling against the Goliath of industrial capitalism. Further publicity was achieved by means of almost daily marches into the west end which Burns usually led, often ending with a morale boosting oration.

It was alleged by the dock employers that many of Burns's speeches were direct incitements to violence. One of their leaders for example, C.M. Norwood, wrote to the Commissioner of the Metropolitan Police asking

> what did Burns mean by 'bombarding the gates with horse, foot and artillery?' He certainly did not mean merely shouting or picketting on the roads. All that had been done before, and the men were now to try something new, which he promised them would be more effective. Moreover, they were to 'bring every blackleg out'. How were the men to be brought out, except by the strikers going in for them?. . . Mr Burns, according to newspaper reports, also said 'they were to remodel their tactics'. Henceforth it would 'be a game of hard slogging'. By this he certainly did not mean hard words, which had already been used abundantly enough, but he clearly meant hard knocks.[3]

Norwood's letter illustrates once again the difficulties, alluded to above, of interpreting newspaper reports, particularly as it is generally agreed that the characteristic of Burns's speeches during the strike was essentially moderation. Without both sympathy and financial assistance from the public the strike could never have succeeded, and there can be little doubt that Burns's moderation was vital in earning this sympathy. Even *The Times* was compelled to concede that 'with all his capacity for wild and offensive speech, he has known how to address at times words of moderation and wisdom to his followers'.[4] Lord Rosebery was but one of several prominent public figures who wrote to con-

1 Quoted in Smith and Nash, *Dockers' Strike*, 147.
2 *The Times*, 10 September 1889.
3 C.M. Norwood to the Metropolitan Police Commissioner, 6 September 1889. P.R.O. MEPO 2/226.
4 *The Times*, 16 September 1889.

gratulate Burns on the orderliness with which the strike was being conducted, and he enclosed a generous donation to the strike fund. [1] The events of 1886 and 1887 had reinforced the view that the east end was likely to be a source of social friction. [2] Yet here was Burns, the villain of 1886 and 1887, leading mass marches into the west end, not bearing the red flag but in earnest conversation with a superintendent of police. Here was Burns appealing to dockers to persevere and win, but to march off peacefully and to keep on the left side of the street. As Champion said:

> As soon as it became widely known that 1,000's of the strikers had marched through the City without a pocket being picked or a window being broken, and that at the head of the procession was a man whose public position was a guarantee that the 'mob' had a responsible leader, the British citizen felt that he might go back to his suburban villa when his day's work was done with full confidence that his warehouses would not be wrecked in the night, and that he could afford to follow his natural inclination and back the poor devils who were fighting with pluck, good humour and order against overwhelming odds. [3]

Administrator, negotiator, but above all publicist — these were the roles that Burns played during the dockers' strike. It is easy to overlook that others played equally important parts. The daily administration of the strike had been undertaken by numerous socialists, east end missionaries, residents of Toynbee Hall, and other well wishers whose sympathies, for a variety of reasons, lay with the strikers. Sidney Buxton, the M.P. for Poplar, distributed thousands of tickets for meals and groceries. Tom Mann was in charge of the monumental task of organising a system of relief for the men and their families — providing food for a quarter of a million mouths each day. [4] Later, when the relief system was operating more smoothly, Mann took charge of the 3,000 pickets who were on duty every day. Further down the river it was Harry Orbell who organized the pickets and it was really on the picket line that the battle was fought out as the companies made intensive efforts to break the strike by importing blackleg labour. Much of the success, both of the relief system and the picketting, came from the participation of the stevedores whose experience of such matters was invaluable, and nearly all the members of the finance committee were stevedores. Yet somehow Burns subsumed them all.

1 Lord Rosebery to J. Burns, 14 September 1889. Burns Papers. B.L. Add. MSS 46282, ff. 2-3.

2 See G. Stedman Jones, *Outcast London: A Study of the Relationship Between Classes in Victorian Society* (Oxford, 1971) and G. Cronjé, 'Middle Class Opinion and the 1889 Dock Strike', *Our History* 61 (1975).

3 H. Champion, *The Great Dock Strike in London* (1890), 6.

4 Burns, 'The Great Strike', 417.

The very appearance of his white straw hat seemed to signify that everything was alright.

> As the straw hat is discerned there are cries of 'here he comes'. As Burns thrusts his way towards his parapet many a hand would fain detain him. Dockers have not received their food tickets, benevolent strangers from the United States wish to present their sovereign for the funds to the wearer of the white straw hat in person, reporters inquire if there is anything new for the press. A nod or monosyllable here and there as he cleaves onward. But is is enough; they have spoken to Burns.[1]

This contrast between the necessary but unseen administration performed mainly by so many others, and Burns's own mysterious ability to epitomise the whole struggle in his own person comes over well in one incident recalled by Tillett. The dockers were preparing to begin their daily march to Hyde Park when Burns strode to the front of the procession 'well washed, clean as a new pin, and having rested wisely and well. . . John's chest swelled with proper pride'. At this point Mann came on the scene, his clothes ragged and dirty from his exertions on the picket line. 'Burns unwittingly ventured an instruction. The sight of his primness and the pomp of John's demeanour outraged Tom, and I shall not print what Mann said in no uncertain docker's English'.[2]

The dock strike of 1889 was an important landmark in the development of unionism among unskilled workers in Britain, even though it has sometimes been given a significance in labour history that it does not really warrant. It did not mark the beginning of mass unionism on the water front, nor was it statistically the largest strike of the year. Many of the gains that the men made were gradually whittled away in the years that followed. But there can be no doubting its importance as far as John Burns was concerned. For one thing it made him a national, not to say international, trade union figure whose very presence was thought to be an almost automatic guarantee of success in a dispute. He was inundated with requests for help in forming new unions, or asking if he would lend his name to particular branches. A rumour that his aid had been sought was sufficient to galvanise a Home Office that had hitherto been handling a dispute with the police in a very dilatory fashion.[3] He was invited by the American Federation of Labor to participate in its current agitation for the establishment of an eight-hour working day, and from an old acquaintance, John Norton,

1 G. Elton, *England Arise* (1931), 157. See also Smith and Nash, *Dockers' Strike*, 36-7.

2 Tillett, *Brief History*, 27-8. Tillett minimises Burns's role in the general administration of the strike.

3 G. Reynolds and A. Judge. *The Night the Police Went on Strike* (1968), 213.

50

there came the very attractive offer of a lecture tour of Australia. 'You are regarded as the great central figure of the strike and all Australians look upon you as the guiding star of the Dock Labourers, and as the Chief Champion of depressed and suppressed labour in England. Your name is enthusiastically cheered everywhere. . .' Norton offered Burns payment of all expenses including a two month boat trip plus £250. He pointed out that he could also expect to receive congratulatory addresses, 'many accompanied by purses of sovereigns'.[1] But Burns had too many demands on his time to spend five months in the Antipodes and in any case money as such held little attraction for him. An appeal to his vanity on the other hand was much more likely to succeed and he acceded very promptly to a request from the Automatic Machines Union Ltd. asking if they could include his photograph in their penny postcard series, 'Celebrities of the Day'.

Burns's participation and the views which he expressed during the strike just about completed his break with Hyndman. He had already formally severed his connection with the S.D.F., resigning in June after he (and several other trade union and socialist figures) had clashed with Hyndman over attempts to revive the Socialist International. So divided were Europe's socialists that two rival congresses were held in Paris in July, as a result of which the Second International was formed. Hyndman, for all his protestations of Marxism, attended the 'Possibilist' conference, mainly because his rivals from the Socialist League went to the Marxist assembly. Burns, sent as a delegate by his union, attended meetings of both factions but his suggestion that more benefit would accrue if the two meetings were merged was heavily criticised by Hyndman. Burns duly exacted his revenge in the columns of the *Labour Elector*.

> How sorely pressed these men must be who with Liberty on their lips, have Coercion in their hearts; and display their fraternity by vilifying and excluding men whose only fault has been the resistance of egotism and jealousy on the part of those who have disrupted the Socialist movement at home. . . [2]

In the same spirit he had broken with the local branch in Battersea after disagreement about his openly expressed support for a Liberal candidate in a by-election at Kennington. The branch was the mainstay of his wages fund and it says much for the loyalty he could inspire that about half the members seceded with him and under the leadership of W.S. Sanders formed the Battersea Workmens Association whose prime

1 J. Norton to J. Burns, September 1889. Burns Papers. B.L. Add. MSS 46289. f. 18.
2 *Labour Elector*, 3 August 1889.

function was to fuel his wage fund.[1] Some members of the Federation tried to keep links with Burns open, praising his vigour in the dock strike and suggesting that he had been misled into accepting a compromise settlement by the 'oily-tongued' Champion.[2] Hyndman, however, was adamant in his bitterness and he was responsible for circulating a handbill which accused Burns, Mann and Champion of misappropriating strike funds. The trio's failure to respond only reinforced his suspicions. 'They have manifestly sold out from the cause of Socialism. Whether money or flattery or promise of place has bought them, or all three together, we neither know nor care. . . Such men are happily no longer Socialists, and if they call themselves so it is only with intent to deceive'.[3] In January 1890 Hyndman levelled similar charges against Burns, bearding him in his own Battersea den. Burns responded by accusing Hyndman of talking revolution but running away as soon as any chance of proving himself appeared.[4] Burns realised that in the popular mind socialism in 1889 was irrevocably linked with the S.D.F. which enjoyed little support and he knew only too well that his help in the dock strike had been welcomed in spite of rather than because of his own socialism.[5] For this reason he had refused the Federation demand that he lead the daily marches with a red flag. From now on, his contacts with the S.D.F. grew steadily less frequent and more acrimonious. Nothing ever changed his view of Hyndman. His conduct had been 'contemptible in the extreme. What a coward he is'.[6]

Finally, the strike of 1889 greatly enhanced Burns's parliamentary prospects. 'Whatever may be the issue of this strike', one paper had commented, 'one thing is quite clear. It will make John Burns inevitable as a candidate for some London constituency'.[7] In fact, the executive of Battersea's Liberal and Radical Federation had approached Burns even before the strike to ask if he would accept nomination in place of the sitting Liberal member, O.V. Morgan, who had decided to retire. Burns had rejected this overture on the grounds that he did not wish to stand as a Liberal. 'I will stand', he replied, 'as a social democrat. If your association likes to support me it may; if not I must fight harder and

1 Members paid sixpence a month and assisted with fund raising efforts such as smoking concerts.

2 *Justice,* 21 September 1889.

3 Ibid. 18 January 1890.

4 *South Western Star,* 11 January 1890.

5 Champion confirmed this in an interview with the Melbourne magazine, *Trident* (September 1908), 93.

6 Burns Diary, 17 January 1892. B.L. Add. MSS 46312.

7 *Birmingham Post,* 4 September 1889.

52

win'.[1] Faced with this response the local Liberals selected, rather unwisely, an outside candidate, Lawson Walton, a lawyer. But Burns had been confident of his ability to win the seat ever since his success in the council contest and he was completely undeterred, the more so since his reputation had grown enormously as a result of his activities during the dock strike. At a public meeting held in Battersea on 1 October 1889 he was adopted as a candidate, in the course of the proceedings pausing to take a swipe at the local Liberal Association and capitalising on the strong sense of local particularism. Why, he wanted to know, were they going to adopt 'a man from the North of England who knew nothing of the labour question and less of Battersea, and who by virtue of his education and training was unfitted and unqualified to represent such a hive of industry as Battersea was today'.[2] The following day Walton drew the obvious conclusions and bowed out, freely admitting the validity of Burns's question. In December the local Liberals met to consider giving Burns their support but it was soon apparent that not all were prepared to let him go forward with their blessing. He had expressed strong views, even in the immediate past. For example, he had threatened in the course of the dock strike to paralyse trade, and asserted at his adoption meeting his wish to sweep away all hereditary authority, and to nationalise the mines, the land, and the post office. This was too strong for more moderate Liberals in Battersea and thus his acceptance by the party in December met some outright opposition and many simply abstained when the matter was put to the vote. Rumours began to circulate that an alternative candidate was being sought and it was perhaps to counter this that Burns launched the Battersea Labour League as an extension of the Workmens Association. In the end, however, most members of the Liberal Association did support their executive's recommendation that they back Burns, although all the members of Branch Four resigned in protest in June 1890.

The Labour League's published programme laid great stress on the need for broad-fronted action on the part of the working classes if they were going to achieve any substantial improvements in their conditions. This was the lesson which Burns was proving almost daily in his council work and it was also one which, for him at least, had been confirmed by the dock strike. In a manuscript entitled 'Lessons of the strike' he noted that 'we must identify ourselves with every movement, social, political, artistic, and by example weave into the lives of others

1 Letter to the *South Western Star,* 12 October 1889.
2 Ibid. 5 October 1889.

the ideal life. . . and that life will be called socialism'.[1] It was to this
policy that he attributed his success in Battersea. 'We have co-operated
with teetotallers, Radicals, Liberals, Trade Unionists, costermongers.
Everyone with a grievance. This policy has done more for socialism
than all the preaching about class war'.[2] Of course as a parliamentary
candidate Burns had every interest in appealing to the widest possible
spectrum of support but it seems that he was preserving the nomen-
clature and trappings of the faith while at heart watering it down to a
programme of radical social reform. 'When socialists as a body have
secured for the people of these islands', he told the crowd assembled to
see him open the new ferry in Woolwich in March 1889, 'some
instalment, however trifling, of the material improvement about which
they talk so much and to attain which they do so little, Socialism will
be a power'.[3] Such sentiments created considerable suspicion among
his remaining socialist friends. Writing to the German social democrat,
H. Schlüter, to point out that middle-class sympathy for trade unionists
was diminishing in Britain, Engels added that 'This is very good and I
only hope Burns will some day go through this experience himself, in a
strike led by himself – he cherishes all sorts of illusions on that score'.[4]
In an earlier letter, written at the start of the dock strike, Engels had
written triumphantly to Laura Lafargue that 'this strike is worked and
led by our people, by Burns and Mann, and the Hyndmanites are
nowhere it it'.[5] In December, however, he was telling Sorge that 'the
most repulsive thing here is the "bourgeois" respectabilĭty which has
grown deep into the bones of the workers . . . I am not at all sure for
instance that John Burns is not secretly prouder of his popularity with
Cardinal Manning, the Lord Mayor and the bourgeoisie in general than
of his popularity with his own class'.[6]

Yet, even though Burns was alarming his socialist friends with his
insistence on broad-fronted political action he was equally passionate
in his advocacy of working-class organisation, since the dock strike had
shown conclusively what combination could achieve. 'Until workmen
of all trades conquered themselves . . . their envy and jealousy of each
other', he told the Engineers' Club in Blackfriars Road, "they would

1 Manuscript headed 'Lessons of the Strike', n.d. Burns Papers. B.L. Add.
MSS 46305, ff. 38-51.
2 Untitled manuscript, written sometime between 1889 and 1892. Ibid. ff. 96-7.
3 *Labour Elector*, 30 March 1889.
4 F. Engels to H. Schlüter, 11 January 1890. *Karl Marx and Frederick Engels
on Britain* (Moscow, 1953), 523.
5 F. Engels to L. Lafargue, 27 August 1889. *Correspondence*, II, 304.
6 F. Engels to F. Sorge, December 1889. Quoted in Thompson, *Morris*, 668.

never conquer their enemies'.[1] Although the gain in wages for dockers was important, he wrote,

> Still more important perhaps, is the fact that labour of the humbler kind has shown its capacity to organise itself; its solidarity; its ability. . .the labourer. . .has learned that combination can lead him to anything and everything. He has tasted success as the immediate fruit of combination, and he knows that the harvest he has just reaped is not the utmost he can look to gain . . . Conquering himself, he has learned that he can conquer the world of capital whose generals have been the most ruthless of his oppressors.[2]

Here then was the message of organisation and co-operation that Burns was to preach from now on. The vehicle of organisation was the trade union, which was to achieve the revolution — though Burns was rarely using this word now — by means of political action, not by blind industrial protest. He often adopted a surprisingly cautious attitude to the rash of strikes that followed the success of the dockers, realising that many were rushing too precipitately into action without adequate financial backing, or even without much due cause. Addressing a meeting on behalf of the newly formed G.R.W.U. in Battersea he told the men not to consider strike action until they had a strong union at their back.[3] A year later he was advising even the dockers to adopt a less militant line as they were short of funds.[4] He counselled Scottish railway workers on similar lines in January 1891 and in February unfolded to members of the Democratic Club a lengthy catalogue of mistakes currently being committed all over the country by newly organised unions. But, as he pointed out in the *Labour Elector,* the failures would be useful because they would press home the lesson that the battle had to be fought in the polling booth as well as on the factory floor.[5] He knew that the combination of favourable economic circumstance and public sympathy which had given the dockers victory could prove to be temporary and that more permanent gains could be secured by using the unions to organise labour as a political force. This would bring gains that were not dependent upon elements as fickle as public opinion or the state of trade. In Liverpool at the end of 1891 he told delegates at the Railway Workers conference to 'stick to their organisation but to use it mainly for legislative purposes'.[6]

Inevitably, although there were many who shared Burns's view about

1 *The Times,* 14 October 1889.
2 Burns, 'The Great Strike', 421.
3 *South Western Star,* 26 October 1889.
4 *Dockers Monthly Record* (September, 1890).
5 *Labour Elector,* 21 December 1889.
6 Burns Diary, 15 November 1891. B.L. Add. MSS 46311.

the political role of trade unions, his policy met opposition. It cost him the friendship of Tom Mann, who did not share his enthusiasm for political action and who, in Burns's view, seemed to be irresponsible in his advocacy of the strike weapon. These differences came to a head during a dock strike at Wapping and by the end of 1891 their relationship was purely formal.[1] More significantly, however, the advocates of political methods came into conflict with the vested interests entrenched in the old established craft unions. Burns had always been critical of the snobbish attitude adopted by these unions towards less skilled men. He believed that they were so obsessed with preserving their friendly society functions that they had degenerated into 'mere middle- and upper- class rate reducing institutions'.[2]   The *Labour Elector,* of whose editorial board Burns was now a member, frequently attacked the old unionists who controlled the T.U.C., especially George Howell, Henry Broadhurst, and George Shipton. Burns was equally scornful in private. When in 1891 Howell published a book which highlighted the differences between the older tradition and the new unionism Burns dismissed it as a 'vulgar lying tirade against men who have completely exposed this Capitalist Hack'.[3] Not that the feelings of hostility were all one way. Beatrice Webb noted that Shipton's view of the dock strike was 'visibly biased by his antipathy, I might almost say hatred of Burns'.[4] This clash between old and new unionists reached a climax at the Liverpool meeting of the T.U.C. in September 1890. The delegates passed many resolutions which had been moved by the new unionist representatives and Burns, sent as a delegate by the A.S.E., joined enthusiastically in the onslaught. Unorganised men everywhere had been looking for guidance, he claimed, and yet the T.U.C. had provided none. Why, he demanded, had they failed to introduce a miners' eight-hour bill into parliament? When he joined in the debate on parliamentary representation he argued that it was insufficient merely to affirm the principle. They needed men who were not tied to the tails of any party but who would support a solid programme of social democracy.[5] At the end of the conference all but three of the existing Parliamentary Committee failed to keep their

---

1 The strike is written up by D. Torr, 'Tom Mann and His Times, 1890-1892', *The Luddites and Other Essays,* ed. L. Munby (1971), 211-17. Burns also ignored Mann's request for help in securing election to the secretaryship of the Amalgamated Society of Engineers.

2 *Justice,* 3 September 1887.

3 Burns Diary, 19 March 1891. B.L. Add. MSS 46311.

4 B. Webb Diary, 1 September 1889. British Library of Political and Economic Science (Hereafter B.L.P.E.S.). Passfield Papers, I, vol. 13, 77.

5 T.U.C., *Annual Report* (1890), 31, 36. See also J. Burns, *A Speech by John Burns on the Liverpool Congress* (1890).

places, and Burns was one of the replacements, although it must be pointed out that the old unionists remained in the majority and Burns only got his place because others with more votes declined to serve. Nevertheless, he interpreted his election to the T.U.C.'s Parliamentary Committee as further endorsement of the policies he had adopted and which he was striving to put into effect on the county council. There, the Progressive majority was a rather heterogeneous group, a mixture of manufacturers, commercial men and lawyers, with a sprinkling of publishers, gentlemen and retired servicemen.[1] They were in euphoric mood after their election victory, 'full of great schemes, mostly framed to secure the millennium for London by return of post. These newly fledged reformers, fresh from the polls, hotly resented any obstruction to their wishes'.[2] Their programme had contained a variety of constructive proposals, but its core was really 'anti-injustice'. Burns shared fully in their zeal and his was the voice that rang out most loudly at the slightest hint of corruption or jobbery. When the appointment of a Mr Duckham as the council's chief engineer was moved Burns created a first-class row in the council chamber by asserting that Duckham knew virtually nothing about sewage systems and that his testimonials had come from council members themselves. Pressed by furious Moderates to withdraw he refused and finally named the two members who had provided the references; one was Duckham's close friend, the other his brother-in-law. Burns was delighted when another applicant was finally given the post. Nor was Battersea's councillor prepared to consent to the lavish salaries which the council in its enthusiasm was recommending for some of its higher officials. 'The people of London', he informed the council during a debate on the salary to be paid to the Comptroller, 'were strongly of opinion, as he was, that the Council was disproportionately increasing the salaries of their permanent officials'.[3] Consistently he moved reductions in salary proposals – of £500 each, for instance, in the case of the £2,000 and £1,500 suggested respectively for the deputy chairman and the chief engineer.[4] His zeal in this matter was such that he often annoyed even his radical colleagues. In March 1891 he noted that after he and another member had made a bid to prevent proposed increases in some official salaries Sir John Lubbock, the council's

---

1 J. Stevens, 'The London County Council Under the Progressives, 1889-1907' (Sussex M.A. thesis, 1966).

2 A.G. Gardiner, *John Benn and the Progressive Movement* (1925), 98.

3 Quoted in W. Saunders, *History of the First London County Council* (1892), 435.

4 It was in the course of such debates that Burns made the comment, often used against him in later years, that he knew no man worth more than £500 year.

Vice-Chairman, had been 'very angry and distinctly unfair in his ruling'.[1]

On the more constructive side Burns devoted most of his time to furthering the interests of London's working classes, operating mainly, though not exclusively, through the various committees of which he was a member — the Parliamentary, the Standing, Main Drainage, and Bridges. He had never before exhibited any great interest in matters as mundane as bridge facilities or sewage disposal but now even the most intimate details of Londoners' daily lives absorbed his attention. When Moderates tried to postpone a move to acquire a new sludge disposal ship until a naval architect had submitted a full report Burns, whose interest in the matter led him to take several voyages on the sludge vessels to Barrow Deep where the sewage was dumped, replied sarcastically but with great feeling. 'What were they to do with the sludge in the meantime? Was London to stink to gratify the fads or theories of one or two gentlemen as against the opinions of their own officers?'[2] His weekends were often spent in examination of council works, for he revelled in seeing council projects actually taking concrete form. Battersea naturally came in for particular attention, especially after his adoption as its parliamentary candidate. In February 1891, for example, he passed a fairly typical day visiting work in progress on Clapham Common, Wandsworth Common and at the York Road pumping station. In the same year he devoted almost the whole month of August to this type of activity, inspecting what he termed 'my district — condition of roads, streets, sewers, gullies, and many dustbins'.[3] He also took good care to publicise his visit to the new Battersea bridge.

This high degree of personal involvement and interest was brought to everything John Burns did on the London County Council. When he was made one of a three man sub-committee to report on the state of the bridges over the Thames, within ten days Burns had dragged his colleagues to inspect every bridge and presented to the council a detailed schedule of suggested improvements, even to the prosiac extent of recommending precise sites for new urinals.[4] Appointed to another sub-committee to examine the working of the Woolwich ferry he organised the committee's meetings actually on the boats themselves and there can be little doubt that this enthusiasm frequently paid

1 Burns Diary, 17 March 1891. B.L. Add. MSS 46311.
2 Quoted in Saunders, *First London County Council*, 341.
3 Burns Diary, 24 August 1891. B.L. Add. MSS 46311.
4 L.C.C. Bridges Committee, *Minutes,* 10 October 1889.

handsome dividends. When the Parliamentary Committee decided to resist a proposed Midland Railway Bill because it would have permitted the building of a track through a children's playing area in St Pancras, Burns got himself appointed to the sub-committee charged with organising opposition. Together with Councillor W.H. Dickinson of Wandsworth he appeared before the House of Commons committee dealing with the bill and turned up having been personally to the playground four times, interviewed the children, and compiled statistics as to its usage. This first-hand presentation of evidence did much to ensure the measure's defeat. It was the same with the Nunhead and Shortlands Railway Bill which also threatened a recreation ground, this time in Lewisham. Deputed by the Parliamentary Committee to assist in organising opposition Burns again based the council case on information gleaned from a personal visit to the playground in question. Small wonder that the *South Western Star,* commenting on the work of the first council in 1892, drew attention to the fact that Burns 'has made himself a kind of inspector-general of London's labourers, and he and others have gone down sewers, investigated pumping stations, looked into personal and staff grievances. . .'.[1]

The comment also highlighted the other important feature of Burns's contribution — his interest in the conditions and wages of all workers connected with the council. Very early on he had argued strongly though unsuccessfully for the institution of a forty-eight-hour week for men employed in the council's pumping stations. He was made a member of several sub-committees charged with investigations into the working conditions of various groups of council employees, including the Woolwich ferryboat men and pumping station workers, and much of practical benefit to the labour force emerged from these committees. The ferryboat committee, for example, recommended a two week annual holiday for all employees. Much council work, however, was done by contractors and during the lifetime of the first council Burns waged unrelenting war against those who refused to pay decent wages or who went in for sub-contracting. Like many Progressives, Burns was resolutely opposed to this latter practice, believing that it encouraged bad workmanship, low wages, long hours, and, ultimately, sweating. On occasion he attended council debates armed with chunks of mortar, dried paint, and screws, not to hurl at the opposition but in order to demonstrate the inferiority of contractors' work. In April 1889 he moved that heavy sanctions be imposed on firms given the council contract to build the new Crossness sewer because some of the brick work involved had allegedly been sub-contracted. He only gave up this

1 *South Western Star,* 23 January 1892.

particular case when the council decided on legal advice that the evidence was too thin to support any penal action. Even a hint of sub-contracting was sufficient to rouse him and he repeatedly raised in committee the question of exactly who had painted and glazed workmen's cottages at the Barking precipitation works until satisfied that the job had not been sub-contracted.[1]

Most of his campaign against sub-contracting was carried out through the medium of the Main Drainage Committee but in June 1889 the establishment of a Contracts Committee provided a new outlet. This committee was established initially to receive a deputation, introduced by Burns, which represented the London building trades and argued for the imposition of fair wage rates and the abolition of sub-contracting. The delegates made two points; that all contractors who paid unfair wages or imposed undue hours on their workers should forfeit their contracts; that the council should consider establishing its own workforce to eliminate the need for contractors entirely. The Progressive majority was generally sympathetic and the Contracts Committee was accordingly instructed to investigate the feasibility of establishing a works department. Burns pushed hard but most members of the committee felt that as the council had had difficulty in raising money, the creation of a works department was too ambitious an undertaking. Their report recommended that the council should employ its own workers for tasks such as road sweeping that did not require much capital outlay. Major works were still to be put out to tender, although contractors would have to agree to pay fair wages. Even this, Burns felt, was too modest, for in his election manifesto he had argued that all men working for the council, whether directly or indirectly, should be paid at the appropriate trade union rate. In November, therefore, he seconded a resolution that every council contract should have attached to it a schedule of the wages to be paid, rather than merely have the contractor make a vague declaration to pay fair wages. For the time being, however, this was as far as he could get.

Of course there were councillors other than Burns who were as keen on direct works, trade union conditions, and reforms to benefit the working classes, and under the whip of John Benn the Progressives soon emerged as a well disciplined political group. Yet it is abundantly clear from the few personal references that the various council committee minutes contain that Burns was the dominant figure with a finger in almost every pie of interest to labour. One council official later affirmed that he was 'very vocal' and that 'his voice influenced

[1] L.C.C. Main Drainage Committee, *Minutes*, 18 April 1889.

more votes in the Council than that of any other member'.[1] Such was Burns's dominance at this stage that when a frustrated Moderate produced an election pamphlet in 1892 it took the form of a fantasy set in 1911 in which year the London County Council, having challenged parliament, was finally crushed by the House of Lords and the Guards. Their leaders were then duly dealt with, their names being Mr McBoodle (McDougall) and Sir John Blazer, a thinly disguised reference to Burns.[2]

Yet Burns was by no means unthinking or unreasoned in his advocacy of working-class interests. He always tried to get as full a picture as possible of any issue before coming to a decision. When gangers and flushers at the sewage stations requested a wage increase of sixpence a day, the Main Drainage Committee at Burns's suggestion asked the engineer to prepare a full report on every aspect of the gangers' and flushers' work, and sent a sub-committee, led by Burns, to watch the workers at Barking before deciding on a new rate for the job. Nor did he believe that the council should get involved in every project for working-class advancement. He was a staunch believer in the value of technical education yet he resolutely opposed Progressive moves to get the council involved in projects designed to further it. He was scornful when it was suggested that £140,000 be set aside to finance technical education in London. It was, he told the council, essentially an imperial question and should be dealt with by parliament. The money was inadequate and would be far better used in building public lavatories 'and they would be doing more good for the people of London than in applying any portion or the whole of it to technical education'.[3] To some extent, his opposition was based on his desire to save the council money. Like many of the Progressives he had a passion for economy that was to become more marked as the years went by. He strongly supported a motion in the Bridges Committee to compel employees to insure against sickness with a friendly society in order to relieve the council of the burden of paying gratuities to men absent from work through illness.

Altogether, Burns attended some 294 meetings of the first council besides devoting untold amounts of his spare time to personal inquiries and investigations into council matters. At least part of two days each

---

1 H. Haward, *The London County Council From Within* (1932), 21.

2 *The Doom of the County Council of London.* Cited in Stevens, 'The London County Council', 19.

3 Quoted in Saunders, *First London County Council,* 337. Burns was elected on to the Technical Education Committee in 1892 but although he attended regularly he took very little part in its proceedings.

week was absorbed by council meetings. The full council met on Tuesdays, the Main Drainage Committee at 2.30 p.m. on Thursdays, which meant he sometimes found it difficult to get to meetings of the Parliamentary Committee which began its deliberations at 4.00 the same afternoon. The Bridges Committee met on alternate Wednesdays at 2.30 p.m. Rarely was Burns absent from council work for very long, and when he was, it was usually because he was busy with trade union agitation or, after September 1890, with the work of the T.U.C. By the early 1890s, therefore, he had carved out for himself a position unique among British labour leaders. Yet it left its marks on him. At the beginning of 1891 while on his way to address striking Scottish railway workers he collapsed on the train and had to get off. In March he was somewhat put out when old friends he met at a football match commented on how he had aged and he noted in his diary that he felt 'tired and very depressed. . .I want a good long rest free of all books, statistics, and all the worry of an agitator's life'.[1] Always, however, he had his refuge, the home in Battersea for which Pattie (his pet name for his wife) cared, and which she was always willing to share with the stream of visitors who trailed up the path seeking the sage's advice. He could find consolation, too, in his books, especially the collection of Sir Thomas More's work that he was beginning to build. He found More appealing partly because of his associations with London but also because one of his guiding political principles, like that of many pre-Marxian socialists, was that of co-operation between different social groups in the cause of progress. Sport as well still afforded some outlet and in the summer of 1891 he took to batting in the Battersea Park cricket nets. 'Health much better', he was able to record in May, 'through cricket and less work than hitherto'.[2] Even this, however, was not without political implications — a parliamentary candidate mixing with his potential constituents on the cricket field.

---

1 Burns Diary, 17 March 1891. B.L. Add. MSS 46311.
2 Ibid. 15 May 1891.

4

THE CLASH WITH HARDIE: PARLIAMENT AND THE TRADES UNION CONGRESS 1892-1895

By the early 1890s John Burns was in many ways a much more respectable figure than he had been six or seven years previously – hero of the dock strike, member of the T.U.C.'s Parliamentary Committee and a London County Councillor. Even so he was still capable of exciting the mistrust and suspicion of authority. As late as 1891, to his intense annoyance, policemen were present at a strike meeting in Stirling, busily noting down the details of his speech. His rather intemperate conduct of a strike against the London Omnibus Company nearly resulted in a legal action being taken against him.[1] Yet his disillusionment with the revolutionary S.D.F. was by now complete. He was sick of the wirepulling and intrigue in which the Federation was involved, fearing that the 'irresponsible people' at its head would damage both the British and international working-class movement.[2] Further, he believed that the rigidity of the Federation was responsible for its failure to make any headway with the workers. He still retained his vision and still referred to himself as a socialist, but he now believed that the vision would be realised, not by revolutionary heroics or perorations on the class struggle, but by solid, practical administrative reform. It was, he told Cunninghame Graham, a 'slow weary fight that *must* be fought.'[3] He evidently derived considerable satisfaction from the fact that William Morris seemed to be coming to a similar conclusion, that 'the workers must learn (as they must) administration'.[4] The clearest exposition of Burns's views came in an interview which he gave to *Le Figaro* in November 1892.

> We go in for progressive reforms. . . . For my part I have two eyes which I make use of, one fixed on the ground on the lookout for practical things immediately realisable, the other looking upward – toward the ideal. . . . I recognise that Socialism has ended its purely theoretical course, and that the hour to construct has come. . . When I have to mount a staircase I climb up step by step. If I want to go up ten stairs at a time I break my neck – and that is not my intention.[5]

1 H.A. Taylor, *Jix – Viscount Brentford* (1933), 43-4.

2 J. Burns to A. Bebel and W. Liebknecht, 17 August 1891. Burns Papers. B.L. Add. MSS 46290, ff. 5-6.

3 Burns Diary, 10 February 1892. Ibid. Add. MSS 46312. The italics are in the original.

4 Ibid. 21 March 1891. Add. MSS 46311.

5 Translation of the interview, 18 November 1892. Ibid. Add. MSS 46291, ff. 39-40.

The essence of his tactical approach was an active independence involving co-operation with anyone in a position to advance the cause of labour. This had been his policy in the L.C.C. and it had been successful, even though inevitably it had brought him into close contact with the radical wing of the Liberal Party. His T.U.C. work on matters like employers' liability also involved working with Liberals, mainly the lawyers such as R.B. Haldane and H.H. Asquith. Yet Burns still retained his innate suspicion of organised Liberalism. In 1890 he had rejected an invitation from Rosebery to stand as a Liberal at Bristol and the following year resisted advances from the Liberal whips to fight Battersea in their interest. He was adamant in his intention to·stand as a socialist.[1] When the L.C.C. elections took place in 1892 the official Liberal organ, the *Speaker,* advocated supporting Labour candidates and indeed ten were given straight fights against Conservative opposition. All but three of the ten had their campaigns organised by their respective local Liberal machine. Burns was one of the three exceptions, his campaign being run by the Labour League. 'The Liberals', he noted cautiously after the first meeting of the new council, 'will do all they can to disintegrate the Labour Councillors'.[2]

But partly as a result of this policy several labour men were returned to the council and the Progressives swept the board, picking up eighty-three seats against the thirty-five taken by the Moderates. The latter's poor showing owed a lot to the way in which the Conservative Government had obstructed the first council, for example, not permitting it to have its own petty cash and wages account, throwing out proposals to extend the South London Tramway over the river, and denying the council, which had responsibility for some forty miles of the River Thames, any representation on the Conservancy Board. The Progressive cause had benefitted, too, from a series of extremely able articles on the council's work which had appeared in the *Daily Chronicle* during the run up to the poll. Behind them lay several lengthy consultations between the newspaper's Fabian editor, H.W. Massingham, and his close friend John Burns. Although Burns had naturally taken good care to see that his own role was not minimised he still interpreted the election result as a spontaneous expression of approval. 'Nascent socialism and the Labour Policy of past three years alone secured it. . . .'[3] His own campaign had passed off fairly uneventfully, even though the energy which he had brought to his electioneering caused some of his friends once more to express concern about his health, and it was alleged that his supporters had deliberately disrupted meetings

1 Burns Diary, 7 October 1891. Ibid. Add. MSS 46311.
2 Ibid. 11 March 1892. Add. MSS 46312.
3 Ibid. 7 March 1892.

organised by Howarth Barnes, one of the Moderate candidates. But Burns was well content with his 5,168 votes. In second place was the other Progressive, James Tims, with 4,470, over twice as many as the nearest Moderate.

Shortly after the council election Burns told the audience at a victory meeting in Battersea that there was even greater scope for a militant labour policy in the House of Commons than in the L.C.C. and it was to parliament that they should now direct their attention. The opportunity to do so presented itself sooner than Burns may have expected, for a general election was called for the early summer of 1892. He had, of course, been nursing Battersea assiduously ever since his adoption, looking after its interests on the L.C.C. and taking good care that his potential parliamentary constituents heard of his efforts on their behalf. At the beginning of each year he had presented to the public a lengthy report of his year's work on the council; indeed Burgess complained that his whole council election campaign had been 'parochial, confined strictly to the constituency of Battersea'.[1] His concern had already been rewarded tangibly. By March of 1890 the Labour League had attracted sufficient new supporters to allow it to increase his weekly wage to £2-10s-0d.

But the League still found it hard to raise the extra money — estimated at £300 — necessary to fight the general election, especially as it followed so closely on the heels of the council campaign. Burns himself had a very puritanical outlook on political jobbery and financial corruption and had no intention of accepting any of the inviting offers that were made to him to solve the problem. During the council election for instance, the returning officer had sent Burns his own fee out of gratitude for some smoothing out of union troubles at his firm. It was an innocent enough gesture with no sinister motive behind it but Burns, determined to avoid even the appearance of evil, sent it back by return of post. So it was hardly surprising that when the Liberal whip, Arnold Morley, offered him £150 to fight the general election, Burns rejected the offer out of hand. The month of May, therefore, found him visiting a local music hall to ask if the proprietor would hire it to him cheaply for a concert in aid of his election fund. It was, he noted wrily, 'a sight for the gods and to me humiliating that the "tribune of the workers" should go hat in hand for an obligation for labour from one who makes his money by punching other people's heads'.[2] The League's appeal for money also evoked promises of help from some trade unions and from Champion via the *Workman's Times* came £100, a contribution

1 Burgess, *Burns, 153.*
2 Burns Diary, 10 May 1892. B.L. Add. MSS 46312.

Burns only accepted once he was sure it had not come from the same source as the Tory gold of 1885.

The campaign in Battersea got under way in earnest in the middle of June. Burns had the support of a surprisingly wide range of advanced opinion. On his inaugural platform the retiring Liberal member, O.V. Morgan, sat next to the Fabian, Bernard Shaw, and the Labour councillor for Woolwich, Will Crooks. Telegrams of encouragement from Kautsky, Engels, and the Avelings were read out. Burns's programme was equally mixed. As he told one audience, 'in things electoral he was a Radical, in things dealing with Government a Republican, in things social and economic he was a Socialist, but in all things he was for labour night and day'.[1]

He demanded radical reforms in the election system, including triennial parliaments, adult suffrage, the payment of M.P.s; hereditary authority was to be abolished; legislation was demanded to establish an eight-hour working day and to control the liquor traffic. The Conservative candidate, Mr Chinnery, took the field a few days later. It was unfortunate that he had hired as his committee room the Lammas Hall which had been long regarded as the Labour League's almost by divine right. Perhaps as a result of this effrontery Chinnery found it almost impossible to get a hearing. Meeting after meeting was disrupted by pro-Burns hecklers. Although Burns himself publicly disowned the hecklers one outraged admiral wrote in high dudgeon to The Times claiming that Burns had won 'by intimidation and coercion . . . it was a mere shouting match . . . a disgrace'. He added that Burns had every reason to try and keep Chinnery quiet, as his own address was the most schoolboyish performance ever inflicted on the constituency.[2] Burns, steaming energetically and almost inevitably to victory by 5,616 votes to 4,057, did not bother to return the admiral's fire. He contented himself instead with a broadside at Chinnery, the drink trade, and the local Conservative Association, observing that the Lammas Hall had been the scenes of disgraceful Baccanalian orgies throughout the campaign. On 5 August he took the oath of affirmation in the House of Commons, beginning a parliamentary career that was to span over a quarter of a century. After a two week session the house went into recess until 1893, and Burns was able to devote himself fully and most fruitfully to the London County Council.

With the assistance of like minded radicals and the help of the Labour group Burns had renewed his efforts to secure a commitment to

1 *South Western Star,* 18 June 1892.
2 *The Times,* 9 July 1892.

trade union wages for all men employed on council work. He continued to maintain a vigilant eye in the Stores Committee on firms supplying the council with equipment to ensure that they paid their employees union rates. Similarly, when the Main Drainage Committee set up a sub-committee to consider the operation of the new sludge ships, it was Burns who insisted that they ask the Sailors and Firemen's Union for a schedule of their wages so that the crews of the vessels should be properly paid.[1] More importantly, however, he moved an amendment on a fair wages motion before the full council which would have had the effect of making all contractors sign a declaration that they observed union practices with regard to wages, conditions, and hours of labour, on pain of penalty if they breached it. The council, of course, was already committed to the principle of fair wages but Burns was determined to give this some more precise form. As he pointed out, 'fair wages' had been widely interpreted by contractors who had frequently argued that in practice it meant the wage at which they could get men to work. This had produced innumerable time-wasting disputes which had held up council projects. The difficulty could be overcome, Burns argued, if the council simply specified that 'union' rather than 'fair' wages were to be paid. A week later the original motion was withdrawn and Burns's amendment became the substantive resolution. Having first taken advice as to whether it could legally impose sanctions of the sort Burns was proposing, the council formally approved his resolution at the end of May 1892 in the face of furious opposition from outraged Moderates. At the beginning of December the Council discussed the form of schedule to be distributed to contractors and it became evident that the proposal was too advanced for some of the Progressives who feared that Burns was opening the way for some sort of trade union tyranny. But Burns made one of his most impressive speeches to date. Packed with facts and evidence, forcefully delivered, it demolished the opposition. Small wonder that a pamphlet written some years later on the history of the fair wages idea singled him out as *the* friend of the movement on the council.[2]

Yet he was not content to rest there. He had always believed that the council should undertake its own contracting work directly. This had been one of his main election platforms in 1889 and 1892. Concurrent with the effort to secure trade union wages, therefore, went the equally successful fight to get the council to establish a works department. As a campaign it was excellently prepared and well co-ordinated, being

1   L.C.C. Main Drainage Committee, *Minutes*, 26 May 1892.
2   G. Dew, *Government and Municipal Contracts Fair Wages Movement. A Brief History* (1896), 14.

launched on a variety of fronts with Burns once again figuring prominently. At the end of September 1892, men employed on the council's new tunnel project at Blackwall sent a memorandum to the Bridges Committee claiming that Pearsons, the contractors, were not paying union rates. At the meeting which discussed the complaint a proposal also came up to invite tenders for the building of houses for the people who had been displaced by the construction of the tunnel. Burns used the memorandum to argue that contractors frequently flouted wage agreements and that therefore the committee should recommend the council to do the work itself.[1] At almost the same time he got the Main Drainage Committee to make a similar proposal in connection with the building of a new sewer under York Road in Lambeth. The two tenders which had been received for this work had both been in excess of £11,000 but Burns presented the committee with a detailed assessment of how much it would cost if undertaken directly by the council. His estimate of £7,000 for wages and materials, plus £2,000 for plant was well below the private tenders and showed just how carefully he and his fellow Progressives had planned their attack. When the Main Drainage Committee accepted the proposal he then successfully moved that there be referred to the council's General Purposes Committee a motion to set up a works department with its own buildings, stores, workshops, and depots, to carry out the various works ordered by the council.[2] When this was discussed in full council Burns was prominent among Progressive voices resisting Moderate efforts to get the report referred back to the Main Drainage Committee. His close colleague in the campaign, John Benn, moved the amendment which required the General Purposes Committee to draw up a plan for the new department's establishment. It was again indicative of much careful pre-planning that the scheme was produced and discussed as early as November. Though he had been the moving spirit behind the whole long struggle Burns took little part in the acrimonious council debate that took place on the report. He was content on this occasion to let others do the speaking, and simply cast his vote consistently against the wrecking amendments that flowed like water from the Moderate benches. Tired at the end of the debate he noted in his diary with quiet satisfaction that the successful conclusion of this campaign for direct municipal labour had been the 'biggest thing yet done for Collectivism and into which I have put as much time, energy and ability for four years as for any piece of work I have yet undertaken'.[3]

1   L.C.C. Bridges Committee, *Minutes,* 28 September 1892.
2   L.C.C. Main Drainage Committee, *Minutes,* 6 October 1892.
3   Burns Diary, 22 November 1892. B.L. Add. MSS 46312.

Resolving to establish a Works Department was only the beginning, however. The amount of work involved in actually setting it up was enormous, particularly in view of the obstacles erected at every step by the Moderates, prompted mainly by Edward Taylor, a master builder. Along with W.C. Steadman and Charles Freak of the labour group, Burns was made a member of the Works Committee and it says much for the general enthusiasm that by March 1893 the department was ready to begin work. Burns had pursuaded the committee to purchase some buildings in Belvedere Road from the Ecclesiastical Commissioners as a main depot even though the then Comptroller of the L.C.C. deemed then totally unsuitable.[1] Ultimately, it cost the council over £100,000 to convert the premises into a suitable headquarters, an indicator perhaps of Burns's total commitment as he was normally very parsimonious in his approach to public expenditure. Increasingly his local inspection activities took the form of keeping an eye on the activities of the Works Department. He did his utmost to ensure that all its workmen got trade union wages by getting most unions to submit to the committee schedules of their current working agreements so that the council could stay in line. Not that he was unduly generous, as he was responsible for establishing the principle that the Works Department manager should get the committee's approval if he ever wished to pay over the union rate for a particular task.[2] He believed that the moral code to which he himself subscribed was also suitable for public bodies, knowing from experience that whenever a working man was elected to a municipal body there were many who expected that he would 'job' for them.[3] In order to guard against this he also moved a resolution that the Works Department manager be directed to ignore any recommendations from members of the committee, the council or its officials, with reference to men seeking employment in the department.[4]

The establishment of the Works Department and the success of the fair wages movement were both impressive achievements and it soon became evident that Burns intended to concentrate on similar objectives at national level in parliament. In the main he eschewed the larger issues of politics and concentrated on matters close to his heart, notably working conditions, corruption, and public amenities. Since 1891 government workers had been guaranteed 'such wages as are generally accepted as current in each trade for competent workmen'.[5] This

1 Haward, *The London County Council*, 319.
2 L.C.C. Works Committee, *Minutes*, 25 September 1893.
3 *The Times*, 1 April 1895.
4 L.C.C. Works Committee, *Minutes*, 9 April 1894.
5 Dew, *Government and Municipal Contracts*, 9.

principle had been conceded largely as a result of pressure exerted jointly by the T.U.C. and radical M.P.s such as Sidney Buxton. The latter clearly welcomed Burns's arrival at Westminster and as early as July 1892 wrote to suggest that they should have a good talk about things. He meant almost certainly about the wage campaigns being fought in parliament and the L.C.C. Certainly Burns gave plenty of notice that he intended to keep the government on its toes as far as its employees were concerned, bombarding ministers with questions about wages in various government institutions. When would the report on wages in the Woolwich Arsenal be issued? Had the government yet decided on any wages policy? Were any increases envisaged for storehouse clerks at Woolwich? When would the Admiralty follow the the army's example and introduce minimum labouring wages in its ordnance establishments? What wages were being paid to men in the Dublin depots?[1] At every opportunity he argued the case for trade union wages to be specified instead of the vague phrase, 'current rate'. All his speeches, like those delivered to the L.C.C., were full of illustrative material and statistics, to such a degree that his hearers must have wondered at his reputation as a public speaker. But this was Burns the patient pragmatist, concerned that there should be economy in the public service, plodding steadily if slowly via shillings on wage levels, benches in parks, and minutes off the working day towards the utopia he had once painted so vividly. The detail, it must be admitted, was considerably less exciting than the overall picture.

The eight-hour day was the other topic to which Burns devoted most of his time during his first parliament. The ideal had a long history among British workers but really caught their imagination in the mid 1880s, due mainly to the tireless advocacy of Tom Mann. Burns, believing as he did that the workers must look to the state and legislation to achieve their objectives rather than to industrial action, had himself been a strong advocate of the eight-hour day, and had participated in many of the demonstrations organised to publicise it.[2] Frequently he had proved the most popular speaker at these meetings and it was no surprise therefore that once he was in parliament the T.U.C. delegated to him the task of introducing its Eight Hour Bill. There was little chance, given the generally *laissez-faire* climate of opinion in Britain, that the bill would pass, but Burns stuck to his brief and whenever possible raised the issue, sometimes in a general way, sometimes with reference to particular groups of employees such as railway workers,

1   Hansard, 4th series, VIII-XVI, February-August 1893, *passim.*
2   See A.E. Duffy, 'The Eight Hour Day Movement in Britain, 1886-1893', *Manchester School of Economic and Social Studies* 36 (1968), 203-22; 345-64.

bakery men, shop assistants and chemical workers. Sometimes he based his case on an appeal to humanity, on other occasions on public safety. Often he stressed the increase of work that would accrue to offset unemployment. He also acted as a parliamentary spokesman for the Government Workers' Eight Hour Committee and the abundance of grateful letters in his papers for 1893 and 1894 are ample testimony to the perseverance which he showed in pursuing the eight-hour day.

Yet it clearly made little sense to put so much effort into securing controls for government workers when so much government work was in fact done by outside employers and so Burns carried into parliament the war against contractors that he had started in the L.C.C. Of course, he could, not influence matters as directly as he could in the council but he made best use of such opportunities as presented themselves to point out the benefits of direct labour and to expose the excesses of bad contractors. His membership of the T.U.C. Parliamentary Committee between 1893 and 1894 was useful here, for he was successful in moving that the committee put pressure on the government to set up an inquiry into the conditions under which contract labour was carried out.[1] His main argument was that firms which produced good work were unable to procure government contracts because their workers were better treated and thus their tenders correspondingly higher than those of less scrupulous employers.[2] Paradoxically, however, he also told the House of Commons that its current expenditure of £600,000 on stationery could be greatly reduced by employing direct labour to produce, it, and that the quality would be better.[3] The Post Office he criticised for its practise of employing contractors to run its mail cart service. He expressed disgust at the dirtiness of the carts, the fatness of the contractors' profits (which was in marked contrast to the thinness of the horses) and he treated the house to a lengthy analysis of the equine death rate.[4]

Given that many Liberals shared his views on these questions and that his own tactical position involved co-operation with people of like mind Burns soon found himself making deeper contacts with Liberal members of the House of Commons. In matters such as home rule and suffrage reform his views were virtually indistinguishable from those of many radicals anyway, but his interest in wage matters strengthened the links he had formed with Sidney Buxton at the time of the dock strike and his involvement as a trade unionist in the Workmen's Compensation

1 T.U.C. Parliamentary Committee, *Minutes,* 9 October 1891.
2 Hansard, 4th series, XIV, 81. 26 June 1893.
3 Ibid. XXVIII, 1572-9. 18 August 1894.
4 Ibid. XVII, 1706-8. 19 September 1893.

bills inevitably brought him into closer touch with the government lawyers. For their part many Liberals viewed Burns very much as he viewed himself — as a sympathetic but independent member whose main concern was with social reform in the interests of the working classes. Accordingly, they invited his co-operation on such matters. James Bryce, for instance, sought his advice on various bills dealing with concilation and industrial arbitration that were before the house in 1894.[1] Within a year of his entry in parliament London Liberal leaders asked him to attend a dinner being addressed by Gladstone. 'It is possible that Mr Gladstone may have some communication to make and may desire to ascertain your views. I fancy that we are all anxious to obtain radical reforms for London and would act together in that direction'.[2] So close did Burns become to the Liberals that it has been said he was offered an under-secretaryship at the Home Office when Rosebery succeeded Gladstone in 1894.[3] If so, then Burns presumably turned in down, because he was as yet unwilling to be identified with Liberalism in this way.

In any case, the general election of 1892 had also seen the return of other independent labour members who looked to Burns for a lead, very much in the way that the labour members of the L.C.C. did. With the sailors' leader, J. Havelock Wilson, Burns was soon able to strike up a good working relationship. In the spring of 1893 Hull was the scene of a prolonged dock strike in which Burns gave Wilson much encouragement and practical assistance. He supported Wilson's efforts to get the activities of the Shipping Federation discussed in parliament and generally formed a high opinion of Wilson's abilities. He was, he felt, 'a regular glutton for work and fighting. With a hundred such in Britain, disciplined, acting together led by a common impulse and aim a great change would take place'.[4] The admiration was mutual. After Wilson had accepted Burns's advice and called a national stoppage of dockers and sailors, an emergency meeting was called in the lobby of the House of Commons. Wilson and Mann attended on behalf of the men, Sir Charles Wilson represented the employers and A.J. Mundella, President of the Board of Trade, was also present. It was Burns, however, who, as Wilson later recalled, 'in his masterful way, immediately took charge of the proceedings' and engineered a settlement.[5]

1   J. Bryce to J. Burns, 29 June 1894. Burns Papers. B.C.
2   Lord Montagu to J. Burns, 7 May 1893. Ibid.
3   Cole, *Burns,* 24.
4   Burns Diary, 16 April 1893. B.L. Add. MSS 46313.
5   J. H. Wilson, *My Stormy Voyage Through Life* (1925), I, 275.

72

But Burns's relationship with James Keir Hardie, the other independent labour member returned in 1892, was not so fruitful. Even beyond their common Scottish parentage the two men had much in common. Both had known a childhood poverty that had turned them to socialism and temperance: both were widely known as champions of the unemployed: together they had served on the editorial board of Champion's *Labour Elector,* and each had made an impact at the T.U.C. as a vigorous proponent of new unionism, the eight-hour day and socialism. Hardie shared Burns's view that labour's political role was essentially that of a pressure group and had a similarly pragmatic view of socialism. 'We are a solid people', he had written in a letter that might easily have come from Burns's pen, 'and very practical, and not given to chasing bubbles. . . We are not opposed to ideals and recognise to the full the need for them, and their power of inspiring men, but we are more concerned with the realisation of the ideal than in dreaming of it'.[1] But despite the similarities between the two men the history of the British labour movement in the early 1890s is dominated by their total inability to work together. Many commentators have suggested that this incompatibility was mainly a matter of temperament. Reared in the secular-rationalist climate of London radicalism and a member of the Battersea Secular Society Burns was highly suspicious of the mystical-cum-nonconformist socialism of the north which Hardie typified. Personally he believed that the church lived on childish delusions and he did not understand a socialism couched in terms of the New Testament. Perhaps more important, however, it has long been argued that Burns was so eaten up by the fear that Hardie would eclipse him as the leader of the labour movement that he refused to co-operate with him at all. Edward Carpenter referred to this when he told Hardie that their greatest problem lay in 'the petty jealousies of Labour leaders'.[2] Another contemporary, writing in the *Sunday Chronicle,* even went so far as to suggest that 'had Mr Hardie gone Liberal Mr. Burns would have gone independent'.[3] Beatrice Webb also took this view. 'Jealousy and suspicion of rather a mean kind is John Burns' burning sin . . . he is unfitted for a really great position by his utter inability to be a constant and loyal comrade. He stands absolutely alone. He is intensely jealous of other labour men . . . his hatred of a Keir Hardie reaches about the dimensions of a mania'.[4]

1 J.K. Hardie to F. Engels, 31 March 1889. Quoted in Pierson, *Marxism and the Origins of British Socialism,* 199.
2 E. Carpenter to J.K. Hardie, 21 October 1894. Quoted in Duffy, 'Differing Policies and Personal Rivalries', 46.
3 *Sunday Chronicle,* 23 June 1895.
4 B. Webb Diary, 12 October 1893. B.L.P.E.S. Passfield Papers, I, vol. 14 (2), 65.

Certainly Burns had shown a liking for popular acclaim and may have feared its loss. Yet there was little reason for him to fear Hardie in the way that Mrs Webb implied. In the early 1890s, still only in his thirties, he had carved out for himself a unique position in the labour movement. He was well thought of by many foreign socialists while his role in the dock strike, and his membership of the T.U.C. Parliamentary Committee and of the London County Council ensured that he was everywhere regarded as the spokesman of labour. Even rank and file members of the S.D.F. continued to invite him to speak and recognised the significance of his council work.[1] As Blatchford put it: 'You stand today for all to see, *the* most useful and hopeful man in London; and *the* head and front of the Great Labour movement in England'.[2] It was to Burns rather than Hardie that trade unions and other groups looked for help in mobilising opinion in the House of Commons, and Hardie made it abundantly clear on more than one occasion that he was willing to accept Burns's leadership. Of course, jealousy is an irrational emotion which may well have blinded Burns to these realities, and it would be unwise to dismiss it lightly, not least because the evidence for it is reliably and widely substantiated. Yet in itself jealousy is too superficial an explanation of the clash between Burns and Hardie. There were other, more complex factors at work.

Friction developed even before they took their seats in 1892. Much to Burns's annoyance Hardie announced that he intended to sit on the opposition benches. 'I venture to suggest', Burns wrote curtly, 'that it would be wise to consult your colleagues as to what should be done before you commit them to any line of action'.[3] Hardie replied that the matter was only a trivial one and that he had done nothing which could be construed as committing the labour members to any particular course. Ultimately, and then only out of loyalty to Hardie, Burns joined him on the opposition benches, but the disagreement did not augur well for the future. As soon became evident, it disguised a fundamental difference of opinion about the precise meaning of independence so far as it concerned the labour members. The incident was glossed over, however, and they agreed to take no part in the proceedings until the new session opened in 1893. Just before this session in Burns, acting as leader of the labour group and apparently anxious to avoid any repetition of the previous misunderstanding, wrote to Hardie about the bills in which they might have an interest.

1 For example, see J. Leatham, *A Socialist View of the New Trade Unionism* (1893).
2 R.Blatchford to J.Burns, 19 March 1892. Burns Papers. B.L. Add. MSS 46287, f. 198.
3 J. Burns to J.K. Hardie, July 1892. Ibid. ff.183-4.

'I have withheld promise to do anything till I have an opportunity of discussing with you what we both shall do . . . I trust we can arrange for a programme of work that will be mutually agreeable'[1] His hopes, however, were misplaced. For one thing, they did not see eye-to-eye on the most pressing social problem of the day, unemployment. Burns believed that it would be best tackled by reforming the conditions of public employment on the lines already undertaken by the L.C.C.; adoption of standard hours and wages, and the abolition of contracting. In this he had support from Sidney Webb and some Liberal M.P.s like Sidney Buxton. Hardie, on the other hand, was much attracted by the idea of a Treasury-financed relief scheme and public works, both of which he suggested when he appeared before the 1895 Select Committee on Unemployment. The depression of 1892-5, however, had served to confirm what Burns had long suspected, that public relief works were costly, inefficient, and really beyond the scope of most local authorities. He was opposed to the idea of building ships simply 'to find work for unemployed labourers and navvies . . . as a Socialist I am, and ever have been, against labour colonies, municipal workshops and such economic nostrums'.[2] As a member of the Select Committee he was therefore very critical of Hardie's suggestions and made every effort to expose his lack of experience in public administration and in unemployment relief.

Even before this, however, relations had been further strained by more procedural wrangles. In April 1893 Hardie moved the adjournment of the House in order to discuss the presence and action of the army at Hull during the dock strike. Under the rules he had to have the support of at least forty other members before an adjournment could be granted but because he acted without previously consulting anyone, the adjournment motion was lost, only seven members supporting it.[3] In spite of his intense annoyance, Burns was one of them, but a week later he showed Hardie how to do things properly. After making sure that he had adequate support Burns himself moved the adjournment to discuss the strike. Three months later Hardie again put Burns on the spot, asking him to take part in a ballot in order to get a debate on government employees – just as the Speaker read out the result of the ballot in question. In part this lack of parliamentary harmony between the two reflected their different experiences. Both were newcomers and unsure of the rules. Indeed, Burns had received a thorough snub when against the Speaker's ruling, he had persisted with his effort to move the closure on a Supply debate in March 1893. James Lowther cuttingly

1   J. Burns to J.K. Hardie, 29 January 1893. Ibid. ff. 186-7.
2   *Star*, 23 January 1894.
3   Burns Diary, 12 April 1893. B.L. Add. MSS 46313.

remarked 'that for an hon. Member of such very limited experience to persist with his Motion for the closure . . . is an incident which demands the most emphatic condemnation . . . the hon. Member will have to endeavour to behave himself according to the Rules of the House'.[1] Pride compelled Burns to retort that his critic should remember that he was not on Newmarket Heath, but he knew that Lowther was right. Abiding by the rules and working with the system had paid good dividends within the L.C.C. and Burns believed that much could be achieved by attention to detail, lobbying and intensive committee work. He was thus willing to spend his parliamentary time in this way and deeply resented Hardie's somewhat dilatory approach to parliamentary work and his apparent preference for histrionics. Tired of the carping critics, Burns drew up a memorandum relating to the labour group's work in parliament in 1893 and 1894. It contained a column headed 'Where was Hardie?' which detailed the latter's absences from divisions which Burns deemed important to labour. He recorded that Hardie had never attended meetings of committees on the Notice of Accidents Bill or Church patronage, that he had missed 98 of the 113 divisions on the Parish Councils Bill, and 242 of the 296 on Home Rule.[2] Hardie was also absent from the House when the Featherstone miners' riots had been debated, 'though he had been accusing Asquith of responsibility all over the country', and Burns began his own speech very pointedly by admitting that he was not in full possession of the facts but intended to speak as other, better informed, labour men were absent.[3] Again, he recorded his annoyance that his own strenuous efforts to improve the terms of the Employers' Liability Bill in Grand Committee had not been supported by his labour colleagues, several of whom had stayed away. [4]

Burns's parliamentary tactics provoked a good deal of criticism from some British socialists. It was Robert Blatchford who took the critics to task, reminding them that in the past Burns's approach had produced good work for labour especially in the L.C.C.[5] The immediate cause of Blatchford's defence was the appearance in Hardie's paper, the *Labour Leader*, of a lampoon attacking Burns for his critical attitude towards the recently founded Independent Labour Party. Beneath all the differences of temperament, experience, and parliamentary tactics, it was over this issue that Burns and Hardie disagreed most fundamentally. Both had radical-socialist ideologies which could be fitted into a broad

1 Hansard, 4th series, IX, 882-3. 2 March 1893.
2 Memorandum, 1894. Burns Papers. B.L. Add. MSS 46308, ff. 59-60.
3 Hansard, 4th series, XVII, 1730-32. 20 September 1893.
4 Burns Diary, 15 May 1893. B.L. Add. MSS 46313.
5 Nunquam, *John Burns and the Labour Party* (1894).

76

progressive alliance based on class collaboration. Yet Hardie had come to believe that within that alliance a labour party should exist as a separately organised entity. Burns did not accept this. True, he had backed a call at the 1890 meeting of the T.U.C. for the establishment of an independent working-class party. But he meant a party based on the trade unions, not an avowedly socialist one and in August 1892 he refused an invitation to attend the inaugural conference of what emerged the following January as the Independent Labour Party. His membership of the S.D.F. caused him to believe that such a party would inevitably be sectarian, intolerant and, therefore, ineffective.[1] Secondly, Burns's success in the L.C.C. had led him to conclude that labour could exert sufficient pressure without taking the necessarily divisive step of establishing a separately organised party which would curtail freedom of action and thought by demanding loyalty to a detailed programme. 'My four years experience on the L.C.C. goes to prove that the less you talk about party making and manifesto issuing . . . the more you do for the cause of labour . . . On the L.C.C. the Progressives have been kept to their work by candid and independent friends in their midst'.[2] In essence this had been at the heart of the rift over where the labour men should sit in 1892. Though agreeing that in general the working classes could expect more from the Liberals than from the Conservatives, Hardie wished to assert his independence by sitting on the opposition benches. Burns, though he had no wish to amalgamate with the Liberals, felt that they should try to exploit the fourteen or fifteen radicals who were nearest to them in political sympathies. 'Hardie's plan will not do this, neither will it convert the Tories to our measures; but it will give the Radicals an excuse for suspecting us unduly and for not fulfilling their pledges. We can do much better for the present by sitting with the Radicals . . . Parnell who knew his business always sat with his tentative allies if only to hold the Whigs in order. That is our line'.[3]

It was also the line then being taken by some leading members of the Fabian Society and it is not without significance that Burns's rift with Hardie coincided with a strengthening of his ties with Fabianism. In April 1892 he referred in a speech at Battersea to his preference for securing reform stage by stage. This, he added, was the policy followed by the Fabian Society and it would lead to great advances in the future.[4]

1 It is worth noting that Bernard Shaw took the view that the I.L.P. was nothing more than a revamped S.D.F. See his letter to the *Workman's Times,* 8 October 1892.
2 J. Burns to R.B. Cunninghame Graham, 29 July 1892. Burns Papers. B.L. Add. MSS 46284, ff. 237-41.
3 Ibid.
4 *South Western Star,* 2 April 1892.

The following year, he formally joined the Fabian Society and his unemployment relief programme appeared as one of the society's tracts.[1] For all her belief that Burns was egocentric and jealous Beatrice Webb, who had been using his collection of labour documents for her study of the trade union movement, felt that she was drawing closer to him. 'Our relationship', she noted, '. . . has never been a cordial one — it promises to be more so in the future'. She went on to suggest that Burns was the man who could make the Fabian Society more influential in politics. 'If John Burns would get over his incurable suspicion and if he could conquer his instinctive fear of comradeship I know no man who could so complete the Fabian trio [i.e. Sidney Webb, Graham Wallas, and Bernard Shaw] and make it thoroughly effective. If Burns would come in and give himself away to the other three as they do to each other — the Fabians would dominate the reform movement'.[2] Burns, however, was incapable of giving himself to any individual in this way and his formal relationship with the Fabians was short-lived and superficial. Yet the threat of Fabian domination was real enough for Hardie, who claimed in 1895 that if the Liberals remained in power then the Fabians would bear most of the responsibility.[3] When the Webbs arranged a political dinner in the same year to co-ordinate the Progressive campaign for the L.C.C. elections Hardie, she noted, would support neither Burns nor her husband because they both 'played to get the vote of the mere Liberal'.[4]

The clash between Burns and Hardie also spilled over into the T.U.C., for the role of the unions was crucial to both of their differing tactical positions. Burns, as we have seen, was in favour of independent working-class representatives backed by the trade unions and at the 1893 meeting of the T.U.C. he again supported a motion to raise funds for working-class candidates who promised their support for collectivisation of the means of production, distribution and exchange. But he was vehemently critical of Hardie's suggestion that such candidates should be supported only if they pledged themselves not to work with either Tories or Liberals. He went on to launch a thorough attack on what he termed 'bogus independent labour parties' and opposed Hardie's candidature as secretary of the Parliamentary Committee. The criticism which his support for the Lib-Lab candidate, Charles Fenwick, evoked was more than offset by his own election to the committee of which he was then made chairman.

1 J. Burns, *The Unemployed* (1893).
2 B. Webb Diary, 12 October 1893. B.L.P.E.S. Passfield Papers, I, vol. 14 (2), 64.
3 *Clarion*, 16 February 1895.
4 B.Webb Diary, 23 January 1895. B.L.P.E.S. Passfield Papers, I, vol. 15, 56.

In 1894 the trade unions met for their annual congress at Norwich. Shortly afterwards the Parliamentary Committee established a sub-committee to investigate the revision of congress's standing orders about which there had been discontent for some years. Burns, who like all immediate past chairmen, was now vice-chairman, was a member of the sub-committee along with J.M. Jack, James Mawdsley, David Holmes, and Sam Woods. In November the full committee met to discuss the report prepared by the five men. It was a far reaching document, for it recommended the elimination of all trades council delegates and all who were not bona fide working men. Together with the proposal to institute a card voting system which would bring greater power to the larger, and generally more cautious unions, the result of the suggested changes would clearly be the curtailment of I.L.P. influence in the counsels of the trade union movement. Broadhurst told Beatrice Webb that Burns was the moving spirit behind the establishment of the sub-committee, a fact which has been faithfully re-echoed by labour historians ever since.[1] In fact the Minutes of the Parliamentary Committee show that Mawdsley moved the resolution calling for its creation and that Broadhurst was the seconder.[2] Certainly it is true that when the recommendations were discussed Burns was in a great hurry to clear away all other business and it is also true that he voted consistently in favour of the changes. But he was by no means alone. Indeed, I.L.P. sympathisers like Thorne and Tillett voted in favour of the proposal to eliminate trade council delegates. More important, on several issues the committee divided evenly and in most cases the revisions only went through on the casting vote of chairman Holmes. When Broadhurst moved that the new orders be first submitted to the trades for approval before becoming operative it was Holmes's casting vote that threw this out.[3] At this point, however, Holmes and Burns left Britain for a tour of the United States as fraternal delegates to the meeting of the American Federation of Labor. It was an exhausting trip for Burns, as he covered 12,000 miles and was much in demand as a speaker. As usual he took full advantage of the opportunity to acquaint himself with the nature of American society and politics, in the process finding still further justification for his gradualist views. When he and Holmes returned it was to find that Broadhurst, who as a trades council delegate was himself in danger, had taken advantage of their absence to get the committee to agree to publicize the new standing orders. As a result, so many protests flooded in to T.U.C. headquarters that Thorne gave notice of a motion to rescind the minute of November approving the orders. He

1   Ibid. 15 January 1895, 52-3.
2   T.U.C. Parliamentary Committee, *Minutes,* 10 October 1894.
3   Ibid. 21 November 1894.

spoke to this motion in February. Burns voted against him but it was again the casting vote of Holmes that defeated Thorne.[1] In April the card voting system was discussed and Burns sided with the representatives of the big unions like coal and cotton who had most to gain — but the resolution only went through when Holmes gave his casting vote.[2] Even as the committee prepared its report for the 1895 congress Thorne tried yet again to amend the paragraph dealing with standing orders. Burns was not even present at the meeting but yet again Holmes's second vote was enough to beat Thorne.[3]

Once more Mrs Webb attributed Burns's primacy in this affair to the fact that he was 'paralysed by a dominant terror that some other labour leader will eclipse him'.[4] Yet it seems clear that Burns did not play the dominant role often ascribed to him in pushing through the new standing orders. Nor did he vote as he did simply out of jealousy or a desire to expel Hardie and his confrères. All the changes could be defended on their merits but Burns's prime motive was to ensure that the I.L.P. lost its influence within the union movement. Rightly or wrongly, he believed that the I.L.P. policy of non-co-operation and party loyalty would wreck the labour movement's prospects of securing reform. His attitude to the matter of the T.U.C.'s standing orders was quite consistent with his view on the nature of working class independence. It was not socialism that he was opposing, but its I.L.P. manifestation. 'Narrow and intolerant exclusiveness was not wanted in trade unionism . . . [it] would lead to friction and decay and disintegration of industrial organisation'.[5] His own high standing within the labour movement he suggested, signified overwhelming approval of his work and his policy over the past six years. 'I am in the position of a man who has been in an overloaded boat and has jumped overboard, not to drown himself, but to lighten the ship. I am strong enough to swim ashore unaided. Some of the rats that have been thrown overboard with me have not got that strength and will inevitably go under.'[6]

Even the result of the L.C.C. election at the beginning of 1895 did little to shake his confidence. Burns himself had been very busy with parliamentary, council, and trade union work since the previous election and had not been able to devote as much time to the constituency as he might have liked. His visit to America at the end of 1894 had taken him

1   Ibid. 6 February 1895.
2   Ibid. 25 April 1895.
3   Ibid. 27 August 1895.
4   B. Webb Diary, 9 September 1895. B.L.P.E.S. Passfield Papers, I, vol. 16, 8.
5   *The Times,* 8 October 1894.
6   Ibid. 17 September 1895.

away at a crucial electioneering time and he had to begin his election campaign late and feeling very tired. During the contest he laid much emphasis on the activities of the Works Department which on the whole had done quite well and saved the ratepayers money on the actual cost of works. The concreting and brick work for the York Road sewer, for example, had cost the council only half as much as the private contractors had estimated. Yet the Moderates, ably supported by the Unionist organisation in the capital and the London Municipal Society, were making much of the sheer cost of establishing the department and also stressed that several projects had exceeded the council estimates. Their propaganda was effective enough to capture over twenty seats from the Progressives and it seems certain that Burns's pre-eminent role in creating the Works Department and his subsequent role as its chief advocate, may have cost him some local support. Certainly the Unionist organiser in Battersea, Allison Webb, used every unfavourable fact he could find about the Works Department in order to maximise the anti-Progressive vote.

Local socialists were also in a hostile mood. Only the Fabian Society backed Burns. Not surprisingly the I.L.P. threw its weight, such as it then was, behind the opposition. More significantly, the influential S.D.F. in Battersea had several specific grievances against Burns and they gave them all full play during the campaign. For one thing, it was alleged that Burns had adopted a very patronising tone towards S.D.F. deputations seeking some action on the local unemployment situation. Then when the Secretary of State for War, Henry Campbell-Bannerman, asked him to arbitrate in the case of a Battersea man who had been dismissed from the Army Clothing Department for persistent absence and trouble making, Burns, having interviewed the man, told him he had been let off lightly and should have been dismissed long ago.[1] This did not go down at all well with the local S.D.F. to which the individual belonged. Finally, the S.D.F. in Battersea had not forgiven Burns for his part in opposing their nominee in a council by-election. James Tims, who had been elected with Burns in 1889, had been imprisoned for fraud and the S.D.F. put up one Rogers. Burns, however, had given his support to Willis, the president of the local Radical and Liberal Association. In part his motive was clearly political, for he himself needed the votes of middle-class radicals and Liberals and did not wish to alienate them unnecessarily. But he had strong personal reasons for refusing Rogers as well, for he had been convicted of criminal offences and his nomination would, Burns argued, bring the local labour

1 G.F. Wilson, *Letters to Somebody* (1922), 73. Wilson commented that as the individual concerned was from Battersea 'I think it will be conceded that he (Burns) well deserved the name of Honest John'.

movement 'into ridicule and disrepute'.[1] The members of the Labour League apparently agreed, endorsing Willis's candidature by forty votes to seven, further embittering the S.D.F.

Feelings ran very high in the campaign itself. Free fights broke out on more than one occasion in Battersea Park as pro- and anti-Burns supporters clashed. On the morning of the poll electors in Battersea woke to find the constituency flooded with anti-Burns leaflets. In the circumstances, therefore, Burns was quite satisfied with the 3,940 votes he obtained, though his pride must have been hurt by the fact that his fellow Progressive, W. Davies, topped the poll with 4,015. The Moderate vote in the constituency was up by over 2,000, the Progressive one down by more than 1,600. Publicly at any rate, Burns did not see this as a comment on either his personality or his policy. It was part of the broader Progressive set back in London, due solely to apathy and ignorance on the part of the electorate. In Battersea, he suggested, he had been opposed by every gambler, drinker and loafer in the constituency.[2] Privately, he blamed the Progressive losses on the fact that some labour elements had tried to fight the election independently.[3]

1 *South Western Star,* 23 January 1894.
2 Ibid. 8 March 1895.
3 See Stevens, 'The London County Council', 23.

5

THE SHIFT TO THE LIBERALS, 1895–1905

In June 1895 the Liberal Government was defeated in a snap vote on the question of the cordite supply for the army. Lord Rosebery, who had replaced the ageing Gladstone as prime minister the year before, secured a dissolution. For the second time in a year Burns had to face the electors of Battersea, much to the discomfort of the hard pressed Labour League. Although funds had come in sufficiently well to permit Burns an increase of a pound a week in 1893, the expenses of a parliamentary election were too much for the league to bear. In the event, it was George Cadbury who came to the rescue, though he took good care to avoid compromising Burns's independence. When his brother somewhat foolishly sent Burns a cheque Cadbury hastily reclaimed this potentially damaging document, telling Burns that '*I* will give you the other £100 when next you call. It is better to be in one person's hands only. We have to deal with the very powers of darkness; and I would not for ten times the amount risk your reputation'.[1] Cadbury's help was all the more welcome as many of Burns's more respectable supporters had been highly alarmed by their candidate's acceptance of an invitation to attend the funeral of Engels, an event which provided useful ammunition for Burns's pushful Conservative opponent, Ridley Smith. A summons of a more formal kind also arrived at his home during the campaign, taken out by one William Sawyer who had insulted the Burns one day in the street. Martha, pregnant for the first time, had reacted somewhat emotionally and her husband, never noted for his meekness, had given Sawyer a boxing lesson. For his rashness Sawyer received a black eye from his M.P. and a bill for three guineas from the magistrates who threw out his assault charge. But the incident was disturbing and as the case was not heard until after polling it created unwelcome publicity.

In view of these local considerations and the fact that the electoral tide ran strongly in favour of the Conservatives, bringing them a majority of 152 in the House of Commons, Burns probably felt relieved that he held on to the seat although his handsome majority of 1892 was slashed by over 1,200 votes in a similar sized poll of over 9,500. During the campaign itself he was inundated with pleas for assistance from Liberal candidates fearful for their own seats. The whips, desperately trying to salvage what they could for a party broken by the home rule

1 G. Cadbury to J. Burns, 10 August 1895. Burns Papers. B.L. Add. MSS 46295, f.204.

issue and divided by personal animosities among Gladstone's successors, turned to Burns, appreciating both his hold over the working-class vote and his hostility towards independent labour candidates who were threatening to split the anti-Conservative vote. From Lord Tweedmouth came a list of constituencies to which he wanted Burns to go and he laid special stress on the Cheshire seat of Hyde, 'where Keir Hardie has settled himself to work for another of his own breed. Now don't anathematise me but take off your coat and dash it in the face of the enemy'.[1] Smarting under the reduction of his own majority Burns drew considerable comfort from the fact that he at least had survived while the 'enemy' in the shape of the I.L.P. had been defeated in everyone of the twenty-eight seats it had contested. It was, he observed smugly, 'the costliest funeral since Napoleon'.[2] Hardie was among the casualties and from his defeat Burns drew the appropriate moral. Entering the House of Commons as a radical pledged to support the government, Hardie, Burns claimed, 'had met with the due reward of his treachery and inconsistency'.[3] He was still harping on this theme long after the election was over, telling one local acquaintance that the I.L.P. leaders seemed to believe that the best way to reach the millennium was to kill off all their best friends and supporters along the road.[4]

Relations between Burns and the I.L.P. thus reached a nadir in 1895 from which they were only seldom destined to rise thereafter. There were those, Ben Tillett prominent among them, who urged Burns to forget the past disputes, to make his peace with Hardie and to assume his place at the head of the labour movement.[5] But Tillett made the mistake of assuming that the differences were purely personal and he was blind to the existence of the underlying conflict between Hardie and Burns over the nature and objectives of the labour movement. In any case if the electoral performance of the I.L.P. was any guide it is arguable that in practice Burns was already regarded by most working men as their leader, even though he did not aspire to the title in any more formal way. Either way, Burns ignored Tillett's pleas; he also managed, for a while at least, to ignore the constant sniping that was directed against him by other socialists.[6] But at last, when sometime in

---

1 Lord Tweedmouth to J. Burns, 17 July 1895. Ibid. f.174.
2 Quoted in D. Lowe, *From Pit to Parliament; the Story of the Early Life of James Keir Hardie* (1923), 86.
3 *The Times,* 5 August 1895.
4 J. Burns to Mr Barrett, 24 October 1895. Burns Papers. B.L. Add. MSS 46295, ff.239-40.
5 B. Tillett to J. Burns, 5 November 1896. Ibid. Add. MSS 46285, f.179.
6 For instance see A.M. Thompson's comments in *Reynold's Newspaper,* 5 July 1896.

1896-7 he was asked to go north to dispel the misunderstanding with Hardie, his frustration and anger exploded across the pages of his reply.

> I am only doing now what I have ever done; and ever will continue to do — that is adapting past experience to present reform in the light of high ideals and future objects. In this work I have received the opposition of a number of men who only advocate the unobtainable *because the immediately possible is beyond their moral courage, administrative ability,* and their political prescience . . . I must firmly adhere to the views I have held and practice, that Socialism to succeed must be practical, tolerant, cohesive and consciously compromising with Progressive forces running, if not so far, in parallel lines towards its own goal. I don't believe that the man who comes furthest my way and nearest to my programme is my most distant enemy. 'He who is not wholly for us is wholly against us' is the plaint of the fool or the fanatic . . . judge men less by the labels they wear than by their persistent labour for sure if slow progress . . . If 'our party right or wrong' is to be the rallying cry of a working class movement then it has assumed the very defects that its advocates decry in others. The recent I.L.P. conference from which I had expected some change in methods and tactics has confirmed my previous views of its leaders.[1]

Burns's suspicions of the I.L.P. were hardened by the repeated efforts being made by some of its members to form a united socialist party in conjunction with the S.D.F., efforts which did not really lose their impetus until 1898.

In January 1895 Burns had told an election meeting in Battersea that if he had to chose between dissolving parliament for ten years and abolishing the L.C.C. he would lock up parliament.[2] Of course this remark must be seen in its proper context, that of a council election campaign, but the parochialism which it betrayed had certainly come through in much of his parliamentary work between 1892 and 1895. He had only made his maiden speech on the Registration Bill in February 1893 because a previous speaker had dared to criticise the work of the London County Council. Constantly Burns had compared government policy unfavourably with that followed by the council. Beatrice Webb claimed that he began to lose his dominance in the council once he became an M.P. and, while this is an exaggeration, there are several indications of his declining influence after 1895.[3] It was odd, for instance, that although he was a member of the council's Parliamentary Committee he was not made sponsor of a single council measure in 1895. To some extent his gradual eclipse was due to the fact that party politics were intruding more into council affairs and growing party commitments made it difficult, even for so pushful an individual as

1 Copy of letter *c*.1896-7 in Burns Papers. B.L. Add. MSS 46296, ff.256-7.
2 *South Western Star,* 25 January 1895.
3 B. Webb Diary, 30 July 1893. B.L.P.E.S. Passfield Papers, I, vol. 14 (2), 56-7.

Burns to assert himself. Positive action was in any case made more difficult as the election had resulted in a virtual stalemate and the Progressives were only able to control the council by enlisting the aid of their aldermen. More probably, however, Burns's relative loss of influence in the council was due to the fact that new issues were coming to the fore in London. Those with which he had been particularly identified, labour conditions and the works department, had been dealt with. Admittedly they were not without their problems. In 1896, for example, irregularities were uncovered in the Works Department account books. No fraud was involved. The manager had simply tried to obscure the losses incurred on some projects by transferring to them profits made on others. But even a hint of impropriety was too much for Burns, especially as the Moderate opponents of the department were able to make a great deal of political capital out of the incident. Burns was appointed to the sub-committee of inquiry and was adamant that the manager and several of his subordinates should be dismissed. But although the incident created a lot of adverse publicity it was soon obscured by other more momentous affairs. Since 1894 the London Municipal Society had been agitating for some restructuring of London government that would establish borough councils to which some of the L.C.C.'s present powers would be devolved. In 1899 the government pushed through the London Government Act which created twenty-eight metropolitan borough councils. Although Burns intervened in the debates on this measure no less than fifty times, and made his longest parliamentary speech to date on it, damning it as an attack on the council, he seems to have taken little part either in the backstage talks that went on among Progressive leaders or in the discussions that began in 1896 to pave the way for the bill.[1]

The other dominant council issues in the 1890s centred on the control of London's water and transport services. Burns was fully committed to the municipalisation of both utilities. If nothing else, his service on the Fire Brigade Committee after 1898 convinced him that the council should take over control of the capital's water supply. Time and again that committee was told of water hydrants that were maintained so badly as to be useless for fire fighting. But although he cast his council vote consistently for municipal ownership he was content to leave the campaigning on the water issue to others. It was not until 1900 that he spoke in a parliamentary debate on the matter. On transport he was slightly more vocal. When the first private tram company leases expired in the 1890s he joined with other Progressives in resisting Moderate proposals that the leases be granted to other private concerns.

1 On the matter of London government at this time see K.G. Young, 'The Conservative strategy for London, 1855-1975', *London Journal* I (1975), 56-81.

The Progressives were defeated in committee and the council about to endorse the Moderates' plan when a furious last minute assault by the Progressives got the suggestion referred back. Drawing on his experiences of American urban transport Burns made a spirited contribution to the Progressive attack but he was eclipsed by John Benn and also by the Progressive member for Finsbury, J. Allen Baker, who was to Progressive transport policy what Burns had been to labour policy. But although he was generally content to leave transport matters to Baker there was one smaller aspect of transport policy that Burns did make peculiarly his own and that was the attempt to establish a municipally-owned steamboat service along the Thames. The council had been giving this matter some rather dilatory thought before Burns joined the Rivers Committee in 1898 and for some time thereafter the matter remained stagnant as the council negotiated with the Thames Conservancy Board about buying up its piers as a first step. Exasperated at the slowness of these proceedings Burns gave notice in May 1900 that at the next meeting of the committee he intended to move a resolution which would commit the council to going ahead. This resolution was approved and six weeks later the committee was discussing the full estimates of the cost which the Progressives had prepared. By 3 December, after much strenuous work by Burns, a bill was ready to go to parliament.

But on the whole this type of activity was exceptional for Burns in the last few years of the nineteenth century. Increasingly, as the various minute books of the L.C.C. show, he became absorbed in the minutiae of London's day to day administration, ordering boots for firemen, discussing the details of main sewer pipes and pricing contracts. After the council elections of 1898 which restored the Progressive majority (he was returned in second place behind Davies with 5,126 votes) Burns's influence was further weakened by signs of splintering within the Progressive alliance between the radicals like himself and the more moderate Liberal elements led by Lord Rosebery. At one time he and Burns had been quite friendly but as time passed so their political views diverged. Burns was too advanced for Rosebery and he resented the fact that, for example, when the council discussed workmen's housing schemes Rosebery adopted the role of 'Political Umpire . . . always giving his own side out leg before or declaring no ball'.[1] Shortly before, he had observed caustically that the 'Rosebery rot has got into the Council Progressive members, a course of Labour creosoting needed to drive it out'.[2] The Roseberyites responded by accusing Burns of trying to dictate council policy and the rift was further widened by their different reactions to the Boer War.

1 Burns Diary, 17 January 1900. B.L. Add. MSS 46318.
2 Ibid. 16 May 1899. Add. MSS 46317.

But if Burns was making less of an impact in council affairs than he had done when first elected, in parliament the reverse was true. In his first session he had got through an enormous amount of work, asked innumerable questions, served on committees and made his fair share of speeches. As his second session wore on so he became increasingly at home in the Commons; so much so that in 1899 he opened the bowling for the parliamentary cricket team against Westminster School.[1] He had never been able to reproduce at St Stephens the excitement of his park oratory, and his speeches, while solid, had generally been dull and on subjects of quite restricted appeal. He was too heated in his advocacy to enjoy the sophistication of parliamentary cut and thrust. John Burns preferred the statistical bludgeon rather than the rapier of wit and innuendo. Yet his mastery of the house grew with time and there was almost a patronising air about his reply to Lord Warkworth's maiden speech opposing the Sunday opening of London museums.

> His only regret was that so good a speaker and so excellent a champion should be identified with so bad a cause (laughter). But, fortunately for London, St George's, Hanover Square, had come to the rescue of South Kensington, and with that magnanimity which characterised a First Lord of the Admiralty asking the nation for a large sum of money (laughter) the right hon. Gentleman had dispelled the unfavourable impression created by the noble Lord's speech . . . (when) people visited the Natural History Museum he sincerely hoped they would see the pliosaurus in a glass case and mark the evolution of the politician who opposed the opening of museums on Sunday, and avoid him in the future as an awful example.[2]

In addition, Burns brought to his parliamentary performances qualities that could only earn respect. He brought passion as when he defended the safety clauses of the Coal Mines Regulations Bill; compassion when pleading for London cabbies, underground bakery workers, or women match makers suffering from phossie jaw. He revealed his fundamental honesty in exposing corruption and jobbery even though this did not always endear him to his fellow M.P.s — in his first parliament he had been ruled out of order for suggesting that all members of parliament should vacate their seats immediately if they accepted any office with a business company. By 1900 his parliamentary technique was so improved that a reporter in the *Manchester Guardian* could refer to Burns holding the house 'rivetted' and 'enthralled'. He was speaking on the London Water Bill.

---

1 Although he was now over forty he bowled nineteen overs and conceded only thirty-eight runs in taking one wicket. When he batted he scored eleven runs. See C.B.H. Knight's letter to *The Times*, 30 January 1943.
2 Hansard, 4th series, XXXVII, 652-3. 10 March 1896.

His sentences are not well rounded, but every now and again an epigram flashes out on you like the lightning from a cloud . . . And then in blow after blow came the sledge-hammer sentences, rugged, rough-hewn, and often unjoined, but always genuine, asserting, original, true, the passionate advocacy. . . . He sweeps aside the sophistry and cunning of self-interest.[1]

As always, these qualities were used mainly in the interests of the working classes. Burns acted as *de facto* leader of the small parliamentary group of labour representatives, mainly miners, returned in the 1895 election, organising their votes and ensuring participation in all matters relevant to labour. In particular, the group played an important part in the debates on the Workmen's Compensation Bill, acting in close liaison with the T.U.C. Personally, Burns continued to be a tireless parliamentary advocate of the eight-hour day and he spent a lot of time encouraging a rather ham-fisted union leadership during the famous engineers' strike of 1897 for the eight-hour day. Although he was hopeful at the start of the dispute that the men could get their objective, by November Burns, always a realist, was urging George Barnes and the other officials of the A.S.E. to beat a dignified retreat, for it had become clear that the employers were too powerful.[2] When in the same year, workers at the Penrhyn slate quarries went on strike, Burns used the House of Commons as a stage on which to voice their grievances and he was savage in his condemnation of Lord Penrhyn's management. So much did Burns reflect trade union sentiment at the end of the nineteenth century that in the spring of 1899 Blatchford was openly espousing his leadership of the projected General Federation of Trade Unions.[3] By contrast, although naturally concerned with the rising industrial tension of which the Penrhyn dispute and the engineering strike were but two manifestations, the I.L.P. lacked a parliamentary voice, and its leadership by the turn of the century was dominated more and more by figures of distinctly non-proletarian origin. Yet ironically, it was this very upsurge of industrial unrest that seemed to give new urgency to Hardie's pleas for labour unity in the face of better organised and more aggressive employers. Although direct socialist influence within the T.U.C. had been much reduced with the adoption of the new standing orders in 1895, Hardie in particular had kept up his propaganda, and other influences were helping to convince trade unionists of the need for some sort of political organization. New technology threatened the position of entrenched skilled groups, for example in the engineering and the boot and shoe industries. Then there

1 Quoted in Knott, *John Burns*, 77.
2 On the strike see H. Pelling, *A History of British Trade Unionism* (1963), 112-14.
3 R. Blatchford to J. Burns, 9 May 1898. Burns Papers. B.L. Add. MSS 46287, f. 202.

was the fear that British employers would seek to emulate their American counterparts by crushing unions through political and legal action. It was largely in the hope of averting this that many unionists began to look more favourably on the idea of independent working-class political representation. The prosperity of the last years of the century had permitted the accumulation of the necessary funds and in 1899 the T.U.C. voted by 546,000 to 434,000 to investigate the possibilities of establishing an independent working-class party and shortly afterwards the I.L.P., mindful of Burns's importance, dispatched two envoys, George Wardle and John Penny, to urge him to attend the foundation conference of the Labour Representation Committee.

Burns did attend — as a delegate from the A.S.E. — but his two short contributions both illustrated his basic mistrust. He supported Hardie's motion to establish an independent group in the House of Commons but added that it was unrealistic to expect all labour representatives to hold identical opinions on every question and that this should not be used as an excuse for excluding those of differing views. More significantly, he added, in an oft-quoted speech, that he was

> tired of working-class boots, working-class trains, working-class houses, and working-class margarine. He believed the time had arrived in the history of the Labour and social movement when they should not be prisoners to class prejudice, but should consider parties and policies apart from all class organisations.[1]

In fact, the conference did reject an S.D.F. resolution commiting it to class war but many delegates affirmed that they believed in this principle, only voting against the Social Democratic motion in the interests of unity. Burns would not go along with this, for it smacked too much of compromise, even hypocrisy. But even without any commitment to class war the formal organisation envisaged for the L.R.C. was in Burns's view too restrictive. He feared that all issues would be interpreted in terms of black and white, and much preferred the freedom to act at the dictates of conscience rather than according to the promptings of party whips. As he told the delegates, the labour group in parliament which he had organised since 1898 had been only loosely structured but it had done the work. All in all, the L.R.C. with its disproportionate leavening of I.L.P. members, was too restrictive for Burns's taste. He responded much more favourably to the foundation of the National Democratic League. The brainchild of W.M. Thompson, the editor of *Reynold's Newspaper,* this was a much more broadly based organisation supported by trade unionists, socialists like Mann and Bob Smillie and by radicals such as Lloyd George. It was designed to act, not as a formally constituted party but as a radical pressure group. But

1 L.R.C., *Annual Report* (1900), 11.

Burns, after his initial enthusiasm, grew distrustful of S.D.F. influence within it, and by 1902 it had faded into insignificance.

Thompson's wish had been to perpetuate the broad left-of-centre alliance that had emerged as a response to the onset of the Boer War in October 1899. Burns shared this vision. He told the Liberal chief whip, Herbert Gladstone, at the time of the 1900 general election of his hopes that Liberal-Labour co-operation would bring down the Conservative government.[1] That this failed to occur was due entirely, Burns felt, to the pro-war attitude of the Liberal imperialists under Rosebery. After a heated council debate on a proposal to allow council employees to construct rifle ranges for their own use, a suggestion which he vehemently opposed, he commented, 'respectability, reaction, thy name is Rosebery'.[2]

Briefly, the war drew Burns closer to the I.L.P. He actually brought himself to approve an anti-war speech delivered in the Commons by Hardie, who had been re-elected in 1900. But although his own anti-war attitude was eulogised in the I.L.P. press, the *rapprochement* with the left was shortlived – the legacy of hostility, his personal differences with Hardie, and his distrust of an independent party – all had too long a pedigree for any more permanent reconciliation to result. What the war did in fact was to strengthen his links, with not the socialists, but with the radical wing of the Liberal party which also came out strongly against it. As early as 1895 Herbert Samuel had observed that his views were practically identical with Burns's 'on almost every question', and to Burns the crowning justification for his resistance to a formal labour party lay in the freedom this had allowed him to work in conjunction with radicals.[3] Just how close he had grown to some of them is suggested by a letter in the Battersea collection. It was from Sidney Buxton. 'I'm quite laid up for the present with a very lame knee', he wrote, 'I was disgusted at missing the Factory Act . . . On the whole I think we have got through the 'higher work' better than was to be expected'.[4] Together, the outbreak of the Boer War and the foundation a few months later of the L.R.C. made it almost inevitable that Burns's political future lay in Liberalism. By January 1900 he was being invited to Liberal conferences on foreign and colonial policy, although generally he remained aloof from formal anti-war Liberal organisations.[5]

1   J. Burns to H. Gladstone, 12 September 1900. Gladstone Papers. B.L. Add. MSS 46058, ff.43-4.
2   Burns Diary, 31 July 1900. B.L. Add. MSS 46318.
3   H. Samuel to J. Burns, 9 July 1895. Burns Papers. B.L. Add. MSS 46295, f.146.
4   S. Buxton to J. Burns, 13 June 1898. Burns Papers. B.C.
5   A.H. Marshall to J. Burns, 11 January 1900. Burns Papers. B.M. Add. MSS

Like many radicals whose reputations sprang primarily from local or sectional interests (as in the case of Lloyd George and Wales) Burns had hitherto shown relatively little interest in foreign affairs. It is true that he had participated in the Hyde Park demonstrations against the Turkish atrocities in Armenia in 1896 and he was also a life-long exponent of home rule who missed few opportunities to turn any discussion of Irish matters into a plea for self-government. In addition, he had travelled quite extensively and frequently drew on his overseas experiences to make telling comparisons or to illustrate points in the course of parliamentary debate. He had never been afraid to express his hostility to colonial exploitation. He had opposed, for instance, an L.C.C. resolution to give a civic welcome to the explorer H.M. Stanley, to whom he referred slightingly as the 'buccaneer of the Congo'.[1] But hitherto he had taken little part in parliamentary discussions on foreign issues. The Boer War changed all this.

John Burns had no doubt that the war was being waged for sordid commercial motives. It was 'war for territory, for gold, for capitalist domination'.[2] The impetus, he believed, was provided by the 'fraudulent demands of Throgmorton Street and the Stock Exchange rascals', and he referred constantly in his speeches to the vested financial interests of men like Chamberlain and Rhodes whom he held primarily responsible for the conflict.[3] Chamberlain especially came in for his abuse and together with Lloyd George, Burns moved a Commons motion banning ministers from having interests in firms tendering for government contracts, a motion which the Colonial Secretary interpreted — rightly — as being a thinly disguised attack on himself. At the beginning of the 1900 session Burns turned his fire on the yellow press, in particular the *Daily Mail* whose proprietors, he alleged, had a financial stake in South Africa. The diamond mine owners in whose interests the British were killing the Boers were so avaricious, he added, that they dosed the native miners with purgatives every week to prevent them concealing diamonds in their bodies. The following year he spoke for C.F.G. Masterman in a by-election at Dulwich and while he quoted freely from an official report on the Jameson raid in which the Conservative candidate, Rutherfoord Harris, had been involved he added so many comments of his own that Harris took out an injunction against him.

46297, f.258. There is a general discussion of Liberal sympathies for the Boers in J.W. Auld, 'The Liberal Pro-Boers', *Journal of British Studies* 14 (1975), 78-101.
1 Quoted in Saunders, *First London County Council*, 212.
2 Hansard, 4th series, LXXVIII, 795-7. 6 February 1901.
3 Ibid. LXXXVIII, 282. 7 December 1900.

There was a strong element of anti-semitism involved in his opposition to the war. In common with many British socialists Burns had an almost pathological dislike of Jews, and expressions of this form a minor but recurrent theme of his diary.[1] Watching the cricket at the Oval in 1899, for instance, he noted several 'frowsy, lousy, greasy Jews. No game but grab, no passion but profit, no human playfulness, parasitic; living to work only and that as a step to exploiting others'.[2] Now with commercial interests so involved in the Boer War he attacked them publicly. The British army, he said, once the Galahad of history had become the 'janissary of the Jews' who were waging ruthless war on the Boers.[3] Nor was it only wealthy Jews who attracted his dislike. On his way to a council meeting in 1900 he saw units of the City Imperial Volunteers marching to the Guild Hall with 'not a Jew amongst the lot'.[4]

Almost paradoxically, hints of patriotism crept into some of his anti-war speeches. Praising the work of the ordinary soldier he asserted in one Commons debate that the Germans could have done no better and that the French would have done a greal deal worse. Further, it was indicative of Britain's very greatness that the war was a matter of public debate at all.[5] But notwithstanding this patriotic gloss there was no doubt in the public mind where Burns stood on the issue of the Boer War. Much of his oratory had a superficially Marxian ring about it, but closer examination suggests that his opposition was grounded not so much in Marxist socialism as in the radicalism of Cobden and Bright. It contained a strong moralistic strain, for Burns felt it was wrong that a power such as Britain should be attempting to impose its will by force upon people who believed that their freedom was at stake. When, later in the war, news of concentration camps and other horrors broke his moral out-

1 Thorne, *Life's Battles,* 49, describes the tricks used by poor Jewish street traders. There is a good discussion of British socialists and Jews in J. Garrard, *The English and Immigration, 1880-1910* (Oxford, 1971), 189 ff.

2 Burns Diary, 12 August 1899. B.L. Add. MSS 46317. L.P. Gartner, *The Jewish Immigrant in England, 1870-1914* (1960), 135, refers to an anti-semitic article written by Burns and published in *Der Vekker* in the 1880s. Certainly Burns had ambivalent attitudes towards the influx of immigrants from eastern Europe. After reading *In the Abyss* he commented that he was 'weakening on alien immigration'. Burns Diary, 10 January 1903. B.L. Add. MSS 46321.

3 Hansard, 4th series, LXXVIII, 795-7. 6 February 1900. See also J. Burns, *War Against Two Republics* (1900), 4.

4 Burns Diary, 17 January 1900. B.L. Add. MSS 46318.

5 Hansard, 4th series, LXXVIII, 781. 6 February 1900. This was not so strange as it might appear. Even members of the S.D.F. produced some very imperialistic arguments in their anti-war propoganda. See N. Etherington, 'Hyndman, the Social Democratic Federation and the Boer War', *Historical Studies* 16 (1974), 89-103. B. Baker, 'The Social Democratic Federation and the Boer War', *Our History* 59 (1974), makes the same point.

raged redoubled. Napoleon had been an ogre, he thundered at a Battersea audience, but at least he had never made war on women and children.[1] Then there was the sheer cost of the war, for in all his public life he had adopted a very traditional radical line on public expenditure and the huge expense of the Boer War appalled him. In 1901 when the government requested money to permit British forces to hunt down the Mad Mullah of Somaliland, Burns referred to the already excessive costs of foreign wars and suggested that the tax payers would resent any further imposition 'in the present strained condition of the finances of the British Empire'.[2] The bunglings of the army in South Africa also provoked his criticism, and it was in this aspect of his opposition that the Marxist ring was perhaps loudest, for it was the officers who attracted his sarcasm. Watching troops preparing to leave Aldershot Barracks in December 1899 he noted with contempt that the officers were taking as much baggage as 'bridesmaids on tour', and this was a theme which he frequently took up in his parliamentary speeches.[3] The initial British defeats afforded him good material. The army was class bound, he told the Commons. Why were N.C.O.s of proven ability not promoted to positions of command instead of the titled and wealthy getting all the commissions? During the supplementary estimates debate in February 1900 he suggested that the need was not for more soldiers but rather for better generals. He went on:

> This war has typified the mental and administrative decay of the governing classes. If the London County Council had managed its fire brigade with no more ability and promptitude than the War Office had displayed in the management of this war people would have been burnt in their beds three nights a week. I am almost inclined to suggest that the management of the next war should be left to the fire brigade committee of the County Council.[4]

Nor did Burns confine his opposition to the House of Commons. In the debating chamber of the L.C.C. he resisted the proposal that the council should provide rifle ranges for its employees and also spurned the suggestion that it should give pensions to widows of its employees killed in Africa. The government was responsible for the war, he claimed, therefore it should also be responsible for maintaining the dependants of the casualties. When council employees sought permission to form a volunteer company many Progressive voices were raised in opposition, but none louder than Burns's. When the General Purposes Committee agreed to send a congratulatory address to the King when the war finally came to an end in 1902, Burns registered his dissent by staying

1   *South Western Star,* 18 January 1901.
2   Hansard, 4th series, XCI, 505. 19 March 1901.
3   Burns Diary, 21 December 1899. B.L. Add. MSS 46317.
4   Hansard, 4th series, LXXIX, 167-75. 15 February 1900.

away from the meeting. He also carried his opposition into the parks of Battersea. Although there was a strong Stop-the-War committee to which the Labour League was affiliated, Burns preferred to plough his own lonely furrow, conducting a series of anti-war meetings in Battersea Park through the summer of 1900. His aloofness may have owed something to the fact that the committee invited Cronwright Schreiner to address his constituents but more probably it was because he disliked the strong S.D.F. element within its ranks. It has also to be seen as part of his general isolation from the formal anti-war organization established to agitate on a national scale. Although the arguments Burns used against the war were very similar to those deployed by its other critics, he would have nothing to do with either of the radical organisations, the Transvaal Peace Committee or the South African Conciliation Committee. He feared the 'constructive imperialism' advocated by the latter body.

It may well be true that the bulk of Britain's working-class population was indifferent to the Boer War except in so far as it impinged upon daily matters such as the price of food or provided employment opportunities.[1] But equally it took a great deal of courage to oppose the war publicly, especially in the emotionally charged atmosphere of 1900 when the critics were very much in a minority. Burns did not come anywhere near being lynched, as Lloyd George may have done in Birmingham, but violence was still directed against him. On Mafeking night — 'people beflagged and befooled' — several of his windows were smashed by an excited mob and for a while he deemed it necessary to stand guard over his wife and son, posting himself in the hallway of his house armed with a cricket bat.[2] Politically as well, opposition to the war required courage, for major figures in the Liberal Party supported the government. So, too, did some of the electorate who would normally have voted against the Conservatives and Burns's stance undoubtedly cost him some support in his own constituency. In May 1900 the *South Western Star* pointed out that he had never been so unpopular in Battersea.[3] His stand was all the more courageous considering the reduction in his electoral majority in 1895 and the fact that in the council elections of 1898 he had slipped marginally further behind his fellow Progressive.

Indeed, it had been no coincidence that since 1895 Burns had been much more assiduous on behalf of Battersea in council affairs. He had

1   R. Price, *An Imperial War and the British Working Class* (1972).
2   Burns Diary, 19 May 1900. B.L. Add. MSS 46318.
3   *South Western Star*, 25 May 1900. See also the critical letters and articles in ibid. 1 June and 28 September 1900.

rushed to the defence of local firemen who had been accused of undue slowness in dealing with a serious local fire. He introduced several vestry deputations to the Main Drainage Committee to protest about the lack of flood protection in low lying areas of Battersea, and almost the only time he troubled to attend meetings of the Council's Parliamentary Committee was when it discussed matters of relevance to Battersea — notably meetings in 1899 to discuss the vestry demand to utilise part of the Latchmere Road allotments for building purposes. He had also taken good care to be seen in and around his parish, availing himself eagerly and vociferously of opportunities to present the prizes at the local polytechnic college and to lay — with considerable gusto — the memorial foundation stone of new baths and wash-houses. But even so, his electoral fate still hung in the balance when in the summer of 1900 the government went to the country on the war issue. The local paper, which had long been a faithful supporter, had turned against him. In February the editor had commented on Burns's entry in the current *Who's Who* that it was 'characteristically boastful . . . vulgar . . . he can never learn anything which may tend to impair his own crude perceptions'.[1] In May it freely predicted that Garton, the Conservative, would win, and on the eve of the poll it advised readers to vote against Burns.[2] A Municipal Alliance had been started in the constituency to unite anti-radical feeling and there were many mutual accusations between Labour Leaguers and members of the alliance about meeting-busting, and there was a good deal of mud slinging in the press. Burns was sufficiently alarmed by the threat to supplement his election manifesto with a special thirty page pamphlet containing his main parliamentary speeches to counter the calumnies which, he alleged, were being spread about him. Altogether he held fifty six election meetings before, visibly relieved, he won through in what he subsequently described as the stormiest campaign of his life.[3] Although his anti-war stand had brought him some tangible financial tokens of support, including another cheque from George Cadbury, he spent over £100 more than his opponent and had had to resort to a bicycle to offset the half dozen or so motor cars at his opponent's disposal. His majority remained at about the level of 1895, pleasing because the swing against him was lower than the national average swing against anti-war candidates. Once more he had illustrated the excellence of his organisation, his own hold on Battersea's working class, and his ability to capitalise on the area's deep seated particularism.

1 Ibid. 2 February 1900.
2 Ibid. 25 May and 28 September 1900.
3 Hansard, 4th series, LXXXVIII, 282. 7 December 1900.

This was reaffirmed when he comfortably retained his seat in the 1901 council elections, only forty-five votes behind Davies. This result was even more satisfying, as his mother's long illness had compelled him to fight a brief and low key campaign. Until her death at the end of January 1901 he attended her bedside constantly, and her loss affected him deeply. After the funeral at Tooting he confided in his diary that 'there welled up in me today too many recollections of her brave fight in my child days to keep home going'.[1] Once the funeral and the election were over he slipped away to Paris — alone and at George Cadbury's expense — for a brief holiday, before resuming his campaign against the war. It was not now such an uphill struggle, for news of concentration camps and the widespread burning of Boer farms created considerable unease in Britain. He now began to address meetings organised by the local Stop-the-War committee. He was encouraged, too, by indications that Liberal opinion was hardening against the war, for he had been greatly exercised at the way in which Liberal divisions had hampered the attack on the government and he had taken advantage of his friendship with Campbell-Bannerman to urge on him the need to secure party unity and to stamp out disloyalty.[2]

Nor was it only the fight against the war that had been weakened by Liberal divisions. They were also affecting the Progressives' work on the council. 'I am afraid of the L.C.C. Progressives just now', Burns commented in 1902, 'the desire to make it a cuckoo nest for Primrose pigeons will break up its municipal work by introducing political differences amongst the majority'[3] His fear was apparently confirmed when the Roseberyites helped to reject the suggested site for new council offices, a suggestion made by a sub-committee of which Burns had been a member. 'Dished by the Imperialists', was his comment. 'This is the meanest thing yet attempted and temporarily carried by the Rosebery-ites'[4] When the Steamboats Bill was rejected by the House of Commons in 1901 several pro-Rosebery Progressives argued that the measure should not be re-introduced in the next session because it needed to be re-thought and Burns did not take kindly to this, as he had devoted a considerable amount of his own time to working out the details. His fears that internal divisions within the Progressive alliance and more particularly within its Liberal section would hamper the council were compounded by the fact that the Conservative Government and its sympathisers were showing every inclination to question the whole principle of municipalisation which was practically the cornerstone of Burns's

1   Burns Diary, 4 February 1901. B.L. Add. MSS 46319.
2   Ibid. 4 July 1901.
3   Ibid. 18 March 1902. Add. MSS 46320.
4   Ibid. 21 October 1902.

political faith. For one thing the government had hedged over the municipalisation of the capital's water supply, even to the extent of ignoring the favourable report made on the L.C.C.'s plans by the government-appointed Llandaff Commission. Burns was bitter when the matter came up for parliamentary discussion. Any other local authority would have been given the go-ahead, he claimed, but because London was becoming the plaything of party politics, they had to go to the trouble of fighting over a parliamentary bill. 'It is a mistake to depreciate your central municipal body in London', he told the Commons, and when, after a rather inconclusive report from a Select Committee on municipal trading, the Liberty and Property Defence League and Professor John Macdonnell succeeded in making the matter a major controversy, Burns joined in at great length[1]. Macdonnell had written a series of anonymous articles in *The Times* attacking municipalisation and Burns replied in what was then the longest letter ever published by that paper; it was reprinted subsequently as a fifteen page pamphlet. Very precisely he exposed the factual errors in Macdonnell's articles, and defended municipal enterprise on the grounds that it was more efficient and more concerned with improving amenities than getting profits – even though in many cases it was in fact cheaper than private enterprise.[2]

The general election of 1900 came too early to allow the newly formed L.R.C. to make much of an impact but it did succeed in getting two candidates returned to the House of Commons, Hardie, and Richard Bell, an official of the Amalgamated Society of Railway Servants. Although Burns's deep seated dislike of railway directors ensured that he struck up a good understanding with Bell almost straight away, it soon became clear that co-operation with Hardie was going to be no easier than it had been in the 1892-5 parliament. For his part Hardie, always hopeful and generous in his assessments of others, was still holding out the olive branch. In March 1900 the I.L.P. invited Burns to address its Glasgow conference of labour representatives on some aspect of municipal socialism, while later in the year Hardie made an approach through H.W. Massingham, asking Burns to lead the labour bloc in the Commons.[3] Burns, however, did little to resuscitate the labour group, which had been quite badly mauled in the election. He seems to have expected Hardie's deference without himself adopting an

1 Hansard, 4th series, CIV, 229. 3 March 1902. On the controversy about municipal trading see E. Bristow, 'The Defence of Liberty and Property in in Britain, 1880-1914' (University of Yale Ph. D. thesis, 1970), 157 ff.

2 *The Times,* 23 September 1902.

3 J.K. Hardie to J.B. Glasier, 15 October 1900. Quoted in P. Poirier, *The Advent of the Labour Party* (1958), 138.

attitude which would have secured it, and when the session began he did not even bother to send Hardie a labour group whip. On many matters the two did work together, if rather informally, but it was not long before there was a clash over parliamentary tactics. As unemployment began to grow in the aftermath of the war, Burns put down a question about it in November. He was annoyed to find that Hardie had also put down a question for the same day without first consulting him.[1]

But the most immediate concern of the organised labour movement in the first years of the new century was not the issue of unemployment. In 1901 the trade union world had been thrown into total disarray by the ruling of the House of Lords in the Taff Vale case that trade unions could be held corporately responsible for damages incurred in the course of a trade dispute. The ability of the T.U.C. to secure a legislative reversal of this judgement had been curtailed by the loss of several trade union M.P.s in the 1900 election, especially severe being the loss of Sam Woods, the secretary of the Parliamentary Committee. Thus it was to Burns that the T.U.C. turned in trying to organise a parliamentary campaign of support for its Trades Disputes Bill. Hitherto consultations among the labour members had been very informal but at the beginning of 1903 the labour members gathered at the request of the T.U.C., for what Burns termed their 'first palaver'.[2] Will Crooks was not very sanguine about its prospects but Hardie took the opportunity to make another and, as it turned out, final appeal to Burns. His open letter in the *Labour Leader* was generous and enormously flattering.

> 'No man in the ranks of labour set out with better qualifications or better prospects . . . no man knows better than yourself that combinations and cohesion are necessary for success. No man can stand quite alone . . . I would fain believe that even now you will come out and openly take your place as one of the active leaders in this work for the emancipation of the class to which we both belong. The mistake you made, as I have heard you sorrowfully admit years ago, was that you buried in a London sewer the talents which nature intended for the nation at large . . . The time, John, is one for drawing together, for consolidating, for strengthening all the forces which make for the emancipation of Labour . . . The thing can be done if we but keep the fact in mind that
>> The individual withers, whilst The Cause grows more and more.[3]

He followed this with flattering references to Burns at the I.L.P.'s annual conference and for a time Burns was 'chummy', as there can be

1 Burns Diary, 27 November 1902. B.L. Add. MSS 46320.
2 Ibid. 19 March 1903. Add. MSS 46321.
3 *Labour Leader,* 28 March 1903.

no doubt that Hardie had touched his essential vanity.[1] In addition, he had based his appeal on Burns's own ground – that of the need for co-operation and collaboration. But the parameters of that co-operation were much wider in Burns's scheme of things than they were in Hardie's. 'It might be', Burns told the 1902 T.U.C., 'that they might do worse during the next few years than copy the tolerant, practical, useful work that the Labour group of the London County Council had been able to do in combination with the sympathetic men of all religions and all views of politics'.[2]

At the beginning of 1904 Burns, after offering to stand down in favour of Hardie, was re-elected chairman of the parliamentary labour group but he resented the private meetings which Hardie organised for the L.R.C. sponsored members. Later in the year Burns clashed with the L.R.C. member for Clitheroe, David Shackleton, about a motion on government workers' wages. He used the disagreement as an excuse to rush into print to damn the L.R.C. as a 'clique of political tyros and economic fledglings' who excluded from their 'petty councils wiser people than themselves'.[3] As it happened, Shackleton's political views were probably a good deal closer to Burns's own than to those of the I.L.P., but nothing could shake Burns's conviction that the L.R.C. and the Independent Labour Party were synonymous. So great was his mistrust that, when the L.R.C. selected George Barnes of the I.L.P. to fight the Blackfriars division of Glasgow, Burns tried hard to get in another, more moderate, nominee, all the while keeping Herbert Gladstone, the Liberal whip, informed of his activities.[4] Indeed, there is evidence that for all his secret negotiation with the L.R.C. about the allocation of seats in the event of a general election, Gladstone tried to use Burns to ensure that the L.R.C. only nominated moderate candidates, and not members of the I.L.P. At Stockton the Liberal candidate, McKinnon Wood, was distressed to find that he was being opposed by an L.R.C. man, Frank Rose of the I.L.P. He asked Burns to put pressure on Rose through his union, the A.S.E., to get him to withdraw. Burns did, but was unsuccessful perhaps because the A.S.E. was, as he put it, 'dominated by a fanatical and vindictive' I.L.P. clique.[5] His own bitterness almost certainly owed something to the fact that the I.L.P. had

1 J.K. Hardie to J.B. Glasier, 1 April 1903. Quoted in F. Bealey and H. Pelling, *Labour and Politics, 1900-1906* (1958), 192.

2 T.U.C., *Annual Report* (1902), 29.

3 *Daily News,* 9 September 1904.

4 J. Burns to H. Gladstone, 22 October 1903. Gladstone Papers. B.L. Add. MSS 46061, f. 30.

5 Burns Diary, 27 January 1904. B.L. Add. MSS 46322.

actually dared to venture into his own constituency in an effort to seduce his supporters. In the course of 1904 he found it necessary to attend meetings of the Labour League much more frequently than had for some time been his custom. So strong was the pressure on organised labour in Battersea to throw its lot in with the L.R.C. that 'at the most serious meeting ever held there' Burns 'warned the T.C. and L.R.C. men that if their policy of capture was persisted in I would fight them even to the point of leaving League, L.C.C., and Parliament'.[1]

At the same time as his relations with the labour movement were being subjected to almost continuous strain, Burns found himself drawing closer to the Liberals. He was writing a labour column for the *Daily News* which was bringing him into contact with advocates of the 'new liberalism' such as Masterman, while his adherence to traditional liberal values such as peace, retrenchment, and temperance, secured his contacts with older forms of radicalism. It was no coincidence that his closest acquaintance in the Liberal Party at this time was John Morley, a true nineteenth-century radical. But once more it was Joseph Chamberlain who was indirectly responsible for strengthening Burns's Liberal links still further. In the autumn of 1903 he launched his crusade for tariff reform, and the Liberal leaders turned to Burns as the man who could legitimately represent the working-class view of the issue. With a parliamentary debate on the subject pending at the end of 1903, Herbert Samuel suggested to Gladstone that, in order to avoid endless repetition from the Liberal benches, the topic should be broken up into different aspects and a speaker allocated to each. Burns, he suggested, should be asked to deal with the likely effects of tariff reform on the condition of the people.[2] It is clear that free trade, which Chamberlain threatened, was a matter about which Burns felt very deeply indeed. Perhaps spurred on by memories of his earlier clashes with the free traders in the 1880s he managed to recapture much of his old fervour. At Dulwich in December 1903 he left his audience 'in a kind of frenzy . . . They say you talked like a man inspired'.[3] So energetically did he attack Chamberlain that by January he was suffering from exhaustion and was confined to bed. Even there, however, he refused to be silenced, taking up his pen to add his own contribution to the flood of polemical literature that Chamberlain had unleashed. In *Labour and free trade*

1 Ibid. 20 October 1904. There is a similar entry for 28 March 1903. Ibid. Add. MSS 46321.

2 Samuel's letter was included in H.H. Asquith to H. Gladstone, 20 December 1903. Gladstone Papers. B.L. Add. MSS 45989, ff. 96-7.

3 C.F.G. Masterman to J. Burns, 20 December 1903. Burns Papers. B.L. Add. MSS 46298, ff. 154-5.

(1904) Burns lashed out savagely against a man for whom he had had little time since the Jameson Raid. Tariff reform of the sort Chamberlain advocated, he insisted, would place severe restrictions on the volume of trade, clearly undesirable for a nation so dependent on trade as Britain, and would also increase the cost of food. Chamberlain, he concluded, was nothing more than a political bankrupt projecting tariff reform to protect a distressed government that had nothing to show for its period in office but war, debt, discredit, and inefficiency.

In floating tariff reform Chamberlain had challenged one of the fundamentals of Liberalism and in so doing inadvertently helped to revitalise a divided and dispirited Liberal Party. In the course of 1904, other topics emerged which strengthened this revival, notably the liquor licensing issue and the importation of Chinese coolies into Africa. Once more, Burns found his views echoing those of the Liberals. The Licensing Bill he condemned as nothing more than a government measure 'shamelessly rewarding their political allies and subsidising their friends. This is a gross piece of political jobbery'.[1] He was equally vociferous in protesting against the use of Chinamen in South Africa, taking part in a mass demonstration in Hyde Park in March 1904, and returning to the subject at a local meeting a few days later. Once more it was Chamberlain — 'the puppet of a diseased ambition' — who attracted his savagery. Lord Milner was not spared either. Burns suggested that he might turn out to be the twentieth-century equivalent of Lord North who would lose Africa solely in the interests of a 'pack of blackguardly cosmopolitan Jews'. The coolies, he claimed, were 'housed like cattle in a compound — neglected when sick — robbed when paid — degraded by confinement — debauched by liquor and vice — used as mere animated implements for the enrichment of plutocratic peers and selfish capitalists'.[2]

All of these matters were, of course, cross-party issues, in the sense that Liberal opinion was barely discernible from that of the organised labour movement. The predominantly nonconformist tradition of labour virtually ensured that on the whole it would react unfavourably to the Licensing Bill. The Hyde Park meeting against Chinese slavery was a Lib-Lab affair and, with a few exceptions, the organised labour movement, swung dutifully into line against Chamberlain.[3]. But there was no chance that such issues would bring Burns back to the labour fold. Rumours that he would get office in the next Liberal administra-

1 Burns Diary, 20 April 1904. B.L. Add. MSS 46322.

2 *South Western Star,* 1 April 1904.

3 For the exceptions see K.D. Brown, 'The Trade Union Tariff Reform Association, 1904-1913', *Journal of British Studies* 9 (1970), 141-53.

tion had begun to circulate as early as 1903 and in the autumn of 1904 there was another burst of such speculation. This time, however the whispers were better founded, for it seems that Liberal leaders were themselves beginning to think in these terms. At the end of the year when Herbert Gladstone put it to Campbell-Bannerman that the party should establish some informal committees to consider policy, he suggested that Burns (and Sidney Webb) should be considered as consulting doctors to the Local Government committee 'because I believe it to be of the utmost importance, and questions connected with it are likely to be to the front at once'.[1] John Morley urged Burns's claims to a place in January 1905 and Burns himself seems by then to have regarded himself as a probable member of the next government. At least, with a fiscal debate pending in February 1905 he referred to his fears that 'we shall have trouble with *our team*'.[2]

Even so, at the beginning of 1905 he was re-elected chairman of the parliamentary labour group, although he had no illusions abouts its co-hesiveness. Beneath its apparent unity, he wrote, there lay 'fanatical discord'.[3] Yet he preserved solidarity in the group's campaign on behalf of the T.U.C.'s Trades Disputes Bill. His efforts were little short of heroic. He acted as the co-ordinator between the T.U.C. and the Irish M.P.'s, and secured the latter's support in return for a vague commit-ment to include in the bill clauses about conspiracy which they hoped to use to protect Irish nationalists. Once the debates came on he marshalled his supporters with considerable skill and delivered a powerful speech himself. In Grand Committee when the Solicitor General refused to accept the conspiracy clause as a basis for discussion Burns led a walk-out of the bill's supporters. But the task was really hopeless. Even with the support of Irish and Liberal members the bill was doomed to fail in the face of opposition carefully organised by the Employers' Parliamentary Council and backed by the government. By May the opposition had successfully killed it off but the T.U.C. was sufficiently appreciative of Burns's efforts to send him five guineas to offset his expenses (typically he returned it), aware of the fact that the bill only survived so many wrecking amendments because of the 'astute statesmanship' of the labour men led by Burns. But there, temporarily at any rate, the matter had to rest.

1 H. Gladstone to H. Campbell-Bannerman, 27 November 1904. Campbell-Bannerman Papers. B.L. Add. MSS 41217, ff. 139-40.

2 Burns Diary, 16 February 1905. B.L. Add. MSS 46323. My italics.

3 Ibid. 14 February 1905.

4 T.U.C. Parliamentary Committee, *Minutes,* 20 April 1905.

In any case by the summer of 1905 the trade unions had other things to worry about. Unemployment had been rising steadily since the previous autumn and was reaching alarming levels. At the end of 1904 the President of the Local Government Board, Walter Long, had introduced a relief scheme for London, which seemed to be worst hit and at the beginning of 1905 he announced his intention of extending a similar scheme to other areas. As it happened, he was replaced at the Local Government Board and it fell to the new president, Gerald Balfour, to introduce the necessary legislation. The scheme had already run into some opposition from other members of the cabinet because it contained a controversial proposal to use the rates in order to pay wages to unemployed men set to work by local relief committees. Once the idea became public the opposition was swelled by powerful vested interests outside the cabinet who feared that it represented the thin end of the socialist wedge.[1] The Prime Minister, Balfour, therefore decided to let the bill die by refusing to name a day for its second reading. In Leicester 500 men signed up to join a march of the unemployed on London and soon Hardie had organised many other similar marches, financed by the soap manufacturer, Joseph Fels. For someone who had made his initial impact on public life as a champion of the unemployed and who was chairman of a labour group which had generally welcomed the bill, Burns took a remarkably detached view of all this. On 16 May he noted in his diary that 'W.C. and others very nervous about Leicester March. I am not surprised. They cannot lay the ghost and are as timid as cats'.[2] Three days later he attended a joint meeting of the L.R.C., G.F.T.U., and the T.U.C., and it became evident that his lack of interest sprang from his disagreement with the bill. Although the meeting passed a resolution approving the government scheme in principle, but demanding that it be applied nationally and funded by the exchequer, Burns was the sole dissentient. He did not believe that public funds should be used to pay wages to unemployed workers. In 1904 the London Unemployed Fund had asked the L.C.C.'s General Purposes Committee to find work for 900 men on condition that the Fund paid all the costs. As a member of the committee Burns had agreed to this but when Colonel Rotton, an old Battersea rival, had suggested that the L.C.C. pay to the London Unemployed Fund a sum to the value of the work done by the 900 men, Burns was vehement in his opposition.[3] Thus when the labour M.P.s met to discuss the govern-

1 See K.D. Brown, 'Conflict in Early British Welfare Policy; the Case of the Unemployed Workmen's Bill of 1905', *Journal of Modern History* 43 (1971), 615-29.

2 Burns Diary, 16 May 1905. B.L. Add. MSS 46323.

3 L.C.C. General Purposes Committee, *Minutes*, 27 February 1905.

ment bill again on 24 May 1905, more disagreement occured. Crooks and Arthur Henderson were very critical of Burns's stand, whereupon Burns confided to his diary that 'this is the beginning of a fight with faction of the most malignant kind'.[1] When the bill, shorn of the controversial rate aid clause, finally went through in August, Burns was totally indifferent, referring to the whole affair as a 'farce'.[2]

The parliamentary session of 1905 was a stormy one, marked by bitter wranglings between government and opposition, internal differences within the Conservative Party, and with the cloud of tariff reform hanging over everything. Soon after it ended, Burns left with J. Allen Baker for another trip to North America. Although it was meant primarily as a holiday Martha as usual stayed behind and the two men covered nearly 20,000 miles in ten weeks. Burns was glad to get home, returning to find a very fluid political situation. Balfour's government, racked by internal dissensions and indecisive leadership, was lurching towards its final collapse and Campbell-Bannerman was turning to the pleasurable if difficult task of considering the composition of the next Liberal cabinet. The press was full of speculation and Burns's name figured prominently among the suggestions for second rank cabinet posts. On 17 November he spent an hour with the Liberal leader and it seems that from this date his appointment to some office was agreed, for 'we discussed every aspect – the personal policy and views – the composite auxiliaries'.[3] Significantly, the following day Burns went to see Morley – who had first suggested to Campbell-Bannerman that Burns should be given some cabinet office.[4] The prime minister-elect had always been impressed by Burns's honesty, ever since their first real contact in 1893, and Burns was one of the few men in politics with whom Sir Henry was on Christian name terms.[5] Politically there were good reasons for including Burns. His 'Little England' outlook would be a useful additional counter weight to the major figures such as Asquith, Grey, and Haldane, who were Imperialists. Moreover, at a time when labour was preparing to fight seats on its own through the L.R.C. it was clearly advantageous to have in the cabinet a man of Burns's origins, experience and record, especially as Sir Henry, following Balfour's resignation in December, decided to go to the country *after* making his cabinet appointments. This was exactly the sort of argument that Morley was using, telling Gladstone

---

1 Burns Diary, 24 May 1905. B.L. Add. MSS 46323.
2 Ibid. 4 August 1905.
3 Ibid. 17 November 1905.
4 J. Morley, *Recollections* (New York, 1918), II, 132.
5 See above, p.80.

that Burns's inclusion would mean that 'the confidence of the labouring classes in the next Liberal Government will be enormously promoted'. His exclusion, on the other hand, would cost them 'thousands of votes'.[1] Ultimately it was the Local Government Board that Burns was given. Campbell-Bannerman had been having some difficulty in providing for the wealth of young talent at his disposal and had considered Lloyd George for this job but Burns's experience of local government and his known interest in working class affairs evidently told in his favour.

At first sight Burns's acceptance of office seems paradoxical. He had always insisted on personal freedom of action and had openly expressed his unwillingness to be tied down by the dictates of party whips. This had been explicit in his opposition to both the I.L.P. and the L.R.C. Yet now he was accepting cabinet office with all its implications of party loyalty and cabinet responsibility. But the paradox is more apparent than real. Cabinet ministers were by and large free to pursue their own policies so long as they fell broadly within the general party outlook. Unlike the L.R.C., the Liberal Party had no formal commitment to a fundamental principle to which loyalty was at all times expected and required.[2] It was rather an alliance of the sort with which Burns had worked so successfully in the L.C.C., though admittedly not quite so broadly based. He certainly regarded it as having better claim than the L.R.C. to be 'the people's party'.[3] For all his faults Burns had shown a consistent desire to advance working-class interests and as organised labour had now thrown in its lot with the L.R.C. he faced the choice of remaining independent but isolated, or taking the opportunity to achieve further reforms. He chose the latter. As he put it when he opened his election campaign at the Latchmere Road baths in December, he 'had to chose whether for the next ten years he should indulge, perhaps, in the futility of faction, perhaps in the impotency of intrigue, or whether he should accept an office which in their day and generation he could make fruitful of good works'.[4]

This was totally consistent with the decision he had taken in 1889 to become a candidate for the London County Council when he had in his own words 'to choose between being an industrial Hal o' the Wynd, a mere advocate of abstract ideas, a propagandist of visionary aims and theories. . .standing alone, free but impotent, or the practical

1 J. Morley to H. Gladstone, 6 December 1905. Nuffield College. Gainford MSS, 82.
2 This point was made forcibly at the time of the election by Philip Snowden, 'The Labour Party and the General Election', *Independent Review* 7 (1905), 143.
3 Burns Diary, 27 February 1906. B.L. Add. MSS 46324.
4 *The Times,* 28 December 1905.

pioneer of the advancing labour host, desiring and slowly winning a higher social, municipal and intellectual life'.[1] Inevitably some of his critics suggested that his acceptance of cabinet office derived purely from his own ambition. Of course ambition had much to do with it, but it is a travesty to suggest that it was the only or even the main reason. Burgess suggests that as early as the 1880s he had detected that the driving force behind Burns was his wife, and that it was she who had her eye on the cabinet office for him. This assertion reflects his belief that Burns had no principles at all but in the context of the 1880s it was sheer nonsense. Martha Burns derived little glory from her husband's career, unless one invitation to a royal garden party in 1905 is counted. Although she acted as a sort of unpaid secretary, keeping up to date his extensive collection of newscuttings, indexing and sorting them, she did not even get much reflected glory.[2] She seldom, if ever, accompanied her husband on his vocational or political trips, never attended political dinners, and herself never entertained. The marriage was happy enough but generally undemonstrative. Burns's emotional fulfilment came through his work and, increasingly, through his son. Most of his time at home was spent either in reading or playing with Edgar, and his delight in the boy bubbles through the diary. 'Played draughts with the boy, and it was delightful to see his young, fresh, and beautiful face all aglow as he captured my kings and won by sheer foresight the game from me. His "father, father", pretty and endearing; the young barbarian grows like a juvenile Spartacus'.[3]

Most of the public reaction to the formation of the new administration centred on the way in which Campbell-Bannerman had outwitted the efforts of Asquith, Grey, and Haldane to push him into the House of Lords, but as the first working man Cabinet minister, Burns's appointment naturally attracted a good deal of comment as well. Conservative opinion was mixed. Several leading Tory figures thought the appointment a good one.[4] The London Municipal Society, on the other hand, was horrified, claiming that Burns's promotion represented

1 Quoted in Donald, 'The Workman Minister', 192.

2 In 1902 Burns had successfully approached some of his friends for financial help which would leave Martha freer to assist him in his political work. See J.A. Baker to J. Burns, 22 January 1902. Burns Papers. B.L. Add. MSS 46298, f. 74.

3 Burns Diary, 13 January 1903. B.L. Add. MSS 46321.

4 See for example Sir Michael Hicks Beach's comment to Seymour Fortescue, 21 December 1905. Quoted in V. Hicks Beach, *Sir Michael Hicks Beach* (1932), II, 220. Also Lord James of Hereford to L. Harcourt, 21 December 1905. Bodleian Library. Harcourt Papers.

a victory for socialism in general and for the rabid type in particular.[1] The society's supporters in the London County Council had fought tooth and nail to prevent the establishment of a municipal steamboat service and it had been largely due to Burns's energy and enthusiasm in lobbying, whipping in support, and debating that the measure had gone through in 1904.[2] It was one in which he took a great deal of pride and he had spent much time visiting the piers and boats, and chatting with the various crews. This was the sort of socialism which, the L.M.S. feared, Burns would implement at a national level now he had the chance.

Labour reaction was similarly mixed. On the far left, his acceptance of office was seen — and has been ever since — as the crowning act of betrayal by a man whose only political goal was personal aggrandizement. When the London Trades Council discussed a proposal to send him a congratulatory telegram, S.D.F. members led by Fred Knee resisted and forced a division. *Justice* commented tartly that a salary of £2,000 a year was 'just reward for his apostasy'.[3] But if trade union journals are any guide the news of Burns's elevation was generally welcomed, a conclusion verified not only by the enormous number of letters from trade unions surviving in his private papers, but also by a resolution of congratulation from the T.U.C. Men like Will Crooks, Isaac Mitchell, and C.W. Bowerman, who were all fighting the election as L.R.C. candidates, told him that his appointment removed the 'last barrier' to British working men having full responsibility for national affairs.[4] A few, however, sounded a note of caution. Hardie was among them, suggesting that a hard working Burns would probably stir up a lethargic department but regretting that he had joined a Liberal government.[5] The *Labour Leader* agreed that he would do his best but felt that he would soon find himself in the difficult position of having to vote either against labour proposals or his own colleagues. Inside eighteen months, it predicted, either he would no longer be reckoned a labour man or else he would have resigned.[6] Harry Snell also warned against expecting too much, as the civil servants at the Local Government Board were notoriously reactionary.[7] Sidney Webb shared this view, for in a somewhat cryptic letter to Burns he said that it was

1 *London Municipal Notes* (January 1906), 337.
2 See Burns Diary, 2, 9, 22 June, 29 July 1904. B.L. Add. MSS 46322.
3 *Justice,* 16 December 1905.
4 Undated memorandum in Burns Papers. B.L. Add. MSS 46298, ff. 214-5.
5 *The Times,* 18 December 1905.
6 *Labour Leader,* 29 December 1905.
7 *Labour Record and Review* (January 1906), 324.

'splendidly courageous of you to accept the L.G.B. and I don't think it ought to have been asked of you. You will be cruelly denounced', he added — ironically in view of his own later denunciations of Burns — 'for not doing impossibilities'.[1]

For tactical reasons Campbell-Bannerman had decided, against advice from his senior colleagues, to form his cabinet before going to the country. Having selected his team he secured a dissolution and initiated one of the most momentous elections in British history. Balfour's government had succeeded both in reuniting a Liberal Party which a short while before had been hopelessly divided, and also in offending many powerful interests in the community by its policies on licensing, education, Chinese labour and, of course, tariff reform. Chamberlain's waving of that particular flag had thoroughly roused the free trade bull, but the result was not quite what he had expected, for the bull dumped the flag and many of its adherents firmly outside the parliamentary fence and returned in triumph to Westminster, carrying an enormous Liberal majority on its back. In Battersea, Burns played on this issue for all he was worth, pleading with his constituents not to be misled by a 'fiscal pervert'.[2] Social reform also figured prominently in his programme and he was one of the few members of the new government to advocate old age pensions. But other older radical themes also found a place. His long-held view that the House of Lords should be abolished had been confirmed when in 1905 the upper house had rejected the London County Council bill which would have permitted a major extension of the council's tram service over the bridges of the Thames. Burns's assertion that all hereditary authorities should be abolished alarmed the King but Campbell-Bannerman, who had to cover up similar indiscretions by others of his colleagues, assured him that it was an error 'due solely to the inexperience in official responsibility of the Minister concerned'.[3]

When the vote was counted in Battersea, Burns, despite the fact that he had spent much of the campaign helping Liberal candidates in other parts of the country, was seen to have shared comfortably enough in the Liberal land-slide that was engulfing the country. He received 7,387 votes against the 5,787 given to his Conservative opponent, Mr Shirley Benn. The announcement of the result was greeted with great enthusiasm by Burns's supporters. 'The cheering

1 S. Webb to J. Burns, 11 December 1905. Burns Papers. B.L. Add. MSS 46287, f. 289.

2 *The Times*, 3 January 1906.

3 H. Campbell-Bannerman to the King, 11 January 1906. Campbell-Bannerman Papers. B.L. Add. MSS 41207, f. 28.

was deafening. . .rain was now pouring down, but it had no dispiriting effect on anyone. Mr Burns took his stand on the waggon, and during the short intervals and breathing spaces that the vast cheering multitude allowed themselves, he contrived to say the electors of Battersea had once more behaved like men and fought like gentlemen'. [1] As seems to have become common by now in Battersea elections there were mutual accusations between rival voters of unfair tactics, but Burns himself took no part in these recriminations. He was too busy settling into his new role. Agitation and lobbying were done with. Henceforth he was one of His Majesty's ministers.

1 *South Western Star,* 19 January 1906.

6

HIGH HOPES, 1906-1907.

John Burns's tenure of office at the Local Government Board was destined to last for slightly more than eight years. For most historians, and indeed for many contemporaries, its length was in inverse proportion to its fruitfulness. Writing of the contribution made by his own father to social reform in the years before the first world war Randolph Churchill suggests that Burns lacked both the will and the inclination to make a similar impact.[1] Christopher Addison, later himself a minister in Lloyd George's coalition government, claimed that Burns's presidency had been noteworthy 'only for a self satisfied waste of precious opportunities'.[2] A similar verdict came from G.P. Gooch, a Liberal back bencher in the 1906 parliament, who felt that Burns the minister had disappointed everyone except himself.[3] Many such assessments of Burns's ministerial career are undoubtedly prejudiced by the observations of frustrated contemporary social reformers like the Webbs and not until recently has it been revealed how considerable were some of the constraints the Local Government Board imposed upon its presidents. Still, however, the judgement has typically been one of 'sheer ineptitude'.[4] Underpinning these unfavourable views has been the belief, common to contemporaries and later writers alike, that Burn's susceptibility to flattery allowed his departmental officials to mould him in their own reactionary image, turning him into a cautious and incompetent minister. Thus Colin Cross claims that he 'fell under the dominance of his civil servants, who convinced him that few changes were necessary in the Local Government Board'.[5]

Certainly vanity had always been one of Burns's besetting weaknesses. It fed upon his success, and particularly on his achievement of cabinet office, for no other man in contemporary politics had advanced so far by dint of his own independent efforts. When Campbell-Bannerman offered him the Local Government Board, Burns is alleged to have

1 R. Churchill, *Winston S. Churchill. Young Statesman. 1901-1914*, (1967), 314.

2 C. Addison, *Politics From Within, 1911-1918* (1924), I, 39.

3 G.P. Gooch, *Under Six Reigns* (1958), 148.

4 R. Davidson, 'Llewellyn Smith, the Labour Department and Government Growth, 1886-1909', *Studies in the Growth of Nineteenth Century Government*, ed. G. Sutherland (1972), 228. See also the verdict of R.R. James, *The British Revolution. British Politics 1880-1939, Vol I. Gladstone to Asquith, 1880-1914* (1976), 240.

5 C. Cross, *The Liberals in Power* (1963), 30.

replied that the prime minister had never done a more popular thing.[1] It would also be rash to deny that the permanent officials of the Local Government Board were anything other than highly conservative when Burns took them over at the end of 1905. The whole administration was shot through with a rigidly conservative outlook, with the exception of the medical department which under Sir William Power had made some progress towards improving controls over food, water supply, and infectious diseases.[2] But the department's general caution was deeply rooted in the circumstances of the board's creation in 1871 as an amalgam of administrative machines responsible for the poor law, public health, and the localities. The chief of the poor law section had become titular head of the new board, in the process imbuing it with the tradition that its approach to all expenditure on the poor and in the localities should be highly restrictive. When Burns became president the permanent head of the Local Government Board, Sir Samuel Provis, was old and nearing the end of an official career which he had devoted to upholding the principles of the 1834 Poor Law Amendment Act. He was very suspicious of the new thinking about poverty and its treatment as epitomised by the Webbs. He even refused to allow the royal commission on the poor law to have free access to the board's records. His deputy, Monro, and the departmental legal adviser, Alfred Adrian, were also survivors of the old school.[3] Almost to a man, the poor law inspectorate shared the disposition of their chiefs, as was made abundantly clear when they were called to give evidence in the course of 1906 to the poor law commission. Nearly all were of the 'charity and character building' school. F.T. Binhan, the inspector for Wales, deplored the absence in his area of the 'better elements', for this meant there was relatively little charitable enterprise. E.B. Wethered was disturbed that in recent years the stigma of shame attached to pauperism had been eroded and he further asserted that drink was a prime cause of poverty. Most reactionary of all was the chief inspector, J.S. Davy. He, too, confessed his alarm that the principles of 1834 had been whittled down and he expressed total opposition to the growth of outrelief which had, he believed, discouraged self help in the form of thrift. He was thirsting for a tightening up of the system's administration.

1 *The Personal Papers of Lord Rendel*, ed. F.E. Hamer (1931), 165.

2 R. Macleod, 'The Frustration of State Medicine, 1880-1899', Medical History *II* (1967), 15-40; J. Brand, *Doctors and the State* (Baltimore, 1965), 36-82; A.S. MacNalty, 'The Medical Department of the Local Government Board', *Journal of the Royal Institute of Public Health* 2 (1948). 9-26.

3 See generally the memoirs of W.A. Ross, 'Local Government Board and After; Retrospect', *Public Administration* 34 (1956), 19 ff.

> If it be that a man by a moderate exercise of self-restraint and foresight can prevent himself from becoming a pauper; if it be that practically no man can become a pauper except with the concurrence of a board of guardians; and if it be that by his own action and with the concurrence of the guardians he becomes a pauper, then his relief is an injury to his neighbours; then I submit that there is the very strongest ground for holding that any outdoor relief which is given must be given with the greatest care and discrimination.[1]

The officials' conservatism was compounded by the red tape which bound the board. The opinions of technical experts were frequently over-ruled by members of the lay secretariat who were usually lacking in any practical field experience of the problems with which they were dealing and who seemed to lack either the will or the inclination to break free and to take on new areas of responsibility. When the Labour Bureaux (London) Bill was under discussion in 1901-2, for example, the L.G.B. issued a memorandum that repudiated any departmental concern in the matter on the ground that the labour market and unemployment were properly the domain of the Board of Trade. There was much truth in Mrs Webb's comment that the board was 'rather a labyrinth. I doubt whether the officials themselves have the Clue to its Mysteries'.[2]

This is confirmed by the memoirs of one of the poor law inspectors, Preston Thomas, who admitted that the complexities of the accounting system used by workhouse masters was totally beyond him.

> I could only hope I should some day learn why [it was]. . . necessary. This, by the way, I have never succeeded in doing; and but for the fact that officialism is a fetish to which I dare not be disloyal, I should contend that at least two-thirds of the [procedures]. . .are absolutely superfluous.[3]

Little enlightenment could be expected from the lower ranks of staff. It had been 1881 before the board had recruited its first Oxbridge graduate, and the overall standard of entrants was low. In Whitehall, first class and principal clerks of the L.G.B. were generally regarded as inferior to their equivalents in other departments and their salaries and promotion prospects were certainly less favourable. Over the years Treasury policy had been directed to keeping L.G.B. salaries, clerical and presidential, low with the result that the department suffered

1 Royal Commission on the Poor Laws and the Relief of Distress. [Cd 4625] Appendix I. Minutes of Evidence. *British Parliamentary Papers* XXXIX (1909), 142.

2 Quoted in R. Macleod, 'Treasury Control and Social Administration: A Study of Establishment Growth at the Local Government Board, 1871-1905', *Occasional Papers in Social Administration* 23 (1968), 54.

3 H. Preston Thomas, *The Work and Play of a Government Inspector* (1909), 224.

from inertia and poor morale, remaining virtually unaffected by the spirit of reform which, in the guise of the national efficiency movement, swept through other departments in the aftermath of the Boer War. All in all, the L.G.B. well deserved its characterisation as 'the ageing Cinderella of Whitehall with an enormous staff and responsibilities'.[1]

Yet it is an over-simplification to assume that the board's officials were able to seduce John Burns *merely* by playing on his vanity. The nature of his own views tended to make him extremely vulnerable as well. There was a very strong streak of puritanism in Burns's make-up, hence his disgust with wire-pulling in the S.D.F. and any hint of graft in the L.C.C. As he told the pupils at a local school's prize-giving ceremony in 1904:

> You come before me this morning with clean hands and clean collars. I want you to have clean tongues, clean manners, clean morals and clean characters. I don't want boys to use bad language. I don't want boys to buy cigarettes. I don't want boys to use their pencils for improper writing. Don't hustle old people. I neither drink nor smoke, because my schoolmaster impressed upon me three cardinal virtues; cleanliness in person, cleanliness in mind; temperance.[2]

This puritanism also manifested itself in his hostility to drink and gambling. 'I am convinced', he wrote in 1903, 'that next to betting and gambling, drink is one of the most serious problems that we have got to deal with'.[3] The following year his pamphlet, *Labour and drink,* was published. It argued that about a fifth of all dismissals from work were directly attributable to the adverse effects of alcohol and suggested that indulgence in it also meant that an individual was often unable to tide himself over a period of temporary unemployment. Burns's distaste for gambling underlay his well-publicised dislike of much professional sport. He deplored the fact that so many people preferred watching and betting on sport to participating themselves. So strongly did he feel about the professionalism of football, for example, that he objected when the L.C.C. Schools' Football Association asked if it could display in the council building the trophy it had recently won in a national competition. But Burns was not yet at the stage where he would have agreed unreservedly with the disciples of the Charity Organisation Society that most poverty was rooted in personal vice. His understanding of poverty was more subtle. On the one hand he knew better than most that low wages were a prime cause of poverty and frequently said so publicly. Further, he believed that

---

1 Macleod, 'Treasury Control', 48.
2 *South Western Star,* 2 December 1904.
3 Manuscript Lecture, 7 December 1903. Burns Papers. B.L. Add. MSS 46306, f. 28.

people often only indulged in drinking or betting because the
municipalities frequently failed to provide an environment which
would render such indulgence unnecessary.

> Individual effort is almost relatively impossible to cope with the
> big problem of poverty as we see it. . .I want the municipality to
> be a helping hand to the man with a desire of sympathy, to help
> the fallen when it is not in their power to help themselves. . .I
> believe the proper business of a Municipality is to do for the
> individual merged in the mass what the individual cannot do so
> well alone.[1]

This would produce in the future 'fewer workhouses and more homes,
smaller charities and larger wages, more pleasures and less drink'.[2]
Opening a new public library in Battersea in 1897 Burns had suggested
that all libraries should provide special facilities for teenage boys
because it was at that age that criminals were made. It was, he added,
more economical for a local authority to spend two guineas on books
than £2,000 to maintain a criminal.[3] Side by side with this environmental approach to the causes of poverty went, on the other hand, a
belief that in some cases at least it was a product of individual defects.
'There are thousands of homes in London', he claimed in a pamphlet
of 1902, 'which are dirty because the dwellers are drunken; filthy
because their tenants are foul; verminous because their tenants are as
lazy as their landlords are exacting. It is not always the pig-stye; it is
sometimes − yea, too often − the pig'.[4] On another occasion, after
interviewing several constituents he noted disapprovingly that 'laziness,
drink, and all the lusts of the flesh at the bottom of their trouble'.[5]
Both of Burns's interpretations of poverty were evident in his attitude
towards many of the suggestions currently being mooted by social
reformers for its relief. 'Pauper ideas of industrial relief and soup
kitchen methods of social reform. . .are being rapidly revealed as
obstacles to real organic change'.[6] Many such schemes, Burns felt,
were too indiscriminate in that they provided relief with no consideration of a particular individual's merits, for like many of his contemporaries he was determined to present the residuum of casual workers,
unemployables and loafers from contaminating the respectable poor.
Equally, many schemes constituted nothing more than wasteful
subsidies to municipal authorities that were shirking their own
responsibilities.

1 Ibid. ff. 19-21.
2 Ibid. f. 16.
3 *The Times,* 10 May 1897.
4 J. Burns, *Brains Better than Bets or Beer* (1902), 5.
5 Burns Diary, 7 August 1903. B.L. Add. MSS 46321.
6 Quoted in Donald, 'The Workman Minister', 198.

Yet it is clear that, exposed to the right sort of reactionary atmosphere such as that provided by the Local Government Board, the flexibility of Burns's ideas about the causes of poverty could quickly ossify into a firm prejudice that personality counted for everything. Such a possibility was made even more likely by two other features of his thinking. One was that he apparently had very few positive ideas of his own. Too often his remedies were couched in terms of empty generalisations. The best he could offer in a debate on unemployment in 1905, for instance, was the suggestion that local authorities should be encouraged to tackle the problems of drink, low wages, and gambling. The other was his passion for economy in government, a trait which had grown more marked as the years passed. There was evident relish in a 1905 diary entry referring to his attendance at a council meeting when he 'defeated all salaries except Sexby's. Led for economy all through and won'.[1] When his supporters organised a victory celebration in the town hall in March 1906 he informed them that the chief duty of government was to practise economy, a message he reiterated at a Labour League meeting later in the same month. It was a mistake, he affirmed, to assume that the largest possible expenditure was synonymous with the maximum amount of public good. There had been far too much extravagance under the previous government and it could not go on.[2] Certainly this attitude made him very susceptible to a line of argument which suggested that if poverty was predominantly personal rather than environmental in origin, government had little moral obligation to spend very much on its relief. This, of course, was entirely out of sympathy with the rising tide of 'new liberalism' with its emphasis on increasing state intervention, particularly in matters relating to welfare. Traditionally, Liberalism had been based on the assumption that there was an anti-thesis between the state and the individual, but T.H. Green and David Ritchie had argued round this, asserting that state action was not a threat but rather a necessity to the individual's moral and material well-being. It was no coincidence that Burns was to find his most vociferous critics among those Liberals most firmly wedded to the new philosophy, C.F.G. Masterman, L.T. Hobhouse, J.A. Hobson, Leo Chiozza Money, Winston Churchill, and David Lloyd George.

Despite the later strictures Burns began his ministerial career with every appearance of vigour. Almost as soon as he assumed his responsibilities he hauled all office late-comers over the coals. He told them that for a good wage they were expected to produce a good day's work, a view which probably did not go down well with staff

1 Burns Diary, 15 May 1905. B.L. Add. MSS 46323.
2 *The Times,* 3 March 1906.

smarting under long-standing grievances about pay and prospects. But he was working extremely hard himself and clearly expected his subordinates to do likewise. In the few days that elapsed between his taking up office and the end of 1905 he appointed a committee to distribute the Queen's Unemployment Fund, amended the regulations relating to the Unemployed Workmen's Act, prepared a circular on housing for the local authorities, issued several administrative orders concerning the poor law, and set up a committee to consider better ways of auditing municipal accounts. At least one back bencher saw in this action an intention to unify accounts and audit, 'just in fact what is wanted to put municipal matters and municipal trading on a sound financial basis'.[1] Official reports became his bedtime reading and the department's surviving letter books reveal that he dealt personally with matters that were often quite trivial and might have been better left to clerks. As often as he could, he made a point of consulting his technical advisers about particular problems and, just as he had in his days on the county council, he spent a great deal of time out in the field personally examining the various works and institutions for which the board was responsible. There is a distinct impression, too, that Burns's arrival at the L.G.B. coincided with a marked increase in the amount of central interference in the work of the poor law guardians. Unfortunately most of the departmental records dealing with the administration of the poor law in this period were destroyed by fire in 1944, but, judging from the pages of the *Poor Law Officers Journal*, poor law administrators themselves certainly believed that the degree of central control had been strengthened. The distribution of alcohol in poor law institutions which had previously been left to the discretion of local medical officers came under such close scrutiny that the journal protested, saying that alcohol was now evidently regarded by the L.G.B, 'in the light of a drug of dangerous tendencies'.[2] Finance was also subjected to much stricter checks. Efforts to raise the salaries of some local officials were persistently and personally ignored by Burns. Often the board exercised its veto over very small matters, such as stopping the payment of a three guinea fee to a specialist called in to attend a poor law patient, or querying a £100 compensation award to the wife of a Strand Union ambulance driver killed at work. By July 1906 the *Journal* was protesting bitterly that 'everyone must have been struck lately with the number of instances of interference with a grant or control of relief by the Boards of Guardians'.[3] But the

1 J.C. Wedgwood to W. Runciman, 23 January 1906. Newcastle University Library. Runciman Papers, 14.

2 *Poor Law Officers Journal,* 25 January 1907.

3 Ibid. 13 July 1906.

clearest indicator of this tendency was one which the *Journal's* editors welcomed, and that was the fact that Burns sanctioned an inquiry into the activities of several London boards of guardians, most notably that in Poplar.

For some time there had been rumblings about corruption and excessive generosity in the administration of relief in Poplar where the guardians included leading labour men like Will Crooks and George Lansbury. These rumblings had grown so loud during the unemployment crisis of 1904-5 that eventually the Poplar Municipal Alliance, backed by the Industrial Freedom League, had laid charges before the Local Government Board.[1] Both Lansbury and G.D.H. Cole later suggested that Burns allowed himself to be coerced into holding an official inquiry because he was in the pockets of Provis and Davy, and wished to show that he was not going to be partial in his attitude towards labour.[2] Certainly there is plenty of evidence in Burns's own papers that he was anxious to be seen as a minister who would act objectively without regard to outside pressures, even if it meant treading on the toes of friends. 'My office', he told Cadbury, 'brings me into conflict with superficial sentiment and pandering politicians who are obsessed with the idea of pauperising palliatives and degrading quackeries. . .nostrums which I have to prevent being costly mistakes. . .I am bumping aside the Charlatans . . . but duty must be done'.[3] But this line owed little to the influence of the L.G.B., for it was perfectly consistent with the attitude he had always taken on the council, where he had insisted on weighing every measure on its own merits and had certainly not given in to demands just because they were made by workers. Again, there can be no doubt that both Provis and Davy saw the allegations against the Poplar guardians as a heaven-sent opportunity to crack down on local officials who had deviated so much from the principles of 1834. But it seems unlikely that Burns would have needed much pursuasion from them to hold an inquiry. He was very keen to cut back on poor law expenditure, especially if, as was being alleged about Poplar, it was being distributed indiscriminately without due regard for a particular applicant's merits. The allegations of bribery would also have roused him, for he had always been particularly vigilant in exposing official corruption, and it is important to note that such allegations were not coming solely from people who had a vested interest in their exposure. Sidney Buxton, one of Burns's government colleagues, told Lansbury

1 For the Industrial Freedom League see *Anti-Labour History,* ed. Brown, 240.
2 Cole, *Burns,* 28. G. Lansbury, *My Life* (1928), 164-6.
3 J. Burns to G. Cadbury, 23 March 1906. Burns Papers. B.L. Add. MSS 46299. ff. 70-1.

that he felt relief had been given out in 1905 'far too lavishly'.[1] After attending a meeting of the Poplar Guardians held to distribute contracts for supplies, Beatrice Webb concluded that the proceedings had been 'utterly reckless. . .if there is no corruption in that Board, English human nature must be more naively stupid than any other race would credit'.[2] All told, therefore, it seems that Burns himself would have had every wish to hold an inquiry into the affairs of the Poplar Union, even without the encouragement he undoubtedly received from his officials. At least one member of the I.L.P. firmly believed that the initiative came from Burns himself.[3] Further, it should be noted that the Poplar Guardians themselves had written to the Board welcoming the prospect of a public inquiry as an opportunity to remove many current misconceptions about their administration.[4] Where Burns did err, however, was in appointing Davy to conduct the inquiry, even though it was a departmental and not a public one. By no stretch of the imagination could Davy have been viewed as an impartial arbitrator.

But while the wheels were being set in motion for the Poplar inquiry Burns had naturally to give some thought to the parliamentary session and in particular what he wished to achieve in it. In February 1906 he paid a visit to Beatrice Webb and, rather to her surprise, suddenly fished from his pocket a set of cards on which he had written down a list of the various measures which he hoped to introduce in the next two years. She was clearly impressed. 'If good intentions, and a strong vigorous and audacious character can make up for lack of administrative experience and technical knowledge John Burns may yet be a success as President of the Local Government Board'.[5] Burns told her that he hoped to bring in measures dealing with the docks, housing, food, offensive matter, burials, land valuation and local taxation. The two final items were particularly important to overall Liberal strategy. Within the Party there was a substantial pressure group calling for a radical land policy which would both raise money for social reform and also, it was hoped, help to solve the problems of urban society, particularly unemployment. With the activities of the poor law commission so widely publicised reform of the poor law was very much in the air. But any reform would have to take into account the

1 S. Buxton to G. Lansbury, 30 July 1906. B.L.P.E.S. Lansbury Papers, I, vol. 2, f. 270.

2 B. Webb Diary, 19 March 1906. B.L.P.E.S. Passfield Papers, I, vol. 26, 83-4.

3 T. Glossop to G. Lansbury, 9 November 1906. B.L.P.E.S. Lansbury Papers, I, vol. 2, f. 300.

4 Poplar Board of Guardians, *Minutes*, 8 November 1905.

5 B. Webb Diary, 9 February 1906. B.L.P.E.S. Passfield Papers, I, vol. 25.

difficulties involved in distributing financial responsibility between the national and local authorities, for local authorities would naturally be averse to accepting new responsibilities and duties until more finance could be raised by them. Already local authorities accounted for over half of total government expenditure. The prime minister himself was anxious to implement rating reform in order to tap new sources of revenue, and a prerequisite for this was a Valuation Bill enabling land to be valued separately from buildings. More immediately, however, Burns had decided to tackle the unemployed question, to tidy up existing legislation on offensive matter, burials, and workers in dangerous industries. Then there was to be a bill dealing with London's rates, and a scheme to establish municipal milk depots to provide milk for children under two. This was a proposal bequeathed to Burns by his pre-decessors at the L.G.B. and in April he instructed Provis to draw up the details of the bill.

Few of these measures, however, featured very highly in the Liberal programme for the 1906 session of parliament. They had been swept to power on a tidal wave of resentment against the Unionists and their main commitments were the essentially negative ones of reversing their opponents' most controversial enactments on education and licensing. Although the cabinet decided that education should have priority in 1906 considerable attention was paid to what Campbell-Bannerman described as 'two sops' for labour — on trades disputes and workmen's compensation.[1] In both, Burns, as the representative of labour, played an important role. He was a member of the cabinet committee set up to work on the Compensation Bill. He argued strongly and successfully for the inclusion of clauses extending protection to workers who con-tracted industrial diseases, a group whose interests he had championed ever since entering parliament. He also took a leading part in drafting a new Trades Disputes Bill. In March, the cabinet, strongly influenced by the arguments of Haldane and Asquith, rejected the advice proferred by Burns and decided instead on a measure that did not go as far as the T.U.C. wished in conferring on trade unions immunity from legal actions. Never afraid to speak his mind, Burns immediately wrote to Campbell-Bannerman, and expressed strong opposition to this 'serious step'. He pointed out that in adopting such a line the cabinet was going against the pledges given by many Liberal candidates during the election campaign.[2] The point was not lost on the prime minister who at the appropriate time overcame the difficulty by advising the Commons to

1 H. Campbell-Bannerman to H.H. Asquith, 21 January 1906. Bodleian Library. Asquith Papers, 10, f. 200.

2 J. Burns to H. Campbell-Bannerman, 26 March 1906. Campbell-Bannerman Papers. B.L. Add. MSS 41239, ff. 74-5.

120

vote, not for the government bill, but for the Labour Party's measure which did confer the desired immunity and which thus became law.

But any gratitude the labour movement may have felt for Burns's part in these measures was more than offset by his attitude on the other issue with which it was concerned — unemployment. It was unfortunately an issue on which Burns had plenty of prejudices but scarcely a single constructive idea. Although the government as such had no specific commitment to deal with the unemployed it could hardly ignore something which had assumed such importance in the previous session, especially as the level of unemployment was still quite high while the election campaign was being fought. A cabinet committee was therefore set up to thrash out a policy. It contained Burns, Lord Ripon, Asquith as Chancellor of the Exchequer, Sidney Buxton, and Herbert Gladstone. According to Burns's diary this committee 'settled policy' at a meeting held on 1 February, and for the next few days he was occupied at the L.G.B. in discussing the unemployment bill with his officials.[1] A little later he told Beatrice Webb that they were working on an amendment of the 1905 Act which would allow greater contributions to be made from the rates, and this seems to have been confirmed by the prime minister who told Lord Knollys that the amending measure would have some of the features of the original bill of 1905.[2] The King's Speech, however, contained only a vague reference to some unspecified amendment and it seems that Burns found himself in something of a cleft stick. Lord Ripon was especially anxious for some action and so, too, was Herbert Gladstone, who at the end of 1904 had been circulating unemployment proposals of quite an advanced nature among his fellow Liberals. Burns himself had opposed the original bill of 1905 precisely because it had envisaged using the rates to pay wages to the unemployed set to work under its provisions. Provis certainly shared this view and it had been at his suggestion that the uses of rate aid had been restricted in the final version of the bill to assisting with the upkeep of labour colonies and labour exchanges, migration, and general expenses. It is doubtful if Burns would even have gone that far, for he had always been severely critical of labour colonies on the grounds that they were very expensive in relation to what was achieved, afforded good opportunities for shirkers, and did not reach the causes of the problem they were trying to remedy — points all freely admitted even by their supporters.[3] In March, Burns personally

1 Burns Diary, 1 February 1906. B.L. Add. MSS 46324.

2 H. Campbell-Bannerman to Lord Knollys, 13 February 1906. Campbell-Bannerman Papers. B.L. Add. MSS 41207, ff. 50-1.

3 See his comments to Commissioner Railton of the Salvation Army. Burns Diary, 3 September 1904. B.L. Add. MSS 46322. Also his pamphlet *Unemployment*.

rejected an application from the Lambeth guardians for money with which to open such a colony. Yet it is further evidence of his initial flexibility in office that at the same time he did sanction the purchase of Hollesley Bay by the Central (Unemployed) Body which wished to use it to provide men with permanent positions on the land. He viewed it however as a 'doubtful experiment' and his attitude hardened even more after an Easter recess spent examining various colonies including Hollesley Bay and Lingfield.[1] The latter he compared very unfavourably with a nearby colony for epileptics.

He therefore had no intention of allowing the rates to be used to provide wages for men involved in such schemes, and thus his scope for amending the existing unemployment act was rather limited. Further, as he quite reasonably pointed out, there was little justification for seeking radical amendment of an act that had only just come into force and which it was hoped, would be replaced by substantial changes based on the report of the poor law commission. It seems, therefore, that initially Burns agreed with his cabinet colleagues to consider some amendment of the 1905 Act. Subsequently, however, encouraged by his officials, he settled on what was really a policy of drift, in the hope that the problem would diminish, to be dealt with when the poor law commission came up with some positive proposals. He must have been further encouraged in this policy by the fact that the trend of unemployment as revealed by official figures was downward. The official figures as we have seen were extremely unreliable, but they would have convinced John Burns for whom statistics held a fatal fascination that turned many of his parliamentary speeches into arithmetical monologues.

But in thus deciding on a policy of drift Burns antagonised the Labour Party which, having won twenty-nine seats in 1906, was naturally anxious to make an impact.[2] When Burns told Will Thorne in March that no day had yet been fixed for the introduction of the promised amending bill, the response was a protest meeting in London, sponsored by the S.D.F. inspired Central Workers' Committee and addressed by Labour M.P.s. In May Campbell-Bannerman refused to see a deputation from the National Right to Work Council, which stimulated yet another demonstration, this time in Hyde Park and again addressed by several of the Labour members. Their protest was boosted by the growing conviction of those immediately responsible for the administration of the 1905 Act that it was virtually unworkable.

1 Burns Diary, 18 April 1906. B.L. Add. MSS 46324.
2 The story of Labour's unemployment policy in this period is told in Kenneth D. Brown, *Labour and Unemployment, 1900-1914* (Newton Abbot, 1971).

The Association of Municipal Corporations passed a resolution to this effect at its annual conference, while the Glasgow Distress Committee had damned it as useless after only a few weeks. In London criticism centred on the fact that the Central (Unemployed) Body was too slow in providing work for the applicants recommended to it by the various local distress committees. All of this, of course, served to undermine Burns's contention that the act should be given an extended trial before any revision should take place, and in May the Labour Party, tired of his continual procrastination, launched a vigorous parliamentary onslaught. This was sustained during the Whitsun adjournment debate and Campbell-Bannerman was presented with a memorandum demanding a clear statement of the government's intentions. But Labour pressure was almost bound to be counter-productive as far as Burns was concerned, for he had no intention of allowing himself to be coerced by a party for which he had no time. After one torrid day in the Commons with Hardie on the unemployment issue he concluded that 'K.H. is intoxicated with sense of newly acquired power and had to be reminded of the fact that he was not the Government time keeper'.[1] Nor was it coincidence that at this time Burns took the opportunity afforded by a banquet at the National Liberal Club — he had been made an honorary member in March — to hit back at the Labour Party along his favourite theme of its narrowness. Campbell-Bannerman's private parliamentary secretary, Ponsonby, noted in his diary that Burns

> has been difficult about 'unemployed'. His views are genuine and well thought out but he is wanting in judgement and tact and will persist in a desire to run rough shod over his opponents in the Labour Party .... his unsympathetic tone will aggravate them more and more. He is frightened of being supposed to 'give in' to them and any anti-labour inclination is very much approved of by the Asquith-Haldane group.[2]

So strongly did Burns feel on this issue that he even considered resignation, as the following, oddly punctuated, diary entry indicates.

> I do not like the Unemployed Bill to amend it is to extend the virtues of pauperised dependency and to inflict I am afraid a serious blow on the morale of the labourers. . .presumably I am for resignation.[3]

But it is doubtful if this was a serious possibility. Burns was enjoying being a minister too much to give it up so quickly, for his every word and action was seized upon by the press and he would not lightly sacrifice his place in the public eye. In any case, rightly or wrongly, he

1 Burns Diary, 10 April 1906. B.L. Add. MSS 46324.

2 Ponsonby Diary, 5 August 1906. Bodleian Library. Ponsonby Papers. MS Eng. hist. c 653, f. 13.

3 Burns Diary, 12 May 1906. B.L. Add. MSS 46324.

believed that in some mysterious way, he had been 'called' to government to work for the good — as he understood it — of the working classes.

But pressure for some more positive approach to the unemployment issue was also building up within the Liberal Party itself. The memorandum which the Labour Party had given to Campbell-Bannerman had been signed by at least sixty-five Liberal back benchers as well, indicative of the degree of discontent that Burns had engendered. Cabinet colleagues were also becoming uneasy. As early as March there had been press rumours of ministerial splits about unemployment and there was an air of desperation in Ripon's letter to Buxton:

> It would be most foolish and even dangerous for the Government not to make provision before Parliament is prorogued for a possible want of employment next winter. I care little how it is done, but done it must be or we shall run a very serious risk.[1]

Faced with added pressure from his own party Burns or his officials — it is not clear whose the initiative was — finally hit on the idea of an exchequer grant to finance the 1905 Act, pending the report of the poor law commission which was generally expected for the autumn of 1908. The idea was very attractive to Burns. Voluntary subscriptions as a means of providing finance had clearly failed but to sanction rate support for wages would be to give aid that could not be controlled. A grant from the exchequer on the other hand, disimbursed by the L.G.B., had the great advantage that it could be directed, reduced, or even stopped at will, in order to prevent excessive expenditure on unworthy projects and individuals. This was the scheme which Burns presented to the cabinet and to the Commons in July. He showed little sign of the pressure he had been under and the negative considerations which had shaped his present policy were very evident in his speech. As the causes of unemployment were multifarious so, he asserted,

> the remedy must be multiform — moral, mental, economic, industrial, municipal, political, and social. If the remedies only created artificial work, that would be bad and mischievous. If the works were state-aided, charity-fed, tax-funded, or rate subsidised they would only be a form of public benevolence. . .in the wrong way to wasteful ends with demoralising results. New works unproductive and unremunerative, fed by rates and taxes, was (sic) about the worst form of relief that could be imagined.[2]

1 Lord Ripon to S. Buxton, 28 May 1906. Buxton Papers. C/o Mrs J. Clay. Uncatalogued. Buxton himself had said as early as November 1905 that some form of public funding would be necessary to work the act effectively. See his letter to C. Buxton, 7 November 1905. Ibid.

2 Hansard, 4th Series, CLXI, 426. 19 July 1906.

He then announced that the Exchequer was to provide a sum of not more than £200,000 which would be granted to distress committees at the discretion of the L.G.B. to finance suitable relief works. Combined with rate monies already available and voluntary subscriptions this would, Burns reckoned, make some £3-400,000 available to work the act. Forthcoming legislation on the army, crofters, and small holdings would also increase the supply of work. Campbell-Bannerman was not over-impressed with his colleague's performance; he confided to Ponsonby that Burns's speech had been 'too rich' and too self-satisfied.[1] Burns certainly did feel well pleased, and at the end of the session went off – as usual, alone – to Europe, to investigate at first-hand the workings of continental labour colonies.

He returned in good time before the special autumn session of parliament to supervise the family's removal to a new house in Lavender Gardens, a move that was effected in a blaze of publicity, for few other cabinet ministers moved their own belongings or lived in houses rented ror £26 per year! Although parliamentary sessions usually ended for the year in August, the government had decided to reconvene in order to press on with some outstanding legislation, notably the Education Bill which had had a very stormy passage. Nothing that occured in the session changed Burns's view that he personally had done quite well. In October the report of the Poplar inquiry was published and although Davy's highly critical verdict on the Poplar guardians hardly seemed justified by the evidence he had been able to produce, Burns's antipathy towards George Lansbury received fresh impetus. So, too, did his suspicions about farm colonies, for Davy had had little good to say about the Laindon colony or about Poplar's country workhouse at Forest Gate. This merely served to confirm the conclusions he had drawn from his recent continental visit and from his continued tours of unemployment relief schemes in the south, '170 men doing the work that 60 could do', he noted at Tonbridge, 'Lansbury killing it everywhere'.[2] In December Burns's measures dealing with burials and the removal of offensive matter in London went through, much to his delight. Satisfaction oozed from his pen. On Christmas Day, after playing with Edgar in the park, he returned home for the customary festive dinner 'as happy as our year's work for the common people entitled us to be'.[3]

But Ponsonby had expressed the view that Burns had lost ground in the House of Commons by his position as a minister, mainly because of

1 Ponsonby Diary, 5 August 1905. Bodleian Library. Ponsonby Papers. MS. Eng. hist. c 653, f. 15.
2 Burns Diary, 9 October 1906. B.L. Add. MSS 46324.
3 Ibid. 25 December 1906.

his conceit and his animosity towards the Labour Party.[1] While a case can be made for his policies on unemployment and Poplar his actual handling of these issues had been tactless and extremely clumsy and had damaged his reputation. His delight in his few legislative successes betrays a very distorted sense of priorities, for his bills had been minor in the extreme. The Burials Bill was short and designed merely to remove an ambiguity in a previous measure exposed by a legal decision in 1905. The Alkali Bill went through with virtually no debate, for it did nothing more than consolidate earlier acts of 1881 and 1892. Similarly, the Removal of Offensive Matter Bill warranted little comment except on the second reading when Claude Hay described this attempt to unify the sanitary authorities responsible for the removal of offensive matter in London as 'a tinkering measure. . .meddling'.[2] The important matters, however, had made no progress at all. Fears were growing among Liberal land reformers that Burns was going to botch the issue of site taxation and in December the Land Values group presented a massively supported memorandum urging prompt action, a manoeuvre described by one of their leaders, J.C. Wedgwood, as 'a thunderbolt for John Burns'.[3] Another leading land reformer, C.P. Trevelyan, was not very sanguine about their prospects of success, however, suggesting that 'Burns showed that he is against us. . .Burns never could carry a bill if his spirit is as hostile as it apparently appears to be; he is simply a Tory on the question'.[4] The Public Health Bill to extend controls over the quality of food had been withdrawn, a victim of the growing log-jam of legislative proposals. The Equalisation of Rates (London) Act Amendment Bill never emerged from the recesses of the Local Government Board despite repeated assurances from Burns that it was almost ready.

In a way this was all very understandable. Burns was new to office and still feeling his way. Indeed, Mrs Webb had the impression that at the outset he had been 'hopelessly confused and blurred in his intentions'.[5] When questioned in parliament he had been generally very cautious about his future legislative plans. He was undoubtedly cramped by the fact that royal commissions were currently examining several subjects for which his department was responsible — the poor

1 Ponsonby Diary, 5 August 1906. Bodleian Library. Ponsonby Papers. MS. Eng. hist. c 653. f. 15.

2 Hansard, 4th series, CLXVI, 1466. 27 December 1906.

3 J.C. Wedgwood to his wife, 27 November 1906. Wedgwood Papers. C/o Mrs Helen Bowen Pease. I am indebted to Dr R. Douglas of the University of Surrey for this reference.

4 C.P. Trevelyan to Molly, 18 December 1906. Newcastle University Library. C.P. Trevelyan Papers, 87.

5 Webb, *Partnership*, 325.

law, tuberculosis in animals, sewage disposal, and motor cars. In other spheres, lack of adequate statistical information held up the analysis of problems and their legislative solutions. The committee appointed to investigate the staffing of the Local Government Board in 1897 had commented on this statistical deficiency, but little had been done and Davy could still lament in 1907 about the 'deplorable state of the *Gazette* and the statistics'.[1] One important outcome of this was the board's difficulty in coping with unemployment, for it had neither the resources nor the expertise to tackle the problem as anything other than an aspect of the poor law. Burns himself suggested that the Board of Trade, which had a highly competent statistical section, was the proper department to undertake the attack on unemployment and this cannot be dismissed merely as an attempt to cover up his own inadequacies.[2] Another result of the L.G.B.'s statistical deficiency, and one about which Burns himself felt more deeply, was its inability to do very much about reducing child mortality. Small wonder then, that few Local Government Board measures of any weight had appeared, still less reached the statute book, by the end of 1906. Yet Burns cannot be exonerated entirely. For one thing, he spent far too much time on trivial matters of administrative detail and on personal fieldwork. In the process he lost sight of the president's real role of providing the department with a general strategy. Further, it is evident that he had a penchant for administration and found the whole legislative process tedious. He had frequently stressed in public speeches that he could achieve most of his objectives by means of administration rather than legislation and in the past his own legislative efforts had not been very remarkable. It had taken him years of hard work to get the L.C.C.'s Steam Boats Bill through the house. The Trades Disputes Bill, the Eight Hours Bill, and Housing Bills had all failed repeatedly, and he had found the whole effort of fighting over measures clause by clause, of whipping in supporters, and reaching compromises, both time consuming and tiring.

By the beginning of 1907 the Liberal programme was running into some difficulty. The Education Bill had come back from the House of Lords so mutilated by amendments that it was eventually decided to abandon it. This raised the whole question of the relationships between the two houses, for the Unionist-dominated Lords showed every inclination to reject the Liberals' main legislative offerings. Faced with this some members of the cabinet had opted for a policy of accommoda-

1 J.S. Davy to W. Runciman, 30 January 1907. Quoted in Davidson, 'Llewellyn Smith, the Labour Department', 255.

2 Hansard, 5th Series, II, 464-6. 10 March 1909.

tion, arguing that the amended Education Bill should be accepted. Burns was not one of them. He argued consistently for its abandonment on the grounds that acceptance would create a very undesirable precedent for all future government bills. Never one to shirk a political challenge, he wished to take up the gauntlet thrown down by the peers and move quickly to emasculate their powers. Every election address Burns had ever issued had stressed his desire to do away with hereditary authority, a sentiment which had caused the king no little concern at the time of the 1906 election. Burns, however, had survived both this and an attempt by a notorious anti-socialist, George Brooks, to discredit him with the monarch. In fact he enjoyed an extremely amiable relationship with Edward VII and was one of his favourite ministers. But this in no way affected his attitude to the legislative powers of the House of Lords. When the cabinet got down to discussing possible courses of action Burns was in no doubt; 'Cut down their power. . . don't clip their wings, prevent them clipping ours'.[1] He wanted the peers' veto of Commons' measures to be restricted to one session only, after which re-introduced bills would be carried automatically.[2] The problems with the Lords might have been more easily resolved had the cabinet been united, but it was split over this and a number of other issues. Mrs Webb had the impression from ministers and leading civil servants alike that 'the cabinet is an incoherent body — intensely individualistic — each man for himself — C.B. presiding merely — R.B.H. asserted that, as with the Government, so with the public — there was no common opinion about anything'.[3] Furthermore, even without the obstacles presented by the House of Lords the sheer size of the Liberal commitment created a major difficulty. The party whips believed that two or three sessions would be needed to deal with the enormous volume of legislation that had been promised.

Burns's own plans for the 1907 session included measures to deal with London's drains, valuation, milk depots, public health, and he told the Commons that he intended as well to introduce bills on vaccination and working class housing. Already somewhat depressed by the L.C.C. elections which despite his own intensive campaigning for the Progressives had for the first time given the Municipal Reformers control of the council, he was further dismayed to discover, when he turned his attention fully back to departmental work, that little progress had been made with anything. On 14 March he summoned Provis to his office and urged on him 'the need for quick and'

1 Burns Diary, 1 February 1907. B.L. Add. MSS 46325.
2 Ibid. 23 March 1907. Add. MSS 46308.
3 B. Webb Diary, 3 May 1907. B.L.P.E.S. Passfield Papers, I, vol. 26.

prompt action in all L.G.B. matters'.[1] Next day he had another long discussion with Provis on the same subject, 'delays in official work, bills, orders and decisions', but privately he does not seem to have been very sanguine about the prospects for improvement, asking in his diary 'will it do any good?'[2] A night's sleep made no difference. He was 'weary of the detailed work and the slowness of officials in responding to energetic example'.[3] So little resulted from his pressure on Provis to get on with the Milk Bill that it was probably in frustration that he personally contacted George Newman, medical officer at the Board of Education, asking for the essential facts about milk depots.[4] It was also at this time that he began work with Provis and Kershaw on the details of the Housing Bill. But here, too, his cajolings evidently had little effect. So little progress was made with the Housing Bill that in the early summer the cabinet decided that it should be brought in as a main measure the following year. The Milk Bill hung around in Adrian's office and was then so badly drafted that it had to be withdrawn. There was more than a hint of truth in Emmott's observation that while Burns was useful in cabinet discussion he 'flunks his bills'.[5] Strictly speaking of course these failings were Burns's own fault, as a more forceful president might have galvanised his staff into greater effort. Yet it is difficult to avoid a certain sympathy for him. After a cabinet meeting in April he came out feeling thoroughly depressed. 'Sixteen months wrestling with fossils inside and fools and firebrands outside'.[6]

The latter reference was undoubtedly to the members of the parliamentary Labour Party who had renewed their pressure on the unemployment front. They affected to believe that the exchequer grant had been a mere stop gap pending legislation in 1907, although Burns had made it quite clear that any legislation would depend on the findings of the poor law commission, which still had not reported. In the absence of government action the Joint Board, representing the Labour Party, the T.U.C., and the G.F.T.U., began drawing up its own bill, in the meantime taking every opportunity to hammer Burns in the House of Commons. The Labour M.P.s were especially critical that by March 1907 well over half the grant remained unspent. This Burns had achieved in a number of rather devious ways. For one thing, on the

1 Burns Diary, 14 March 1907. B.L. Add. MSS 46325.

2 Ibid. 15 March 1907.

3 Ibid. 16 March 1907.

4 J. Burns to G. Newman, 2 April 1907. Wellcome History of Medicine Library. Newman Papers.

5 Emmott Diary, 23 April 1907. Nuffield College. Emmott Papers, I.

6 Burns Diary, 19 April 1907. B.L. Add. MSS 46325.

basis of information available to him he had circularised a large number of distress committees in October 1906 telling them that they could expect no help from the exchequer grant. Those that objected had their cases reconsidered, but it is evident that very few thought it worthwhile to protest. Again, in announcing the grant Burns had stated that the only condition for its use would be the degree of distress in the locality making application for it but it seems that in practice he had insisted on the locality making some contribution to its own problem before he would sanction any central aid. This accusation was first made in a *Labour Leader* editorial and was taken up by Hardie in an Easter adjournment debate when he cited Burn's refusal to make a grant to the Newport Distress Committee.[1] As Hardie quite reasonably pointed out, the knowledge that the government had set aside a sum for unemployment relief would almost inevitably lead to a drying up of local voluntary sources of help. Nor had Burns allowed any of the grant to go towards assisting schemes of the sort which he personally regarded as fruitless. He refused grants for women's workrooms set up in London by the Central (Unemployed) Body and personally vetoed a request (already accepted by one of his own inspectors) from the Glasgow Distress Committee to buy land for a labour colony.

All of this provoked immense anger on the Labour benches, but Burns remained obdurate. He preferred to interpret the rage as being personally motivated against himself and his steadfast adherence to principle. After yet another of his seemingly interminable clashes with Hardie, he observed that it was 'a pitiful sight to see this vain wild dervish preaching his Jehad of hate'.[2] Burns tried to defend his cautious allocation of the exchequer grant by arguing, logically enough, that to use it all up too quickly would be unwise in case the winter was unexpectedly prolonged. Yet he could not see that this was a criticism of the whole idea of treating unemployment through the medium of a fixed finite sum. Clearly, he would have been on much stronger ground had he had any concrete proposals of his own to offer, but he had very little. In March he convened a conference of large employers of labour to discuss the problems of casual workers but nothing practical resulted. There is some evidence that he was keeping a watchful eye on the labour exchanges set up in London under the provisions of the 1905 Act. At least he interviewed the manager of the Battersea exchange and went to see it at work. But he was not very impressed. W.H. Beveridge, the main exponent of exchanges who kept Burns well supplied with information, was regarded as being as foolish as

1 *Labour Leader,* 1 March 1907.
2 Burns Diary, 27 March 1907. B.L. Add. MSS 46325.

Lansbury.[1] Briefly, too, Burns toyed with afforestation. He had been impressed by a scheme in Leeds which he had visited in the autumn of 1906, and had asked other bodies to keep him informed of their own similar experiments. In March 1907 he announced that he would make grants to any distress committee applying immediately for help in undertaking such projects. Yet his sympathy for this sort of scheme sprang from his belief that afforestation, unlike most other relief works, was useful and not simply work for its own sake. Accordingly he stressed to a deputation on the subject that all submissions must be practical and economic. As a solution for unemployment, however, it could never be anything other than peripheral. Afforestation required suitable land, time to prepare, men able to learn the necessary skills, and suitably qualified instructors.

The poverty of Burn's unemployment policy was thrown into greater relief when in July the Labour Party produced its own solution in the form of the Right to Work Bill. Its basic premise was that local unemployment authorities should have a statutory obligation to provide work or maintenance for all unemployed registered in their area. This was absolute anathema to both Burns and his officials, for it made no attempt to discriminate between organised labour, the deserving poor and wastrels, a cardinal distinction in Burn's opinion. Contemptuously he dismissed the measure, therefore, as the 'right to shirk' bill and a prescription for universal pauperism.[2] A good number of his colleagues, however, were not prepared to be so dogmatic. True, there were few who actually supported the idea of a right to work, but they were alarmed by the electoral repercussions of Burn's sterility. In July, Victor Grayson, standing as an independent socialist, won the Colne Valley by-election largely, it was claimed, because of his advocacy of the Labour Party's Unemployment Bill. There was a note of urgency in Buxton's comment to Ripon that he had been able to get nothing in the way of policies from Burns, only a bland assurance that

> 'it is all going very well' which it is not (he will lose us all our seats in London if he's not careful) ... It is important for us in our autumn speeches and before cabinet begin again to be able to say the Government intends to deal with the matter by *Bill* in view of the expiring of the Act next year ... I also want Burns to get pinned to something.[3]

But, other than a renewal of the exchequer grant for a further year,

1 W.H. Beveridge, 'The Birth of Labour Exchanges', *Minlabour* 14 (1960), 2-3.

2 Burns Diary, 9 July 1907. B.L. Add. MSS 46325.

3 S. Buxton to Lord Ripon, 19 August 1907. Ripon Papers. B.L. Add. MSS 43555, ff. 166-7.

Burns produced nothing, prompting Mrs Webb's conclusion that he had become

> a monstrosity ... an enormous personal vanity feeding on the
> deference and flattery yielded to patronage and power. He talks
> incessantly, and never listens to anyone except the officials to
> whom he *must* listen in order to accomplish the routine work of
> of his office. Hence he is completely in their hands and is becoming
> the most hidebound of departmental chiefs.[1]

For all this, in September Burns went to Germany and made a point of examining at first hand the working of the labour bureaux system there. He returned with his prejudices confirmed, seeing in the great collection of unemployed at the Berlin exchange a fruitful source for unscrupulous employers of blackleg labour.

On other minor fronts, however, rather more progress was made in 1907. The Public Health Bill, withdrawn in 1906, passed through parliament despite opposition from those who thought it too radical in conferring on the L.G.B. powers of control over all food but drugs and all drinks except water. Once more, though, there is clear evidence of Burn's impatience with the niceties of parliamentary struggle. 'Busy all day', he wrote after one lengthy debate on the bill, 'and all the while good causes are delayed. Very sick of it all today'.[2] At about the same time, royal assent was given to the Vaccination Bill. Although this was only a modest measure simplifying and cheapening the procedures for getting exemptions from vaccination, it too encountered opposition, for compulsory vaccination was still an emotive issue. Once more Burns found it difficult to reconcile his own views with those of his opponents and his technical experts. After a parliamentary discussion on the bill in May he referred to his dislike of the 'restraints that office imposes upon me. Every word and act is weighed at its real value and the quality of caution is construed as fear but it must be done'.[3] What he wished to do was to transfer the administration of the Vaccination Act to public health authorities but he felt unable to do this because 'everyone sees that the Poor Law system is in the melting pot. The Poor Law Commission is now sitting and until that Commission has reported I cannot carry out what I would like to do ...'[4] He did derive some comfort, however, from the thanks of J.W. Wilson who, on behalf of a number of Liberal and Labour members, had introduced a second Public Health Bill in 1907. It was designed to codify the many clauses which had been passed in various private members' bills relating to items such as street

1 B. Webb Diary, 30 October 1907. B.L.P.E.S. Passfield Papers, I, vol. 26.
2 Burns Diary, 15 July 1907. B.L. Add. MSS 46325.
3 Ibid. 24 May 1907.
4 Hansard, 4th series, CLXXIV, 1276. 24 May 1907.

lighting, buildings, sanitation, milk supply, lodging houses, slaughter-houses, and to permit the Local Government Board to extend its regulative powers over such matters to rural areas. It was extremely long and complex, containing 142 clauses. In standing committee Burns, ably supported by his officers, did most of the work in tidying the bill up, in the process adding fifty-three new clauses. Wilson wrote gratefully to Campbell-Bannerman, emphasising that the bill's passage had been 'greatly facilitated by the thorough way in which Mr. Burns (and the L.G.B. staff) had revised the clauses.'[1]

On the whole, however, it remained true that at the beginning of 1908, as A.G. Gardiner pointed out, Burns's claims to be a legislator on a grand scale still remained to be proved.[2] All the measures so far dealt with were extremely trivial and the frustrations which they had caused Burns did not augur well for the future programme of the L.G.B. Departmental work was continuing on the Housing and Valuation Bills but the latter was running into problems. It was a very complex issue and the Lords had further confused things by throwing out a modest measure relating to Scotland.[3] Campbell-Bannerman was so anxious for progress that at the beginning of the year he had appointed T.J. Macnamara to the Local Government Board as its parliamentary secretary. Macnamara had already co-operated with Burns in the intro-duction of a private members' Housing Bill in 1901 but Campbell-Bannerman's main reason for sending him to the L.G.B. was that he was excellently qualified to deal with the matter of land valuation. Having himself been involved in the introduction of Valuation Bills between 1902 and 1904 he was an expert in local rating. In cabinet discussion, however, Burns had insisted that the bill would have to wait until measures had been taken to arrange the actual machinery of valuation. This was described by Ponsonby as 'quite unreasonable' and he ascribed it to the fact that Burns had been ever-influenced by his officials.[4] But Macnamara, too, had taken a similar line and it seems that on this issue Burns had preferred to do as his subordinates advised him, for he possessed neither the intellectual equipment nor the patience to cope with such a tangle as the existing rating system.[5] 'The point you make as to the basis of valuation' he told Crewe, 'is a difficult one but it is I

1 J.W. Wilson to H. Campbell-Bannerman, 1 July 1907. Campbell-Bannerman Papers. B.L. Add. MSS 41240, f.1.

2 Gardiner, *Prophets, Priests and Kings*, 175.

3 See generally J. Brown, 'Scottish and English Land Legislation, 1905-1911', *Scottish Historical Review* 47 (1968), 72-85.

4 Ponsonby Diary, January 1907. Ponsonby Papers. Bodleian Library. MS Eng. hist. c 653, f. 22-3.

5 T.J. Macnamara to C.P. Trevelyan, n.d. Newcastle University Library. C.P. Trevelyan Papers, 17.

am afraid only one of the many difficulties which beset this much talked about and little understood subject'.[1] Although he told the prime minister at Christmas 1907 that the Valuation Bill was making steady progress, Pease, deriving his information from Macnamara, told Asquith that it had made no progress at all.[2]

The other matter still being mooted was the Milk Supply Bill. Burns had been frustrated in his efforts to get a satisfactory bill prepared and at the end of 1907 he replaced Power, his retiring medical officer, with Arthur Newsholme who had sponsored a very successful programme of tuberculosis control and prevention in Brighton. Almost the first task Burns gave his new official was to prepare a memorandum on the question of a safe milk supply with particular reference to the tuberculosis danger. Mrs Webb claimed later that it was she who, with some backing from George Newman and Robert Morant, pursuaded Burns to appoint Newsholme. Yet this is strange, for Burns was increasingly distrustful of the Webbs' machinations, and it is unlikely that he would have taken much notice of Morant who believed, rightly or wrongly, that Burns hated him.[3] And if, as Mrs Webb alleged, Burns was in the hands of his departmental officials, why should he involve himself in a row with them merely to act upon her suggestion? Burns went through what he described as 'a long and dogged fight against the Departmental view that an inside man should be appointed ... saw Parsons, dealt with him as with P(rovis) and insisted upon outsider as best fit for the Department. The interests of the public must override Departmentalism everyone must adapt themselves to this or go'.[4] It seems more likely that, irrespective of Mrs Webbs' encouragement, Burns, who had met Newsholme before and been impressed by him, saw him as a capable and active man capable of dealing not only with the milk matter but also of galvanising his sluggish department.

The year of 1908, therefore, promised to be make or break year for Burns. He had made enemies, but had pushed through some useful if minor legislation, and had become a byword for economy in administration. He himself was hopeful that the poor law and unemployment issues would finally be open to attack in the light of the poor law commission report which was expected in the autumn of 1908. It was as well that he was essentially an earthy character. Had he not been, he

1 J. Burns to Lord Crewe, 4 June 1908. Cambridge University Library. Crewe Papers, MSS C/3.

2 J.A. Pease to H.H. Asquith, 15 December 1907. Nuffield College. Gainford MSS, 85.

3 R. Morant to B. Webb, 1 May 1907. B.L.P.E.S. Passfield Papers, II, 4c, f. 237.

4 Burns Diary, 11 January 1908. B.L. Add. MSS 46326.

might have been disturbed by the horoscope cast for him by one Sepharial. It suggested that 1908 would be the year in which his star began to wane. In retrospect he may well have wished that he had taken more notice.

7

ACHIEVEMENT AND SETBACK, 1908-1910

The year began badly for Burns when the Labour Party moved an amendment to the King's Speech that regretted the absence of any reference to the unemployment problem. Exasperated by his refusal to promise anything more than a renewal of the exchequer grant pending the report of the royal commission, seventy Liberals backed the Labour action. But Burns stuck doggedly to his guns in a cabinet memorandum occasioned by the second reading of the Right to Work bill. Privately he had already damned it as a 'Bedlam bill establishing the right to shirk'.[1] Now he claimed that if the measure became law no-one would have any incentive to look for work, and casual labourers would only take well-paid jobs. He expressed doubt about the ability of the proposed unemployment committees to find suitable work simultaneously for thousands of housemaids, clerks, and labourers. There was no reason, he concluded complacently, to change the existing policy of waiting for the poor law report.[2] Some of his colleagues were not so sure, however. Lloyd George was one who wanted to let the measure through.[3] Asquith, who chaired the discussion in the absence of the ailing Campbell-Bannerman, told the King that while the right to work principle was 'obviously inadmissible', something really needed to be done for the sake of appearances, a view shared by Burns's own parliamentary secretary, Macnamara. Sidney Buxton confided to Lord Ripon that if the government opposed the bill then it should be able to put up some practical alternative. Ripon, on the other hand, did not believe that public opinion was ready for such a radical measure as the Right to Work Bill and refused to lend it his support.[4] Neither was the party rank-and-file any less divided. At one extreme were radicals like Masterman who had consistently demanded government action and who had voted for the Labour amendment on the Royal speech: on the other were those like the member for Preston, Harold Cox, who believed that the whole tenor of Liberal legislation was increasingly socialist and who had no time for Labour remedies for unemploy-

---

1 Burns Diary, 9 March 1908. B.L. Add. MSS 46326

2 PRO CAB 37/91. *The Unemployed Workmen Bill.* 9 March 1908.

3 Burns Diary, 11 March 1908. B.L. Add. MSS 46326

4 For Macnamara's view see ibid. 14 February 1908. For Asquith see his letter to the King, 11 March 1908. Bodleian Library. Asquith Papers, 5, f. 14. For Buxton see his letter to Ripon, 4 March 1908. Ripon Papers. B.L. Add. MSS 43555, f. 273. Ripon's view is contained in his reply to Buxton, 6 March 1908. Ibid. f.276.

ment.[1] The bulk of the party seems to have felt very much as Asquith did but it is clear that the existence of these divisions strengthened Burns's hand on what he personally saw as 'the real and vital issues of my official career. . .I don't like what appears likely to terminate my office. Better that than devitalising the proud spirit of the workmen'.[2]

Despite the considerable interest generated by the Labour Party's well organised publicity campaign the House of Commons was little more than half full when a radical, P.W. Wilson, rose to move the second reading on 13 March. It seems that a good number of Liberals had decided to evade the issue by non-attendance, for not all the absentees were paired. The rejection of the bill was entrusted to two 'Lib-Lab' members, Henry Vivian and Fred Maddison, both of whom succeeded in thoroughly antagonising even the most moderate Labour men. Neither was the mood on the Labour benches improved when Burns delivered his own speech. For one thing it was larded with self-pity. 'I have been the Derby dog', Burns told the house sorrowfully, 'running down the Parliamentary course, hon. members throwing sticks and stones at me all the time'.[3] Still worse it was packed with gratuitous insults, most of them directed against the Labour Party, and was redolent with self congratulation. It was left to Asquith to try and salvage something for the government which he attempted in a highly placatory speech, although it was not enough to prevent 116 members voting for the bill.

Shortly after this debate Campbell-Bannerman, finally shattered by the recent death of his wife, gave up his struggle against failing health and resigned. Less than two weeks after his resignation he, too, was dead. Asquith, the long-standing heir apparent, now assumed the premiership, but in the ensuing ministerial reshuffle Burns was retained at the Local Government Board — or as Vaughan Nash rather disparagingly put it, 'J.B. hasn't been got rid of'.[4] This was a decision which surprised many and openly disgusted leading radical editors like Scott and Massingham, particularly as the general effect of Asquith's changes was to give the cabinet a more radical bent. Yet despite the abundance of junior talent pushing its way to the front of the party Asquith does not seem to have tried very hard to find a replacement for Burns. Apparently the only man whom he considered as a possible alternative was Winston Churchill who rejected the idea:

1 H. Cox, 'The Right to Work', *Quarterly Review* 202 (1908), 203.
2 Burns Diary, 16 February 1908. B.L. Add. MSS 46326.
3 Hansard, 4th series, CLXXXVI, 66. 13 March 1908.
4 Quoted in J. Wilson, *A Life of Sir Henry Campbell-Bannerman* (1973), 629.

Five or six first-class questions await immediate attention – housing, unemployment, rating reform, electoral reform, old age pensions. Administration I presume, to say nothing of minor measures and exacting day to day administration. On all of them I shall be confronted by hundreds of earnest men who have thought of nothing else all their lives, who know these subjects. . .from experience learned in hard schools.[1]

Perhaps this assessment of the difficulties involved in running the Local Government Board explains why Asquith could not find a replacement for Burns and was content to inject some radicalism into the department in the shape of a new parliamentary secretary, C.F.G. Masterman. This was certainly an appointment which neither Burns nor Masterman relished. Burns apparently tried to prevent it, though assuring his chief that if his mind was made up he would 'receive in a friendly spirit any man you consider desirable to send here'.[2] For his part Masterman, who had been a vociferous critic of the Local Government Board, appears to have regarded the job as akin to swimming in glue and at least one leading Liberal concluded that he only took it on out of a sense of moral obligation.[3] Before accepting finally, though, he secured assurances from Asquith that he would be given some specific area of board work to deal with, that the Housing and Valuation Bills would be introduced in the present session, and that there would be some major internal restructuring of the department under a new and more radical permanent secretary when Provis who was near retiring age, finally left.[4]

Yet it is probably wrong to view the retention of Burns in such wholly negative terms, for there was no shortage of talent available to Asquith and cabinet rank was cabinet rank, however, difficult and unglamorous the position involved. Furthermore, there were good prospects that the President's status and salary would soon be raised. Had Asquith really wanted to remove Burns, he would have done so, but there were some positive reasons for retaining him. There was first of all the general consideration that ministerial changes needed to be minimised in order to avoid too much disruption in the middle of the government's term of office. Secondly, Burns had not done as badly in all his departmental work as he had in unemployment and the pro-

1 W.S. Churchill to H.H. Asquith, 14 March 1908. Bodleian Library. Asquith Papers, 11, f. 13. Violet Bonham Carter, *Winston Churchill as I Knew Him* (1965), 153-5, asserted that Churchill actually asked for the Local Government Board. In a letter to the press dated 1 April 1965, she subsequently withdrew this suggestion.

2 J. Burns to H.H. Asquith, 13 April 1908. Bodleian Library. Asquith Papers, 11, f. 89.

3 Emmott Diary, 28 April 1908. Nuffield College. Emmott Papers, I.

4 C.F.G. Masterman to H.H. Asquith, 13 April 1908. Bodleian Library. Asquith Papers, 11, ff. 95-6.

spects for major legislation on milk, housing, and valuation were promising, as far as Asquith knew. Indeed on 12 May Asquith gave the House a definite promise that the Valuation Bill would be introduced by the Local Government Board. Churchill's eventual appointment to the Board of Trade, where he could work on long term proposals for tackling unemployment through labour exchanges and insurance, relieved the government of some of the embarrassment that Burns had caused it on this score and yet allowed him to continue with his administration of the poor law where in Asquith's own words there remained 'useful gardening' to be done.[1] And Burns could be relied upon to do this gardening in the most economical manner, a not unimportant consideration for a new Liberal prime minister. Indeed, Asquith had had personal experience of Burns's parsimony when the two men had co-operated in the drawing up of the old age pension scheme in 1907. Burns had worked assiduously in the cabinet committee charged with this task, helping to design the administrative machinery but also supporting an abortive proposal, emanating from the Chaplin Committee of 1900, to exclude all who had received poor law relief in the past twenty years. Again, personal factors may have entered into Asquith's calculations. As Home Secretary under Rosebery, Asquith had been ultimately responsible for troops firing on striking miners at Featherstone in 1893 and even now his public speeches were sometimes punctuated with shouts of 'Featherstone' or 'murderer'. Clearly it would have been impolitic to add to this unfortunate reputation by dropping from the cabinet its one authentic labour member, especially as he was also in the view of some of his colleagues, its best known member.[2] W.H. Beveridge certainly attributed the retention of Burns to the fact that because he dropped his aitches he appeared to be the genuine voice of the working classes.[3] Putting Burns out altogether might also have been seen by the Little Englanders as a hostile gesture by a prime minister of known imperialist sympathies; in this context it is perhaps significant that just before Asquith became prime minister the cabinet's radicals, including Burns, had combined in a threat to bring down the government if the naval estimates were again increased. Further, Burns has a long standing admiration for Asquith dating back to his passing of the Factory Act in 1895.[4] He would be a loyal follower and prime ministers even then

1 H.H. Asquith to J. Burns, 16 April 1908. Burns Papers. B.L. Add. MSS 46282, ff. 48-9.
2 A conclusion reached by Birrell, Grey and Masterman at a dinner held in March 1909. L. Masterman, *C.F.G. Masterman* (1939), 127.
3 W.H. Beveridge, *Power and Influence: An Autobiography* (1953), 92.
4 See his comments in Hansard, 4th series, XXXV, 163. 4 July 1895.

had to construct their cabinets with at least half an eye on their own personal security. All in all it was not surprising that Beatrice Webb commented gloomily that 'they can't be rid of him'.[1] The Clerk of the House of Commons, Sir Courtenay Ilbert took a similar view, suggesting to James Bryce that if Churchill did take the Local Government Board 'J.B. would have to be provided for somewhere'.[2]

Burns himself had mixed feelings about remaining at the Local Government Board. It was indicative of his growing capacity for self-delusion that he believed he deserved promotion and in a moment of depression, deepened perhaps by a bad cold or the black eye accidentally inflicted by his son, he toyed with the idea of resigning. But resignation, though it would confer greater freedom of action would, he felt, be 'less useful for one's aims' and there is here further evidence of Burns's belief that he had a peculiar destiny to fulfil as the people's representative in the cabinet.[3] In any case he revelled in being a cabinet minister and would have found it hard to readjust to the relative obscurity of back bench life.

One of his 'aims' had already assumed tangible, if somewhat amorphous form, in the long awaited Housing and Town Planning Bill which had had a first reading at the end of March. The introduction of this measure sprang from Burns's very real concern with the amenities of ordinary people, well illustrated in his work on the London County Council. In 1901 he and Macnamara had introduced a radical Housing Bill which would have empowered local authorities to levy rates on empty houses and to establish fair rent courts. His interest had waned when the bill had made no progress either then or in 1902 and 1903 when it was reintroduced, and although it had been repeatedly introduced by labour and radical members since, it had got nowhere. But almost as soon as Burns has assumed his ministerial office he had circularised local authorities in rural areas to see what building they had done and had been appalled at the response – five authorities, for instance, had managed to build forty-four houses between them in the space of fifteen years. Accordingly, he had been suitably sympathetic when a bill to amend the Housing of the Working Classes Act was brought before the Commons in 1906. But he had been opposed to the measure's financial arrangements and had agreed to let it go to a select committee and then be used as the basis for a suitable bill later on. The bill which Burns now presented to the House did in fact contain several

1 B. Webb Diary, 15 May 1908. B.L.P.E.S. Passfield Papers, I, 26.
2 C.P. Ilbert to J. Bryce, 26 March 1908. Bodleian Library. Bryce Papers, 13, f. 141.
3 Burns Diary, 19 April 1908. B.L. Add. MSS 46326.

of the ideas from this measure as well as some from his own earlier bills. It aimed to make all urban and rural authorities adopt the provisions of the 1890 Housing of the Working Classes Act relating to the clearing or renewal of housing. To encourage building cheap fixed interest loans were offered over eighty years. The inclusion of the section on town planning also owed a lot to Burns's personal interest in environmental conditions. He had been impressed by the carefully planned towns he had seen in Europe and believed that something on similar lines could be beneficially undertaken in Britain. Public interest in planning had been developing too, and it is perhaps significant that Burns's acquaintance, George Cadbury, was a leading light in the National Housing Reform Council, one of several important pressure groups founded round the turn of the century. In 1906 this body sent a deputation to Burns and Campbell-Bannerman, each of whom responded enthusiastically to its request for the introduction of a planning scheme. The following year, the Association of Municipal Corporations also sent a deputation to Burns for the same purpose and submitted a draft bill. Burns's own bill aimed at securing greater co-ordination in land development by encouraging local authorities and landowners to plan future development in the vicinity of towns. But Adrian, the department's legal adviser, had been totally unable to see the wood for the trees. The measure was thus incredibly complex, full of references to previous bills and with many very technical points. Nor did Burns himself do much to clarify matters. His speech was couched in his worst flowery and alliterative style, figures and metaphors tumbling over each other as he described his plan to secure 'the home healthy, the house beautiful, the town pleasant, the city dignified and the suburb salubrious'.[1] In a rare moment of modesty he later confided to his diary that it had taken him a long time to get into his stride and in fact he spoke for the best part of two hours, spending most of the time on an historical introduction to housing legislation but saying relatively little about the current proposals.[2] The press was suitably scornful; the local paper commented for example, that the bill's production ranked with the building of the Tower of Babel and was thus 'performed with appropriate confusion of speech'.[3] For the opposition Walter Long professed utter bewilderment. 'I can safely say', he complained, 'that never yet have I had to read a Bill that has given me such infinite labour which left me with so appalling a headache, and even after the labour and with the headache, such a minimum of practical information as to what the Bill proposes to do'.[4]

1 Hansard, 4th series, CLXXXVIII, 949. 12 May 1908.
2 Burns Diary, 12 May 1908. B.L. Add. MSS 46326.
3 *South Western Star,* 15 May 1908.
4 Hansard, 4th series, CLXXXVIII, 972. 12 May 1908.

But, these criticisms notwithstanding, the bill was referred to standing committee and it was then that the battle really began. Standing committees always tended to attract to them people vitally interested in the subjects under discussion and Burns now found himself, defending a measure which, as so often with L.G.B. bills, had been incompetently drafted, against enthusiasts, many of whom were disappointed that the town planning section made no provision for municipalities to buy up land on their fringes, nor made town planning a mandatory activity. Sourly, Burns commented that the committee was full of his 'friends' and the 'faddists'.[1] Things were not made any easier either by the fact that Masterman had strongly differing views about housing policy. Burns regarded him as a source of weakness in the committee while Masterman could only watch in dismay as meeting after meeting dissolved into interminable wrangling which reduced progress virtually to a standstill. It took nine days for the committee to get as far as the third clause of the bill. When Asquith sent the King a list of measures which the government intended to complete in an autumn sitting, the Housing and Town Planning Bill was not among them.[2]

As the summer drew on, Burns's attention was increasingly being diverted back to the seemingly intractable problem of the unemployed. Once again events seemed to move too fast for him. The Valuation Bill upon which so much reform depended was ready by the autumn of 1908 but never reached parliament. It was a very cautious measure, designed to unify the national and local valuation systems, but it made no provision for the separate assessment of site values, and it was far too mild for most Liberal land reformers. Thus when a trade recession set in and showed distinct signs of worsening in the autumn Burns's department still had nothing to offer. Even allowing for the distortions produced by prolonged strikes in the shipbuilding and engineering industries, official unemployment figures were running at high levels in what should have been the low season − 7.4 per cent in May, 8.5 per cent in August, 9.3 per cent in September.[3] During the summer the Local Government Board sanctioned some ninety loans to local authorities totalling nearly three quarters of a million pounds, in addition to grants from the exchequer fund. Early in September, a worried President summoned a departmental conference to consider action. In many cities civil unrest was growing as socialists organised the unemployed into hunger marches, and a stream of anxious lord mayors

1 Burns Diary, 14 July 1908. B.L. Add. MSS 46326.

2 H.H. Asquith to the King, 8 July 1908. Bodleian Library. Asquith Papers, 5, f. 43.

3 Board of Trade, Seventeenth Abstract of Labour Statistics [Cd. 7733]. *British Parliamentary Papers,* 61 (1914-16), 322.

followed one another to the Local Government Board. As always, however, the pressure was counter productive as far as Burns was concerned. He was resolved not to give in 'to menace or ignorance' and to go on as before 'giving help without pauperism'.[1]

Although rising unemployment was providing the tariff reformers with valuable ammunition in their campaign against free trade – the Conservatives had already won several Liberal seats in by-elections in 1908 – it was the Labour Party which took up the offensive when parliament re-assembled on 12 October. Although the cabinet had intended this extra session for the completion of the Licensing Bill which had run into difficulties in the House of Lords, it was immediately apparent that unemployment required urgent action. Indeed Churchill, Lloyd George and Reginald McKenna had already been trying to tackle the problem in the engineering and shipbuilding areas quite independently of Burns.[2] On 14 October the cabinet over-rode Burns and established a small sub-committee of seven to work out a programme of short term measures which Asquith could present to the House the following week. Although Burns was naturally enough a member of this committee he could do nothing to prevent his colleagues using the services of Vaughan Nash to consult the Labour Party about acceptable remedies. Churchill, Masterman, and Buxton all responded favourably to Arthur Henderson's suggestion that the exchequer grant should be increased and that rate monies should be used to pay wages to men employed under the provisions of the 1905 Unemployment Act. To Burns this was unthinkable. For years he had argued that the best way to approach the problem was to allow local and national authorities maximum flexibility in arranging their own work schemes. For the rest, as he told Beatrice Webb in May when she had explained to him that they could either revert to the principles of 1834 or create an entirely new national authority to deal with the unemployed, 'I should prefer to make the police the authority for vagrants and able bodied men'.[3] It seems clear from this comment that by 1908 Burns's suspicions that in many cases relief schemes were subsidies to the idle had ossified into prejudice of the most unreasoned kind, in the process swamping his belief that unemployment and poverty also had environmental origins. Devoid of any constructive ideas of his own, he was content to leave long-term remedies to the Board of Trade and to repeat that he was waiting for the report of the poor law com-

1 Burns Diary, 8 September 1908. B.L. Add. MSS 46326.

2 W.S. Churchill to R. McKenna, 19 September 1908. Cambridge University Library. McKenna Papers, 3/20, ff.8-10. D. Lloyd George to R. McKenna, September 1908. Ibid. f.3.

3 Webb, *Partnership*, 411.

mission which was clearly imminent, as Mrs Webb had already circularized members of the cabinet with details of her own proposals. All Burns was prepared to concede in the present crisis, therefore, was an increase in the exchequer grant — if it was really thought necessary — and the relaxation of some of the administrative regulations pertaining to the 1905 act. Further, he claimed, it would require legislation to permit local authorities to pay wages from the rates and once the principle was conceded strong pressure would inevitably be exerted to increase the proposed penny rate. Three days passed before the cabinet sorted out its differences and it was Burns who triumphed, finally wearing down the opposition led by Churchill and Lloyd George. His victory came partly because the other members of the cabinet committee had been unable to agree on any adequate short term measures, and, as Mrs Masterman noted, 'partly because he came armed with figures. . .partly because the distrust of the Ll. G. — Churchill combination is so profound in the Cabinet'.[1] On 21 October, therefore, Asquith presented the government's emergency proposals to the House of Commons — an increase of £100,000 in the size of the exchequer grant, and an increase in recruitment by the post office, army special reserve and the admiralty shipyards, together with some administrative relaxations of the 1905 act. Burns was exultant. 'I've smashed 'em', he told Masterman, 'and there's more behind them than George and Churchill. . .41 Grosvenor Road', (i.e. the Webbs).[2] But if he had overcome the opposition within the cabinet and out-generalled the Labour Party on the matter of the penny rate he had also been instructed to report personally to Asquith each week on the state of the labour market and on what had been done for the unemployed. Neither was the Labour Party in any mood to let him further off the hook. At the beginning of November Ramsay MacDonald contacted all local authorities, drawing their attention to the effects of Asquith's statement and urging them to try to secure a share of the extra relief for their own unemployed. In parliament the more militant Labour members launched a vigorous campaign of questions. It began on 27 October when Snowden asked if the local authority at Keighley had asked for permission to create a distress committee and with what result. There followed a spate of questions, always couched in exactly the same terms, culminating on 3 December when eight were put. It was clear from his answers that Burns was still taking a very restrictive line, for he turned down all but fourteen of the fifty-two requests made to him. But his policy soon produced a clash with the prime minister. Replying to a question from Will Thorne on 12 November

1 Masterman, *Masterman*, 112.
2 Ibid.

Burns stated that his recently issued departmental circular allowed full discretion to local distress committees to relax the 1905 restrictions on applicants for relief. Henderson promptly rose to ask if this was what the prime minister had meant by relaxation of the regulations, and later in the day he moved an adjournment in order to get the matter discussed more fully. Asquith replied that Henderson was quite correct in assuming that he intended local committees to lift the restrictions, not merely to give them a discretionary power to do so. He added that he had discussed the matter fully with Burns and that the misunderstanding had been resolved. This was tantamount to a public rebuke and it upset Burns who believed that he had made his own wishes very clear to the prime minister and was annoyed that his attempt to ignore Asquith's view had been thwarted. But although the incident did occasion some press comment, it was nothing more than a temporary set back and it was not long before Asquith was telling Burns that the unemployment situation was now highly satisfactory and had completely vindicated his policy.[1]

At about the same time, however, he sustained another, more serious, if not so unexpected, setback in connection with the Housing Bill. During the unemployment crisis, the bill had been pushed back and forth in standing committee. Burns, subject to considerable lobbying had grown daily more intransigent and fought almost every suggested change.[2] Masterman, already thoroughly disillusioned by his chief's handling of the unemployed, was in despair. Frequently he had to conduct negotiations behind Burns's back. Twenty three days in all were needed to finish with the bill and by the time it came back from standing committee it was much too late in the session to continue with it. Burns was bitterly disappointed when it was axed by the cabinet at the beginning of December. 'Twenty-three days in committee', he wrote, 'through the ordeal of a Cranks Committee, a veritable Freak Museum vain of their own proposals, dogmatic in their plans and several obviously determined to wreck the bill'.[3] Masterman was so disheartened that he drafted a letter of resignation to Asquith, claiming that the committee discussions had consisted mainly of departmental officials opposing amendments wanted by the majority of Liberals.[4] In fact Masterman did not resign at that time, but he did so

---

1 H.H. Asquith to J. Burns, 3 January 1909. Burns Papers. B.L. Add. MSS 46282, F. 75.

2 See for an example of the lobbying that went on a letter from the Metropolitan Public Gardens Association to W.H. Dickinson, 6 November 1908. G.L.C. Record Office. Dickinson Papers.

3 Burns Diary, 9 December 1908. B.L.Add. MSS 46326.

4 Masterman, *Masterman*, 122.

soon after, having decided that it would be interesting to have some experience of 'an efficient and progressive Government department'.[1]

This lends further weight to the belief that Asquith retained Burns in his cabinet mainly for personal reasons. Since becoming prime minister he had found it necessary to appoint a committee to deal with the unemployment crisis, and had caught his minister out in a serious error about the regulations of the 1905 Unemployment Act, and must have known of the discontent caused by Burns's handling of the Housing and Valuation Bills. Indeed Masterman claimed that Asquith regarded Burns as something of a child requiring careful nursing.[2] Yet Asquith still made no move to dispose of him. On the contrary, he seems to have been anxious to help him out, for when the cabinet discussed what to do with the Housing Bill Asquith had argued in favour of breaking parliamentary procedure and carrying it over to the following session. Perhaps this was why when Sidney Webb was discussing possible replacements for Burns with Haldane, the latter *'seemed* to indicate that nothing could be done in that matter'.[3] Certainly Burns was sufficiently sure of himself to launch another biting attack on the Right to Work Bill when it reappeared in April 1909, and when Churchill introduced his insurance proposals to the cabinet Burns insisted on preparing a paper on how to prevent any scheme being abused by malingerers. Nor was he any more generous in his disposal of the augmented exchequer fund. The workrooms established by the Central (Unemployed) Body for women in London were refused a grant on the strict economic grounds that they had already sustained a loss of over £9,000. He was annoyed too, when Walter Runciman publicly committed himself to an extension of the period over which local authorities could repay loans from the Local Government Board.

But substantially this was the beginning of the end of his difficulties with the unemployed question. The numbers of men out of work were falling, and long term policy was now in the hands of Churchill and Lloyd George. By May he was rejoicing that most of his worries about unemployment were clearing up and that 'but for loans period difficulty sprung upon us without notice or consultation our trouble of first 3 years almost over'.[4] This was in marked contrast to the depression which had plagued him during the unemployment crisis,

1 C.F.G. Masterman to H. Samuel, 6 July 1909. H.L.R.O. Samuel Papers, A/155 (iv), f.12.

2 Masterman, *Masterman,* 123.

3 S. Webb to B. Webb, 29 January 1909. B.L.P.E.S. Passfield Papers, Correspondence Section II, 3 (i), f. 225.

4 Burns Diary, 8 May 1909. B.L. Add. MSS 46327.

and there is little doubt that both that crisis and the struggles over the Housing Bill had taken a heavy toll. Physically they had left their marks. Celebrating his own fiftieth birthday early in 1909 J. Bruce Glasier noted that Burns (almost exactly the same age) looked 'fifteen years older. . .quite grey'.[1] It was perhaps ironic that just as the unemployment figures began to fall, a trend that was to continue until 1914, the poor law commission on which Burns had for so long leaned in the absence of any ideas of his own, presented its report; or rather its reports, for there were two. Both the majority and minority reports recommended labour exchanges and a state-backed scheme of insurance against unemployment, suggestions with which Burns was not especially enamoured but to which he was *de facto* committed by his very membership of the government. He did not like the majority's support for labour colonies nor the minority's suggestion for the creation of a ministry of labour. His economically orthodox mind was outraged by the minority's further suggestion that the government should spend some £4,000,000 a year on countering cyclical unemployment.

As far as the poor law generally was concerned, both reports took the view that local authorities should assume responsibility for its administration. But while the majority wished to make the revamped poor law into an all purpose relief organisation the minority, inspired by the Webbs, wanted to destroy it entirely and replace it with a series of separately organised local authority bodies each responsible for a different function such as education, health, and pensions. This was far too radical for Burns while he was in any case profoundly suspicious – as indeed were many other Liberals – of the bureaucratic terms in which the Webbs' proposals were couched.[2] When in June 1909 the Webbs plunged into a propaganda campaign to break up the poor law Burns opposed them at every turn. As it happened, neither L.G.B. officials nor Burns himself were particularly opposed to the municipalities taking over the poor law, for Burns had suggested to a conference in the Potteries in 1907 that 'the poor law may be municipalised to keep pace with the urbanisation of the working classes and consequent poverty attendant thereon'.[3] But by now Burns was liable to oppose on first principles anything the Webbs proposed and his dislike of the legislative process had deepened as a result of his experience with the

1 Bruce Glasier Diary, 25 March 1909. Quoted in L. Thompson, *The Enthusiasts* (1971), 178.

2 For a critique of the minority report on the grounds that it went in for over-classification, see U. Cormack, 'The Welfare State; the Formative Years, 1905-9', in *A Reader in Social Administration,* ed. A.V.S. Lochhead (1968), 80-112.

3 *Poor Law Officers Journal,* 19 July 1907.

Housing Bill. Consequently he took the view that it was a waste of time to construct a massive general poor law reform bill (The very prospect of this must have given the highly incompetent Adrian many a sleepless night). 'If the country knew its business', he told an audience at Carshalton, 'it would relegate both reports and the whole of the problem to the President of the Local Government Board for his. . . practical action whenever he determined that action should be taken'.[1] He expressed similar sentiments to a deputation of poor law officials, telling them that if they wished to avoid being destroyed their best hope was to back his policy of implementing what was best from each report.[2] The hostile attitude of the poor law establishment and Burns's own general reticence must go some way to explaining why, having toyed with the reports for a few months, the cabinet ultimately did little about either. The Webbs were their own worst enemies in this respect, however, for their intriguing and aggressive propagandising alienated several cabinet members who at heart were probably quite sympathetic.

That the government was able to get away with virtually ignoring such a major and long-awaited report was due partly to the fact that it had alternative proposals and partly to the fact that this programme was predicated upon a budget whose terms created a major political sensation and precipitated a constitutional crisis. The Chancellor of the Exchequer had no intention of being stampeded into Fabian socialism by the Webbs and had been quietly at work, with Churchill and Masterman, on schemes to tackle unemployment and sickness by means of insurance. Given that the government was also committed to its old age pensions scheme and faced the possibility of rising expenditure on armaments, Lloyd George decided that the necessary monies should be raised by the simple expedient of taxing the wealthy few in the interests of the penurious many. The ensuing budget stunned the Opposition. Writing thirty years after the event, Lucy Masterman could still recall the gasps of astonishment and rage rising from the Conservative benches as the Chancellor flung out one controversial proposal after another: a more steeply graduated income tax; maximum death duties levied on estates at £1½ million instead of £3 million; higher legacy and succession duties; a sharp increase in stamp duty; an unearned increment tax of twenty per cent on land; a ten per cent determination of lease tax; a tax on undeveloped land and minerals.[3] It was the land taxes in particular that produced most hostility; Lloyd George's own intemperate oratory only inflamed

1 *The Times,* 17 May 1909.
2 Burns Diary, 1 July 1909. B.L. Add. MSS 46331.
3 Masterman, *Masterman,* 133.

feelings still more. The opposition was equally outspoken, the Duke of Beaufort, for example, telling his tenants that he would dearly love to see the chancellor caught in the middle of a pack of foxhounds.[1] Soon the whole country was aroused and everywhere it was the budget and the Tory alternative of tariff reform that was under public discussion, eclipsing even the controversies about Britain's naval strength that had dominated earlier in the year. Lloyd George was delighted, for he rightly divined that the land taxes had succeeded in rekindling the enthusiasm of his party which had wilted steadily before the Lords' rejection of one major bill after another.[2]

Yet about this controversial radical budget which went so far towards making possible the reforms to which he was pledged John Burns said nothing. While the debate raged around him, he remained silent and no pro-budget meetings were organised in Battersea. To some extent his guarded reaction was a matter of personalities. According to Edwin Montagu, his first sour reaction to the budget was that the members of the cabinet were like 'nineteen ragpickers round a 'eap of muck', and there is plenty of evidence that Burns, contrary to some opinions, disliked Lloyd George intensely.[3] In many ways they invited public comparison because, of all the cabinet ministers, Lloyd George was closest to Burns in both his social origins and in his early radicalism. They had even been near-neighbours in Wandsworth at the time of the Boer War. Yet the Welshman had quickly forged ahead of Burns in political stature. Burns had been annoyed that as the representative of labour in the cabinet he had not been asked by Campbell-Bannerman to arbitrate in the 1907 railway strike, a task which had been given to Lloyd George. When Lloyd George had been made chancellor, Burns had been extremely catty, suggesting that Asquith had only given him the job in the belief that he would make a mess of it.[4] Certainly Burns was piqued because Lloyd George got on as well as he did with Edward VII. On one occasion he remarked waspishly that the chancellor had done so much cringing to royalty that he was suffering from "ousemaid's knee'.[5] His view of Lloyd George, not to mention Churchill and Masterman, had further diminish-

1 D. McCormick, *The Mask of Merlin* (1963), 67.

2 D. Lloyd George to J.A. Spender, 16 July 1909. Spender Papers. B.L. Add. MSS 46388, f. 202.

3 A. Fitzroy, *Memoirs* (1925), II, 430. Lloyd George himself said that his least effective supporter was Burns. See R. Lloyd George, *Lloyd George* (1960), 120.

4 Emmott Diary, 31 May 1908. Nuffield College, Emmott Papers, I. See also J.H. Lewis Diary, 23 February 1908. National Library of Wales. Lewis Papers, 10/131/72. I owe this reference to Dr Chris Wrigley of Loughborough University.

5 Fitzroy, *Memoirs*, II, 419.

ed during the unemployment crisis of 1908 and it is significant that from about that time he took to referring to these colleagues as the 'three musketeers', revealing perhaps his belief that they were carefree, irresponsible and swashbuckling in their approach to politics.[1] Certainly he believed that Lloyd George was deliberately clouding the budget with noisy rhetoric for party advantage.

Yet his reaction was not solely a matter of personalities. He genuinely believed that some of the budget's proposals were too extreme and that some of its financial calculations were suspect. When he did finally make a public pronouncement it was to tell a constituent that he would support the budget but only to the extent that it was reasonable, businesslike, and equitable.[2] On the night that it was presented to the Commons it is alleged that he told Sir George Younger, a leading Unionist, to be thankful for what was *not* in it.[3] Nor was Burns very favourably disposed towards the chancellor's proposals to establish a Development Commission and a Road Board. Both measures would incidentally do something to reduce unemployment, a fact which Burns interpreted as a criticism of himself, but his opposition rested mainly on his belief that both bodies should be subjected to much more rigorous financial control than Lloyd George envisaged, and although in cabinet he pressed for such control to be vested in his own department he was overruled by Asquith.

There is also some evidence that Burns was annoyed at the way in which the controversy over the budget had stolen the thunder from his Housing Bill which had been re-introduced. His opening speech had been much improved from the previous year, better constructed, less flowery and much more precise. But it was clear that, even as amended by standing committee, the bill would expose fundamental differences between M.P.'s about how the agreed objectives of more houses and more planning should be achieved, and the second reading was deferred nineteen times. At the committee stage, over 360 amendments were tabled and once more it seemed likely that the bill would be lost for lack of time, most of which was perforce being devoted to the budget. The main thrust of Conservative criticism was that the bill would confer enormous bureaucratic power on the Local Government Board. One M.P. accused Burns of wishing 'to go back to the days of Louis XIV. . . and have everything done that he, with the best intentions, decides', a

1 For examples see Burns Diary, 31 October 1908. B.L. Add. MSS 46326. He also referred to Churchill and Lloyd George as 'the two romeos'. W. Runciman to R. McKenna, 27 March 1910. Cambridge University Library. McKenna Papers, 3/22, f. 12.

2 *The Times*, 4 January 1910.

3 Quoted in A.C. Murray, *Master and Brother* (1945), 26.

charge which might equally have been made about his policy on the poor law reports.[1] Finally, however, by dint of some hard whipping, long argument and, in the end, the parliamentary guillotine (which annoyed the Tories) the bill got through and went to the Lords. But although Burns spent hours discussing it with the Liberal leaders in the Lords, Crewe and Beauchamp, they were unable to prevent the huge Tory majority in the upper house whittling away some of its most important provisions. The Lords rejected the view that in the case of a disputed compulsory purchase order there should be no right of appeal except to the Local Government Board. They wished further to restrict to rural areas only the ability of the L.G.B. to enforce housing orders. Clauses designed to compel landlords to remedy defects caused by tenants were also amended out. In the planning section the Lords wanted schemes to be approved by provisional order, not by the Local Government Board. Nor did they agree that the board should have the final say in the dismissal of local officers of health.

These were the main amendments that the House of Commons rejected on Burns's advice and it was now that he entered into tortuous and lengthy negotiations to try to reach some agreement with the peers. In the first week of November, he met almost daily with his principal housing officers and with Lords Salisbury, Lansdowne, and Onslow, here making a concession but there sticking his heels in and generally displaying a degree of firmness and resolution that surprised Masterman.[2] By 10 November compromise had been reached on all but one point − who should arbitrate on the value and necessity of those schemes of housing and planning which involved compulsory purchase. The peers voted that the county court should be the appropriate body, but Crewe was so strongly opposed to this that he suggested the bill be abandoned if the government view could not be enforced.[3] But Burns, perhaps fearing that the bill would again be axed and with success so nearly in his hand, would not accept Crewe's suggestion to refer this matter to the cabinet. On 12 November he again conferred with Salisbury and Lansdowne, giving them 'a bridge to cross tho' a ricketty one'.[4] Knowing they would soon have to turn their attention to the budget the Unionist peers finally accepted Burns's suggestion that when compulsory purchase orders were disputed on points of law the High Court, not the county court, should be the

1 Quoted in J. Minett, 'The Housing, Town Planning etc Act, 1909', *The Planner* 60 (1974), 680.

2 Masterman, *Masterman*, 150-51.

3 Lord Crewe to J. Burns, 10 November 1909. Burns Papers. B.L. Add. MSS 46301, ff. 5-6.

4 Burns Diary, 12 November 1909. Ibid. Add. MSS 46327.

arbiter. For the rest, it was clear that Burns's firmness had paid off. He agreed that compulsory purchase orders should lie on the table of the two houses for thirty days, but only for information, not so that addresses could be moved against them. He had refused to give in on the question of medical officers of health and had insisted that town planning schemes be confirmed by the board rather than by provisional order. On 19 November the Liberal peers successfully resisted efforts by a few Unionist dissidents to wreck the compromise and a week later the bill passed into law.

It was Burns's most important legislative achievement. The bill conferred wide permissive planning powers on local authorities, allowing them to ensure that considerations of amenity, health, and convenience were duly weighed in any housing programme. The housing section quietly introduced for the first time the idea of local authority home ownership. Previous acts had insisted that a local authority divest itself within ten years of such property as it had had built. Burns's act made no such stipulations. In retrospect it seems a modest measure but several contemporaries were alive to the possibilities it created – even if in practice they were hardly realised in the years before 1914. Lord Jersey, for instance, claimed that in this one act Burns had done 'more to benefit the people than any other Minister before him'.[1] Another contemporary referred to his 'great service to his country'.[2]

To Burns himself the passage of the act represented merely one aspect of his programme to improve the general environmental conditions of ordinary people. It was this aspect of his office which really interested him, much more so than the administration of the poor law, and in the course of the first Asquith administration he had been able to take other steps to this end. At the end of 1908 the board issued a circular making tuberculosis in poor law institutions a notifiable disease, a move which, Burns felt, represented 'a new stage of warfare against this social disease'.[3] Critics pointed out that the order left untouched the sufferers who were not paupers but Newsholme, after much thought, concluded that universal notification was not possible until such time as local authorities were prepared to follow notification with remedial action. He therefore advised Burns that a gradual extension of notification was best. Despite the fact that something like forty per cent of all T.B. deaths took place among paupers, the department had long resisted its notification on the curious grounds that T.B. was a chronic disease whereas notifiable

1 *The Times,* 24 September 1909.

2 H. Aldridge, *The Case for Town Planning: a Practical Manual* (1915), 155.

3 Burns Diary, 20 August 1908. B.L. Add. MSS 46330.

diseases were generally acute ones like smallpox or typhoid. But Newsholme had built up a good system of notification and treatment while at Brighton and wished to take advantage of his new office to extend it, a desire which Burns encouraged. Even then, Burns had to put a great deal of pressure on the hapless Adrian to find some way in which the order could be enforced, Adrian eventually suggesting rather reluctantly that it could be done by reference to the 1875 Public Health Act which contained provision for the notification of pthisis.

The other aspect of the campaign against T.B. had not made such good progress, however. In 1907 the Royal Commission on Tuberculosis had issued its report stressing the relation between the drinking of milk from cows infected with the tubercle bacilli and the infection of humans. It had urged stringent measures against the sale of infected milk. By February 1909 a draft bill to strengthen regulations regarding the sale of milk and the conditions of dairies was ready, but once more progress was hampered by the deficiencies of civil servants, though Burns himself seems to have had little idea of how to speed things up. The problem really lay with the Board of Agriculture which wanted compensation for those farmers whose cows were slaughtered because they were infected. Provis objected to this on the grounds that it would be far too costly, a consideration which may also explain why Burns himself did not intervene more decisively. The L.G.B. officials suggested instead that all cows should be tested before their milk was offered for sale but by the time a compromise had been reached the session was too far advanced for the measure which Burns introduced to have much chance of success and in August it was withdrawn. But he continued to publicise the department's efforts against T.B., pointing out when he opened the summer exhibition arranged by the National Association for the Prevention of Consumption and Tuberculosis that the disease was a product of poverty which the Local Government Board was doing its best to eliminate.

In the course of this speech Burns also made reference to the crusade which he had initiated against infant mortality. His long standing interest in children was well in tune with rising public concern at the very high death rate among newly born babies, for almost alone of the indices of public health it had failed to improve during the nineteenth century. The British Medical Association had raised the matter in parliament in 1904 but Walter Long had replied that as the cause was related mainly to improper feeding there was nothing that the government could do. Burns had taken a very different view, organising and presiding at a special London conference in 1906 on the subject, and instructing his departmental officers to begin collecting statistics with a view to bringing in some sort of legislation later on. He was beaten to it, however, by Lord Robert Cecil who in 1907 introduced a bill requiring the notification of births within thirty-six hours instead of six weeks, the object being to permit health visitors to have access to infants much earlier in the vital first few days of life. The measure was much criticised in the Commons and also in the medical press.[1] Burns and Macnamara, however, joined the standing committee to which the bill was referred, and in the course of a single day changed it into a measure which the L.G.B. could utilise and control in the interests of children. A second national conference followed in 1908 and in the same year Burns, desirous of establishing a medical institution exclusively for children, took over the Southern Hospital at Carshalton for this purpose, in the process creating what was then the largest childrens' hospital in the world. The next year he authorised a national survey of the incidence and control of infant mortality, the first time that central government had shown much indication of taking the matter at all seriously. At about the same time ophthalmia, a disease which annually blinded about three thousand children at birth, was made notifiable.

Inevitably, however, all of this quiet but significant administrative change was obscured in the dust clouds raised by the poor law reformers and by the budget. At the end of November 1909 the Lords brought the incipient constitutional struggle with the Commons to a head by taking the unprecedented step of rejecting the Finance Bill, whereupon the cabinet decided to go to the country. Though he had no doubts as to the constitutional impropriety of the peers' action, Burns did not have any particular wish for an election. It is true that one delegate at the annual meeting of the National Liberal Federation in July had referred to him as 'a brilliant success' but in his own constituency there had been growing complaints that he never visited it and that his obligations to Battersea had been secondary to his ministerial duties. Certainly it had been a long time since he had delivered a speech to his constituents and he began his election campaign by explaining to the Liberal and Radical Association why he had neglected the constituency for the past two and a half years. In his absence, Burns's opponent of 1906, Shirley Benn, had secured almost as strong a personal hold on Battersea as Burns himself, and local Conservatism had been further strengthened by the formation of a branch of the Tariff Reform League. From the other side, Burns was threatened by growing labour disillusion. Socialists of varying shades had taken every opportunity to blacken his name through their recently launched journal, the *Battersea Vanguard,* and in particular had attacked his

1 *British Medical Journal,* 31 August 1907; *Lancet,* 7 September 1907.

unemployment policy – or rather his lack of one – taking full advantage of high unemployment in the constituency itself. More worrying still, perhaps, were the cracks beginning to appear in his own power base. Some Progressives had also been very critical of his handling of unemployment but by 1908 serious differences about tactics and policy were threatening the cohesion of the Labour League. There had been defections from the local trades council and a constituency Labour Party had been formed. Burns had observed these events with some concern and had devoted his infrequent appearances at Labour League meetings to making impassioned pleas for unity. His dismay was redoubled when the Progressives were totally routed in the borough council elections of November 1909, securing only two seats. He chose to open his campaign by addressing the local Liberal and Radical Association, but even there his reception was cool, for he had caused considerable offence by his refusal to help that body out of its financial difficulties by paying the salary of its registration agent.

Yet the issue on which the election centred was one close to the heart of his democratic philosophy and one on which he had held unwavering views all his life. Even though he had eventually found a way out of the impasse the peers' treatment of his Housing Bill had embittered him. 'I have always been a single chamber man but this confirms me absolutely', he wrote when he received notification of their amendments in September 1909.[1] He had not expected that the Lords would actually reject the budget and privately had expressed some irritation at the lengthy cabinet discussions about what to do if they did. But once the gauntlet was thrown down he had no doubt that an election was the right course of action, for he sensed that the peers' decision was 'the first decisive act in either a great victory or a great tragedy for the British race. Will present snobbery, past jobbery, ancient robbery unite with dogma and drink to fetter our hands and chloroform our minds again?'[2] Now, almost for the first time, he began to make public reference to the budget, telling an election meeting at Walthamstow that Lloyd George's proposals should be passed because they were popular and just. But his attitude, as we have seen, was cautious and in most of his speeches he concentrated on the constitutional crisis rather than the merits of the Finance Bill. Similarly, his election manifesto attacked the Lords not so much for their rejection of the budget as for their rejection of other major Liberal bills.

1 Burns Diary, 22 September 1909. B.L. Add. MSS 46327.
2 Ibid. 1 December 1909. Add. MSS 46331.

It was a tiring campaign in more ways than one. Shortly after it began the departmental store of Arding and Hobbs at Clapham caught fire. Hearing of this Burns (perhaps capitalising on his experience as a member of the L.C.C.'s Fire Brigade Committee!) rushed to the scene and organised some of the crowd into impromptu firemen. Eight people died in the blaze, but it provided valuable publicity and illustrated once again Burns's uncanny knack for stealing the lime-light, because the presence of Shirley Benn at the scene passed virtually unnoticed. But he still had a lot of ground to make up and pledged himself, rather rashly, to visit every home in the constituency. The local S.D.P. considered running Victor Grayson against him but ultimately resorted to a campaign of heckling so successful that Burns responded by making his meetings all-ticket affairs. Nor were the socialists the only source of disruption. The suffragettes were also busy and Christabel Pankhurst took advantage of his absence at a Finsbury meeting and addressed the residents of Battersea. Burns, she told the audience, should be rejected because he did not allow women into his meetings. The immediate charge was true, but unlike many of his cabinet colleagues who were being similarly harrassed, Burns could point to a lifetime's advocacy of womens' rights. His early trade union work had done much to advance the position of female workers and he had been extremely friendly with one of the most influential of women trade union leaders, Clementina Black. It was Burns who had urged Asquith to let women serve on the pensions committees created to administer the Old Age Pension Act, and he had also moved the second reading of Lord Crewe's bill in 1907 permitting women to serve on those public bodies for which they were allowed to vote. Burns had been disappointed when Campbell-Bannerman refused to pledge the government to a measure extending the parliamentary franchise to women, but he nonetheless stood condemned in the eyes of the Pankhursts because he had not dropped everything in the cause of womens' suffrage.[1] But this single-mindedness and the violence in which the suffragettes indulged were equally repugnant to Burns. Militancy as far as he was concerned was entirely counter-productive. As he told the Forward Suffrage Union, the best argument against giving women the vote rested in the activities of the suffragettes themselves.[2]

But neither the intervention of the 'vixens in velvet' (Burns's own

---

1 Ibid. 19 May 1906. Add. MSS 46324. He noted later that the pro-suffragists in Asquith's cabinets had not been forceful enough. 'We were all too deferential to his view'. Ibid. 28 March 1917. Add. MSS 46339.

2 J. Burns to the Forward Suffrage Union. 17 November 1909. Ibid. Add. MSS 46301, f.15.

description) nor of the socialists had any decisive effect on the outcome of the campaign in Battersea. Burns received his largest vote to date, though this was a reflection not so much of his popularity as of the great local interest in the election, for his majority of 1906 fell by over 1,100 votes to 555. This result was consistent with what happened elsewhere, for in the south of England the Unionists, fighting mainly on a tariff reform platform, regained much of the ground lost in 1906. The swing in London, however, was sufficient to give them only an extra eleven seats, fewer than even their least optimistic forecasts. Burns, although he came nowhere near getting the 3,000 majority he predicted on the eve of polling, had won his fifth successive election, and duly celebrated by slipping across the Channel to France for a five day rest.

8

EXHAUSTION, 1911-1914.

The general election of January 1910 was inevitably accompanied by speculation about the composition of the next government. Rumour had it that in the event of a Liberal victory Burns would succeed Herbert Gladstone at the Home Office but it is an interesting indication of the social prejudice with which he still had to contend, even after four years of office, that Elsie Pease commented tartly that 'John Burns would be hopeless there. You can't have a man of that class there'.[1] Others, like the Webbs, were not so much concerned with Burns's destination as with the probability of his moving. 'Whatever happens', Beatrice Webb noted gleefully on the eve of the election, 'John Burns leaves the Local Government Board. He will probably lose his seat. . .Winston means to go to the Local Government Board. . .with the intention of carrying out the Minority Report'.[2] She added that Churchill intended to appoint Morant as the new head of the L.G.B. in place of Provis who was retiring. This appointment had long been deemed by the Webbs to be crucial to their hopes of securing poor law reconstruction and to this end they had been urging Morant's claims since 1908. Although their canvassing had annoyed Asquith, the prime minister still appeared to be toying with the idea of Morant in December 1909 when Burns went to see him to tell him of his own wish to appoint Monro as Provis's successor. At least, Burns noted afterwards, 'he appeared to have someone else in mind. I pressed the necessity of an experienced man and a firm one. . .I left him feeling that something would happen to me'.[3]

Yet nothing did, and not one of Mrs Webb's prophecies was fulfilled. In January 1910 Monro's appointment was announced, much to the chagrin of the Webbs who saw in it clear indication that however much the cabinet might nibble at the poor law reports there would be no major reconstruction of the sort they wished to see.[4] Even worse from their point of view, Burns retained the presidency while shortly afterwards Asquith sanctioned the raising of its status to that of a secretary-ship of state with a salary of £5,000 a year. Asquith himself had come down in favour of retaining a distinctive poor law administration and while he may have had some vague notion of ultimately appointing a

1   Elsie Pease to J.A. Pease, November 1909. Nuffield College. Gainford MSS, 87.
2   Webb, *Partnership*, 436-7.
3   Burns Diary, 18 December 1909. B.L. Add. MSS 46327.
4   Webb, *Partnership*, 443.

158

new president to undertake a major reconstruction, in the short term he was much more concerned with the constitutional deadlock. On the whole he had shown himself to be unwilling to override the chosen policies of his ministers, being content to act as a general co-ordinator. He was thus happy enough to let Burns get on with his own approach of implementing revolution via reform since, as Burns himself put it, reform via revolution was impossible.[1] Burns himself found things somewhat easier after the shakeup among his senior civil servants which followed the announcement of Provis's departure. In the course of 1910 Adrian was replaced as Legal Adviser by John Lithiby whose place as Assistant Secretary in the Public Health division was taken by F.J. Willis, a man with very progressive ideas about the treatment of T.B. As Burns began to put administrative reform of the poor law into effect — for example, discussing new ideas on relief or considering whether London should be made into one separate union — Asquith seems no longer to have regarded him as a source of weakness in the cabinet. Writing to Crewe in the autumn of 1911 he said that there were only two weak spots, at the Admiralty and the Board of Agriculture.[2]

Burns's whole reaction to the poor law commission reports had been coloured partly by the fact that they would involve the creation of a vast new bureaucracy, partly by the fact that the implementation of either would cost millions, a point he stressed in a general circular issued to guardians in March 1910. So intent was he on saving money that he now changed his mind about pauper pensioners, advocating an extension of the pension scheme to those hitherto barred on the ground that they had previously applied for relief — because this would reduce the burden on the poor law rates, shifting it instead to the pension fund of the imperial exchequer. In March, Burns instituted a departmental committee to investigate what changes could be made in the administration of outrelief and there were few in Whitehall who doubted that he was hoping for recommendations that would save still more money. As far as the machinery of poor relief was concerned he took the opportunity afforded by the debate on the Prevention of Destitution Bill, introduced by advocates of the Minority Report, to argue strongly for the retention of the guardians, quoting statistics to show that their devoted public service has produced a general reduction in the incidence of pauperism while allowing an increase in per capita expenditure. It was unfortunate that his passion for figures did not also extend to their comprehension, for his argument allowed nothing for

1   In a speech at Bow. *The Times*, 2 March 1912.
2   H.H. Asquith to Lord Crewe, 7 October 1911. Bodleian Library. Asquith Papers, 46, f.191.

rising prices. Similarly in October 1910 he forecast proudly that the incidence of pauperism would fall to an unprecedentedly low level in the approaching winter, apparently unaware of the fact that this owed far more to the impact of pensions and a healthy labour market than to his own administration. The other argument Burns used to defend the current system was that it allowed a variety of approaches to pauperism, a feature he believed to be important and one which was stressed in a series of new orders promulgated between 1910 and 1914. In a circular of June 1910, for example, he emphasised the advantages of having several different types of institutions into which pauper children could be slotted and he criticised the grey regimentation proposed by the Minority Report. By the middle of 1911 he had removed nearly all London's pauper children from mixed workhouses and distributed them among a variety of specialist institutions. By 1913 his administrative reforms had resulted in an increased deployment of medical staff and the handing of authority to professional staff in the infirmaries.

In the nature of things, this approach to the poor law was essentially a holding operation. The actual causes of poverty as Burns understood them were to be reduced by a variety of flank attacks through housing and town planning, pensions, insurance, and measures to reduce the incidence of pauperising diseases. To this end, the 1910 Census Bill which he piloted through the Commons differed from its predecessor of 1900 in that it sought to obtain more information about both family structure and urban conditions in order to facilitate the development of further policies to tackle infant mortality, slum dwellings and similar conditions. But although in many of his parliamentary and public speeches at this time Burns appeared to be stressing the overall coherence of government social policy, the Housing Act stood as his only legislative contribution. Further, he often gave the impression that he was at the centre of government policy, yet his contribution to pensions, insurance, and labour exchanges had been essentially peripheral and government policy emerged more by accident than overall design.

In any case social policy was firmly in the wings in 1910. The centre of the stage was dominated by the continuing dispute with the House of Lords which was absorbing enormous amounts of both parliamentary and cabinet time. Burns took little part in the formulation of government strategy. His views on the Lords were well known, – and totally unrealistic as far as his colleagues were concerned. On the whole, therefore, he was content to go along with the policy devised by Asquith, and as cabinet meeting followed cabinet meeting so his admiration for the prime minister's handling of the situation grew. 'No P.M.', he noted, 'ever had a more difficult task and none behaved

160

better all through it than he has done'.[1] In May, the drama took an unexpected twist with the death of Edward VII, and a constitutional conference was therefore convened in the hope of producing a settlement. It failed to reach agreement, however, and in November when Asquith unfolded the government's intentions with regard to the Finance Bill and the conduct of future business Burns commented that he had never heard a statement 'so admirably made and achieving in such a short time a complete exposition of his difficult call without raising a difficulty or doubt in any quarter as to what he meant'.[2]

Faced with the deadlock between the nation's main political parties the new King, George V, had little choice but to agree to Asquith's demand that if a fresh election produced a Liberal majority then he would put pressure on the Lords to accept the government's Parliament Bill severely restricting their powers. In December, therefore, the country went to the polls for the second time in a year. It was Burns's sixth contest in Battersea and was not without its difficulties. When his salary had been raised to £5,000 a year the London Liberal Federation had announced, not unreasonably, that it was no longer willing to find all the £3,000 a year necessary for the work of registration in the constituency. Burns replied that he had no intention of assuming financial responsibility for the Liberal Association which was neither democratic nor controlled by himself, a response which left him in very bad odour with local Liberals. Although he set both the terms and tone of the campaign in Battersea by referring in his opening speech to the peers as 'hereditary imbeciles', four womens' suffrage organisations joined in and tried to concentrate the electorate's mind on the franchise issue with the one aim of keeping Burns out.[3] The contest was further enlivened by the candidature of C.N.L. Shaw, an independent socialist, backed by the local S.D.P. His intervention made little difference to the result, however, for Burns romped home with a majority of 1,300 and the swing against the Unionist candidate, Colonel Harrington, was the greatest in any South London constituency, though this may have been due mainly to the fact that he was something of a last-minute choice.

The announcement of yet another victory for Burns in Battersea was greeted by his supporters in characteristically exuberant style. They shouldered him through the constituency, said the local paper, 'like one of the popular kings of the Gallic tribes, whose right to rule was proclaimed by his standing on a shield upheld by the arms of

1 Burns Diary, 29 March 1910. B.L. Add. MSS 46332.
2 Ibid. 18 November 1910.
3 *South Western Star*, 25 November 1910.

veterans. . .'[1] But the effort had told on Burns, and as 1910 passed into 1911 his diary entries suggest that he was physically run down, pessimistic about the general situation and doubtful about his own future — all sentiments that were to recur with increasing frequency in the future. Not that he had any doubts about the validity of his work at the Local Government Board. He had, he felt, been too reticent, not daring enough, but his record showed 'much useful work slavishly carried out for the benefit of all'.[2] But, he added, he was finding the daily routine of office work wearisome and increasingly tedious, and certainly he had shown little inclination of late to continue his struggle against official inertia within the department. What he wanted was 'resignation of office, 2 to 4 years of private membership and a free hand on social and economic matters, education of Edgar and reparation to Pattie [Martha] for her years of devotion to us in the interests of our public work'.[3] Nor apparently did he manage to cover up his feelings at this stage very well, for the political gossip columnists were soon busily purveying rumours of his impending resignation. Yet he did not resign, and the question therefore arises of just how serious his diary jottings were at this time. Did he write with one eye on a future historian and deliberately try to create the impression of a minister trapped in office by considerations of loyalty and duty against his deeper wishes? Almost certainly not. Burns appears to have believed quite genuinely that resignation at this juncture would have seriously damaged the government which still had to settle its dispute with the Lords, and that it would also be an act of betrayal against Asquith to whom he was devoted. Although by general consent he had made no useful contribution to the government's handling of the constitutional issue, his resignation, given his well-known views, could only have been interpreted as a criticism of government policy for being too moderate. Yet Burns's belief still betrays a vastly inflated sense of his own importance and it was this vanity rather than anything else that trapped him in office. On the whole, therefore, it seems likely that his gloom had more to do with his own personal circumstances and the vagaries of his political fortune. At home Edgar was showing every sign of growing into an obstinate and self-willed adolescent, a fact which Burns naturally preferred to attribute to his own prolonged absences on official business and his wife's over-indulgence of their only child rather than to any hereditary factors. Two election campaigns inside twelve months had taken a physical toll and there were signs that the

1   Ibid. 9 December 1910.
2   Burns Diary, 11 December 1910. B.L. Add. MSS 46332.
3   Ibid. 28 January 1911. Add. MSS 46333. For other entries in similar vein see ibid. 20 January, 5 February, 5 March 1911.

robust constitution in which Burns had long revelled was beginning to show marks of wear. For years he had boasted of the fact that he had never worn an overcoat, only the reefer jacket that had become a familiar sight in the streets of London through which he loved to walk. Now he was increasingly troubled by rheumatism and early in 1911 he had to resort to spectacles for close work. His morale undoubtedly suffered too, when Burgess published his book portraying him as 'a political octopus. . .a titanic and satanic monster, casting mountainous shadows over the centuries'.[1] Although he affected to ignore the appearance of Burgess's work, Burns hung eagerly on condemnations of it from men like Snowden and Barnes with whom he normally had very little to do.

Politically too, 1911, began badly for the Local Government Board when the departmental committee issued its report on poor law administration in the form of a draft order which Burns helped personally to prepare. The order stressed the value of the principle of less eligibility and really represented an attempt to rehabilitate individuals by restricting relief to an absolute minimum. Only in cases of exceptional hardship were the able bodied poor (i.e. the unemployed) to get outrelief. A storm of protest broke out, led by the Prevention of Destitution Committee which the Webbs had created to press for the implementation of the Minority Report. Emergency resolutions condemning the order were tabled at the conferences of both the Labour Party and the Independent Labour Party, and both Asquith and Balfour were inundated with protests. So too, was the Local Government Board which received nearly 200 letters in just under eight weeks.[2] Even the guardians objected as the order recommended that their powers of deciding on the validity of an application for out relief should pass to the local medical officers of health. In the Commons, Ramsay MacDonald asked for a day to be devoted to discussing the new order, Asquith replying that such an opportunity would occur during the debate on L.G.B. estimates. Faced with this concerted opposition, Burns hesitated, announcing that he wished to consider fully all the points made to him before finalising the terms of the order. In this way he avoided what would have been a highly acrimonious debate on his departmental estimates.

It is possible to detect behind these recommendations the influence of Arthur Newsholme who, like Morant and Newman, believed that the medical functions of the poor law system should gradually be diverted

1   *Clarion*, 19 May 1911.
2   PRO MH 60/13. Letter Books. 28 January - 24 March 1911.

into the hands of the local authorities.[1] Burns's own motive, however, apart from any conviction he had about the necessity for an 1834 type poor law administration, was one of economy. 'Go on with . . . economising', he told Davy in November, 'now that Pensions are taking over many poor law dependents'.[2] Similar feelings informed his reaction to the insurance schemes that were now coming before the cabinet for discussion. Although he conceded in a parliamentary speech in May that insurance was the government's main weapon in the fight against pauperism he was less than helpful to Lloyd George. He feared that in the chancellor's too generous hands it would become nothing more than a subsidy to malingerers, although in fact there was very little relevant evidence to substantiate this. Privately Burns complained that he had not been asked for his assistance early enough and according to Braithwaite, who was responsible for drafting the health insurance scheme, Burns was reluctant to allow Newsholme to help with some of of the medical clauses. When the measure came under detailed consideration by the cabinet Burns allowed his prejudices to get such a grip that he actually opposed recommendations of which in the past he had often approved. He objected, for example, to clauses placing a special levy on employers whose workers suffered exceptional sickness because of the unhealthy nature of the work or the place of work; and he also opposed the proposal to grant to local health committees powers of closure over public houses in cases where excess sickness was related to too much drinking.

As 1911 drew on, however, the public had eyes for two issues only. On the most absorbing, that relating to the House of Lords, Burns continued to play a relatively passive role, his opinion of Asquith rising almost daily as the drama reached its climax. On 7 August when to all intents and purposes the government won the battle and the Parliament Bill was accepted by the peers, Burns sat silently in his seat, revelling in the discomforts of the opposition on whom Asquith's measured tones fell 'like flails'.[3] The scenario was pitched against a background of unparalleled summer heat and there were some who attributed to this the outburst of militant industrial unrest that was the other main topic of public concern in 1911. Unrest had been growing steadily since 1909 and owed far more to the combination of falling real wages and low levels of unemployment than to any fluctuations in climatic conditions. But it was the militancy that went with the strikes

1 See F. Honigsbaum, 'The Struggle for the Ministry of Health', *Occasional Papers in Social Administration* 37 (1970).
2 Burns Diary, 1 November 1911. B.L. Add. MSS 46333. Also ibid. 6 November 1911.
3 Ibid. 7 August 1911.

that was so disturbing, for by contemporary standards it was unusual. The strikes were centred in three related industries, coal, the docks, and the railways. In the docks trouble had begun in Southampton during June and spread rapidly to other principal ports. In London an arbitration award by Sir Albert Rollitt satisfied the dockers but not other groups like carmen, lightermen and stevedores and the strike continued to spread. Asquith, busy with the constitutional crisis and a railway strike, deputed Burns and Sidney Buxton as President of the Board of Trade, to deal with a situation not made any easier by the militant proclivities of the Home Secretary, Winston Churchill. Churchill had already shown himself willing to sanction the use of troops against strikers in Hull, a suggestion which Burns had opposed passionately in cabinet, arguing that if any supplementation of the forces of law and order was necessary then it should be provided only by the Metropolitan Police.[1] Constantly Burns had to counter Churchill's tendency to over-dramatise, and reassure his colleagues that matters were not as serious as they were being painted.

The task of conciliation was made even more difficult when in the middle of the strike an international crisis threatened in Morocco. When the German government dispatched a gun boat to Agadir, it was argued that Britain should show her support for threatened French interests by herself sending a warship to a nearby port. Many seized on this to appeal to 'patriotic' workers to return to work so as not to jeopardise national security at a time of international tension. But such appeals fell on deaf ears as far as Burns was concerned. He had no sympathy for a diplomacy that led Britain to risk her own interests for those of other nations, and along with Morley, Harcourt and Lord Loreburn, he opposed the proposal for British intervention. He also managed to overcome all difficulties and secure an agreement in the dock strike at the end of August. It was a remarkable achievement. Burns had been very sympathetic with the case of the dockers, observing that 'there is great and proper discontent of the poor at their lot and it must go on. Carmen, labourers, workmen are educated enough to understand their grievances, intelligent enough to define the causes, and they are now too sober to be drugged as of yore with the opiates that passed for medicine and the quackeries that are not remedies nor relief'.[2] Yet he had little time for some of the leaders, particularly Ben Tillett, of

1   Ibid. 28 June 1911. For other comments about Churchill's aggressive tendencies see ibid. 8, 10, 12, 14, 16, 18, 19, 20 August 1911. Haldane told his sister that 'Burns is working splendidly, but he and Winston quarrel. The latter is too impulsive'. R.B. Haldane to E. Haldane, 19 August 1911. Haldane Papers. National Library of Scotland MSS 6011, ff.154-5.
2   Burns Diary, 15 August 1911. B.L. Add. MSS 46333.

whose syndicalism he was deeply suspicious. Nevertheless Tillett himself recognised the contribution Burns had made to getting a settlement favourable to the strikers.

> Burns must have his due; it is given generously. One has seen the picture of the old war horse answering to the call of the huntsman and galloping furiously with mane and tail flowing: well, not even one of these ever entered into a fight with greater zest than did John. He coaxed and bullied, reasoned and flouted, ever at the service of both sides . . . fussing like an old hen as he hovered about us; he ran like a being possessed from room to room, a sort of interrogation mark linking both sides. [1]

If Burns's involvement in the 1911 dock strike served to confirm his suspicions of Winston Churchill, so the drafting of the health insurance scheme heightened his distrust of Lloyd George, a resentment constantly fed by his officials who disliked the intrusion of the exchequer into what they regarded as their own province. In particular Burns saw the chancellor's decision to appoint special commissioners for Wales instead of permitting the Local Government Board to administer the scheme in the Principality as a breach of faith, but he got nowhere when he tried to enlist Asquith's support. But his reaction to Lloyd George was based on something far deeper than policy differences. Ultimately it was Lloyd George's political ambition that Burns distrusted, the more so as it could only be directed against Asquith for whom Burns had nothing but admiration. Writing a private memorandum on the prime minister in 1911 Burns commented that 'his fine record as H(ome) S(ecretary), his great chancellorship and his successful premiership place him in the ranks of Great Commoners whose crowning credit will be that he effected a political revolution without martial accessories'. [2] So much did Burns fear for Asquith that early in 1912 he made some very unguarded comments about Lloyd George's ambitions on 10 Downing Street. The upshot was that in February he was summoned by Asquith to a very uncomfortable meeting at which Lloyd George accused him of spreading rumours that he was intriguing against the prime minister. Burns denied having said anything that was not current in the political press but he was eventually compelled to withdraw completely, which he did with a very bad grace, still protesting that he had said nothing that was not true. Years later after Asquith's death, Burns still felt strongly enough about this incident to complain that 'it was a sign of weakness on his part to close his eyes and ears to what was evident to others. He thought no

---

1 B. Tillett, *A History of the London Transport Workers' Strike* (1912), 36. Masterman paid Burns a similar tribute. Masterman, *Masterman,* 205.
2 Memorandum, 10 January 1911. Burns Papers. B.L. Add. MSS 46306, ff.260-1.

evil. Instead of crediting a story of intrigue, he thought poorly of the man who told it'.[1]

In fact Burns was having a difficult time with Asquith at the end of 1911 in more ways than one. He had made plans to issue an amended version of the poor law order withdrawn earlier in the year, hoping to slip it through after parliament rose and to endorse it before the new session. News of this somehow leaked out and Labour M.P.s, led by George Lansbury, turned on him angrily. Ramsay MacDonald made strong representations to Elibank, the Liberal whip, and also wrote to Asquith drawing his attention to the ambiguities in the order, implying that they were deliberate. It was unclear, MacDonald, said, whether certain groups of applicants for outdoor relief were to be entirely exempt from getting medical support or whether they were to be exempted only from getting a fresh medical certificate upon each application for a renewal of relief. It so happened that MacDonald's support of the government was crucial at this stage — in return for Labour support for the Insurance Bill he had been able to extract a pledge that the government would introduce the payment of M.P.s — and Asquith agreed, therefore, to have the order held over until the following session when it could be fully discussed. Burns was furious at the Labour intervention and showed every inclination to resist, even according to one source, to the point of resignation.[2]

The upshot was a renewal of introspection and self pity which lingered on well into the spring of 1912. 'I am after quiet reflection wearying of office. Its restraints, its denial of freedom to your thought, liberty to your speech, its conventions and servitude fall on me like fetters. I am a pinioned bird. I want to soar. I want a change. I desire to do quickly what must be done oh so slowly. The last 3 months have given me great concern'.[3] Yet the truth was that Burns lacked the ability and the drive to do anything in office very quickly. In the course of 1911 the department had finally produced a bill dealing with the sale of rag flock, the material used to stuff cushions and pillows. Questions on this matter had been raised in parliament regularly since 1906, yet it was not until 1909 that a departmental inspector had been directed to investigate and it had taken two further years to prepare legislation. When the bill finally did appear it was so uncontroversial and straightforward that it went through with virtually no discussion at all. The Milk Bill,

1 A. Mackintosh, *Echoes of Big Ben* (n.d.), 111. At a cabinet dinner in February 1912 Asquith shocked his colleagues by referring openly to rumours that he was about to retire and that Lloyd George and Grey were competing for the succession.
2 C.D. Sharpe to S. Webb, 16 December 1911. B.L.P.E.S. Passfield Papers, IIe, ff.200-12.
3 Burns Diary, 9 December 1911. B.L. Add. MSS 46333.

another measure which had lingered for years on the departmental drawing boards, was still not on the statute book and Burns seems to have given up all hope of ever getting it there. Certainly the initiative in resurrecting it in 1910 was not his, and it was not until July 1911 that he hit on a possible solution to the problem of compensation for farmers whose cows were slaughtered, suggesting to the Board of Agriculture that they make a joint approach to the exchequer asking for a grant for this purpose.[1] It was another year, however, before his own officers got round to approaching the Treasury. True, Burns did tell one of his chief housing officers, J.A.E. Dickinson, to be less punctilious about minor points in planning applications but on the whole he appears to have given up almost completely the struggle against departmental inefficiency and lethargy. 'At office I deal with the endless letters, the daily routine of small things that now are dutifully done but I sigh for bigger things'.[2] Yet the fact of his being so enmeshed was entirely of his own making and sprang from his understanding of the function of a government minister. Perhaps at bottom the difference between Burns and Lloyd George was that between an unimaginative administrative plodder, obsessed with economy and detail, and the great visionary legislator to whom economy was of secondary importance and detail a mere nuisance. Burns once commented that if 'you throw him a few facts, suggest a few arguments on any subject, give him the detailed stones . . . he produces at short notice the most harmonious and pleasing mosaic'.[3] By the same token Burns was nothing more than a bricklayer's labourer.

It is noticeable, too, that Burns was attending the House of Commons less frequently than before and that he was growing less inclined to speak. After spending a day clearing up outstanding matters at the L.G.B. before the Christmas holiday of 1911 he noted that while he had been very busy with administration, 'so far as legislation and speaking (to which I get disinclined as years roll on) we have not been prominent'.[4] Public speaking generally seems to have been less attractive to him, for the local press in Battersea continued to harp on his prolonged absence from the constituency. At the beginning of 1912 he failed to appear at a meeting arranged since the previous October, telling his old colleague, Willis, that he was tired, in ill health, and deserved a holiday. Not that he felt any better when he returned from a Christmas motoring

1   The initiative came from Monro. See his memorandum on the bill dated 8 February 1910. PRO MH/4 E.R.D./2173.
2   Burns Diary, 16 April 1912. B.L. Add. MSS 46334.
3   Ibid. 10 March 1914. Add. MSS 46336.
4   Ibid. 10 December 1911. Add. MSS 46333. This point was also made by P.W. Wilson in *Everyman*, 1 August 1913.

holiday on the continent. 'I have almost had enough of it for a time at least'.[1] According to his diary it was still loyalty to his colleagues that was preventing him from actually resigning, especially as by-elections were going badly for the government. 'My inclination is to resign; my reluctant duty is to stay, comradeship and loyalty alone induces me to remain'.[2] But vanity alone kept him from resigning without a suitably important cause. His frustration was not yet such that he could contemplate disappearing from public life altogether. But this would have been the inevitable result of any resignation at this stage for as Ben Turner noted about this time, Burns was a lonely man and felt it.[3] Within the cabinet he was at loggerheads with both Lloyd George and Churchill while at least one of the other leading members, Haldane, had been complaining for years about Burns's conservatism at the Local Government Board. His commitment to economy in public expenditure and his fear that growing state activity would sterilise personal initiative and self help increasingly isolated him from the 'new liberalism' and it was no accident that his closest friends within the cabinet were old fashioned radicals like Morley and the Lord Chancellor, Loreburn.[4]

Neither was it coincidence that at the very time when thoughts of resignation were in his mind, if not very serious at this stage, his diary shows a renewed interest in the problems of London government, and also in the labour movement. Thus during a parliamentary debate on the coal strike in July 1912 he would only look on 'disarmed by office . . . but burning to take a hand and rebuke the lions led by asses on both sides'.[5] He attributed the continued rash of strikes to excessive government expenditure in recent years which, he felt, had helped to fuel the inflation that had driven down the purchasing power of work-men's wages. He was particularly depressed by the violent nature that continued to characterise industrial relations, and was once more directly involved when in the course of 1912 unrest flared in the docks when the settlement he had negotiated the previous year broke down. By the autumn he had managed to patch the situation up again but the experience confirmed his pessimism.

1   Burns Diary, 21 January 1912. B.L. Add. MSS 46334.
2   Ibid. 12 October 1912; See also ibid. 14 April 1912; 27 June 1912.
3   Alf Mattison Diary, 14 January 1912. University of Leeds Library. Mattison Papers. Notebook B, 11.
4   When H.W. Massingham sought to sub-divide the cabinet into its various political groupings he commented that Burns was 'a little difficult to classify'. Quoted in A.F. Havighurst, *Radical Journalist. H.W. Massingham, 1860-1924* (Cambridge, 1974), 208.
5   Burns Diary, 23 July 1912. B.L. Add. MSS 46334.

> I am depressed rather at the wave of brutality sweeping over the
> country . . . the new spirit is manifesting itself in a bad way.
> Impatience with serious grievance, resistance to solid injustice,
> revolt even against intolerable wrong certainly but the revolutionary
> spirit is now evoked and responded to in matters that disciplined
> patience for a short period would resist and a contemptuous
> indifference could dispose of. [1]

Yet Burns could have been under no illusions about the reception he
might receive either from the trade unions or the Labour Party after
the mutual recriminations of the past few years. In any case he had no
time for a class-based party, stressing while in office that he had sought
to do his best for all sections of the community. The type of labour
politicians he admired most were those who had remained as moderate
but distinctly labour men within the broad framework of Liberalism.
Neither had he anything to offer the labour movement. The charisma of
his early days was gone and in any case was irrelevant to the needs of
the Edwardian labour movement. It is probably true to say that the
Labour Party had hardly a single practical and distinctive policy in its
programme but Burns was hardly a fount of constructive ideas. But he
could still comment in 1912 that 'personally I have been anxious to
resign and resume my place in the labour movement', further evidence
of his growing capacity for self-delusion. [2]

The immediate cause of this diary entry was yet another political
reversal, this time over a private member's bill designed to replace the
Local Government Board as the agency responsible for encouraging
house building under the Housing of the Working Classes Act and the
Small Dwellings Acquisition Act of 1899. It proposed to replace the
board with a commission of experts whose job it would be to tour the
country making recommendations to local authorities about possible
house building schemes. Burns set his face resolutely against this bill.
He bitterly resented the implied and often explicit criticism of his
department's housing section — it was shortly after this that he told
Dickinson to be less officious about planning applications — and he
disliked both the creation of another commission, not responsible to
parliament, and the proposal that the bill be funded by a grant from the
exchequer. This, he asserted (in common it must be said with many other
Liberals) would in practice turn out to be a subsidy to bad landlords.
But the whips were not put on and Burns's attempt to get the measure
referred to a committee of the whole house where it would have to take
its chance along with a host of other bills which had been similarly
referred, was defeated. It went instead to a standing committee. He
had already decided that the way to defeat the measure was to delete the

1 Ibid. 23 September 1912.
2 Ibid. 15 March 1912.

provision for an exchequer subsidy on the ground that only a minister could bring in measures involving increases in state expenditure.[1] Although he was added to the standing committee he took little active part in the proceedings, leaving the hatchet work to his parliamentary secretary, Herbert Lewis, and contenting himself with venomous diary entries about the bill's sponsors.

It was an essentially negative triumph and one which unleashed a torrent of press criticism around his ears. *The Times* accused him of talking nonsense, the *Daily News* claimed he had been 'pedantic and intemperate' while the *Telegraph* suggested that his hostility was based mainly on the fact that the bill was an intrusion on his domain. 'It trod on his grass. And that with Mr Burns is an act which is past forgiveness'.[2] Nor did Burns derive much relief from his victory, for the pages of his diary continued to reflect the by now familiar mixture of schizophrenic musings about the drudgery of office, his loyalty to the government, the domestic difficulties concerning Edgar, all combined with an inability or unwillingness to do anything about the situation. Everywhere the forces of social advance, as he understood them, seemed to be on the defensive against either reaction or extremism. In London the Progressives suffered further reverses in the elections of 1913 and the malaise seemed to Burns to be reaching parliament itself. 'No interest, no enthusiasm, disillusioned and depressed; all sections are wearied with their 7 years hard labour ... '[3] There is no doubt that he was feeling like this himself and certainly all the values which he had upheld in office did seem to be under attack. He was a constitutionalist and yet other groups in society seemed to be determined to use unconstitutional methods to secure their aims. Burns himself had tangible evidence of this at the beginning of 1913 in the form of a chemical parcel from the suffragettes, a gentle irony this in view of his speech about chemical parcel post in the 1880s.[4] Fortunately the post office had detected the device *en route*. He had always been the epitome of integrity in public life, yet the Liberal Party had been shaken by the Marconi scandal in which some government ministers, including Lloyd George, had allegedly used their political position to reap financial benefits. Burns felt that their indiscretions had involved both the party and the government in 'endless trouble' and 'much discredit', and could easily have been avoided had Lloyd George admitted that he had been

1 J. Burns to Lord Crewe, 14 March 1912. Burns Papers. B.L. Add. MSS 46302, f.124.
2 All quoted in Kent, *Burns,* 228.
3 Burns Diary, 4 June 1913. B.L. Add. MSS 46335.
4 See above. p.25.

at fault.[1] Burns was a champion of individual effort. 'In all their work', he exhorted the infant mortality conference in August 1913, 'they should remember that they could not supersede the mother, and they should not by over-attention sterilise her initiative and capacity to do what every mother should be able to do for herself'.[2] But this, too, seemed under attack when a fresh poor law order restricting outdoor relief still further was issued in 1913, and another storm of protest broke out. Over 400 angry letters descended on the Local Government Board, many of them from local Liberal associations, showing just how out of touch Burns had become in his approach to social problems.[3] Again, economy in administration had been Burns's watchword, but some of his colleagues seemed determined to ignore all financial considerations. After a day with Lloyd George discussing the sanitoria for T.B. patients proposed under the terms of the health insurance scheme, Burns commented privately that 'we are spending on rates, taxes, officials, and institutions what, if spent on wages, food and housing, would make, if added to wise spending on higher wages, consumption disappear in a generation'.[4] Yet when he opposed the Tory Housing Bill which reappeared in 1913, suggesting that it would result in a further growth of national mendicancy, he was again subjected to a good deal of press abuse, and the newsmen's placards that evening were everywhere proclaiming that he had killed a good bill.

He felt profound dismay therefore when in October 1913 Lloyd George launched a new campaign on housing and the land which borrowed some of the features of the hated Tory bill. As Burns pointed out in a lengthy letter to Lloyd George the suggested creation of an entirely new department - either within the Board of Agriculture or in a new Ministry of Lands - to deal with housing was an implied snub on his own housing department which had done well with the legislation of 1909.[5] In fact his enthusiasm was misplaced. Although demolition work had been spreading, the act had come into force at a time when private house building was at a low ebb in Britain and it did not provide the sort of encouragement really needed, for example, in the form of direct aid from the exchequer. Neither was the town planning part proving very fruitful. As usual Burns had devoted enormous amounts of time to examining projects for himself, but he had been so concerned to allow everyone affected by planning schemes to express their

1 Burns Diary, 19 July 1913. B.L. Add. MSS 46335. See also his comments to Almeric Fitzroy. Fitzroy, *Memoirs*, II.514.
2 *The Times*, 5 August 1913.
3 PRO MH 60/16. Letter Books. 18 September - 16 December 1913.
4 Burns Diary, 16 May 1913. B.L. Add. MSS 46335.
5 J. Burns to D. Lloyd George, 9 October 1913. Beaverbrook Library. Lloyd George Papers C/3/9/1.

opinions that the act's regulations, issued in May 1910, were bureaucratic and labyrinthine in the extreme. By the beginning of 1914 only two schemes had been finally approved, both in Birmingham. In any case, Lloyd George was not worried by the prospect of snubbing Burns whom he had found to be 'wholly obstructive and troublesome' on the insurance bill, and in cabinet he swept aside his objections, plunging Burns once more into the mood for resignation,[1] 'I am confronted', wrote Burns, 'with a serious issue, personal, political and administrative. My personal inclination is to go'.[2]

Instead, however, he found a much more congenial outlet when at the beginning of 1914 Asquith offered him the presidency of the Board of Trade. It was perhaps indicative of his flagging enthusiasm for L.G.B. work that the news of the offer reached him in the billiard room of the National Liberal Club where he had latterly become something of a regular. Asquith had first offered the post to Herbert Samuel who had turned it down in favour of the Local Government Board, but giving it to Burns was an ingenious move on the prime minister's part. It allowed him to remain in government and also afforded him the satisfaction of an apparent promotion, as the Board of Trade was generally regarded as being of superior status. Further, it had had a series of highly energetic presidents and it was questionable as to whether there was much of importance still to do.[3] Burns therefore could be safely left to concentrate on administration at which he was nothing if not diligent and economical. The comprehensive mandate exercised by the Board of Trade over all matters relating to trade, the collection of statistics, regulations of railways and shipping, and the maintenance of industrial standards, also included industrial relations and would thus permit Burns to become involved in the one area which he had found rewarding in recent years. Indeed, his appointment was welcomed for this very reason by some union leaders. Tillett, for instance, wrote to say that 'I am making a fight of it and shall be glad to see you give our side a fair chance'.[4] Certainly the appointment appears to have rejuvenated Burns and lifted his spirit. 'Today', he observed, 'begins another advance ending where?'[5] Like so many ventures in 1914 it was to end unexpectedly and abruptly in the aftermath of a political assassination in the Balkans.

1 Newman Diary, 5 May 1912. Department of Health and Social Security Library. Newman Diary, I.

2 Burns Diary, 17 October 1913. B.L. Add. MSS 46335.

3 This was Herbert Samuel's reason for turning it down. See H. Samuel to his mother, 11 January 1914. H.L.R.O. Samuel Papers, A/156, f.1052.

4 B. Tillett to J. Burns, 13 February 1914. Burns Papers. B.L. Add. MSS 46285, f.195.

5 Burns Diary, 31 January 1914. Ibid. Add, MSS 46336.

9

RESIGNATION AND RETIREMENT. 1914-1943

Superficially at least, Burns's new job seems to have raised his spirits. The Board of Trade was staffed by some very able civil servants, including Beveridge, George Askwith, and, at its head, H.Llewellyn Smith, who had organised picket lines for Burns during the London omnibus strike of 1891. At his first official meeting with his staff Burns gave every appearance of enthusiasm and energy, telling them that they had better be as good officials as he intended to be president, and within six months he was exulting in his diary that 'I have never had such luck as this year. Bills, Orders, Estimates, Administration, Deputations'.[1] Yet it is difficult to avoid the conclusion that while Burns's mood may have changed, his underlying attitude had not, for he was generally content to leave well alone. 'Our new president', Beveridge confided to his mother, 'is not particularly active and this gives us a very peaceful time'.[2] It is true that after the régimes of Lloyd George and Churchill there was not much left in the way of major legislation to the Board of Trade anyway, but Burns certainly had few ideas of his own. The need for the measure he introduced in April to tidy up the administration of the unemployment insurance scheme had long been apparent and was already prepared when Burns became president. Furthermore, the old failings were still much in evidence. After listening to his chief floundering during standing committee on the bill Beveridge observed tactfully to his mother that Burns was not 'very good at explaining the complicated provisions of a Bill in Committee'.[3] When the Commons considered the amendments made by the standing committee Burns left it to his parliamentary secretary, J.M. Robertson, to deal with the debate, contenting himself with voting. The only other legislative measure of any import that he introduced before world events intervened was the Merchant Shipping (Convention) Bill, based on the recommendations of an international conference on sea safety, held before Burns went to the Board of Trade. Here he did find it necessary to exert himself a little. Within a few days of his appointment he had set up a departmental committee against the wishes of some of his civil servants to examine the whole question of health and safety in the merchant navy. By April he had a bill in his hand which was referred to standing committee. Yet he was not

1 Burns Diary, 9 July 1914. B.L. Add. MSS 46336.
2 W.H. Beveridge to his mother, 8 May 1914. B.L.P.E.S. Beveridge Papers, IIa, f 60.
3 Ibid.

sufficiently interested to see the measure through to the statute book. The amendments made in standing committee were considered by the House on 5 August. By this time Burns had resigned but no successor had been appointed and he could at least have attended to see it through. He preferred, however, to leave this to Robertson.

But if, as Beveridge claimed, the officials of the Board of Trade were having a quiet time in the first half of 1914, the same could not be said of the nation as a whole. In addition to militant strikers and suffragettes, in Ireland, Ulster protestants, encouraged by signs of disaffection in the Irish garrisons, were showing every inclination to resist by force the establishment of home rule. Burns had a lifelong commitment to Irish independence and took a firm line in the cabinet, urging his colleagues to press on in spite of the threats of opposition. 'If P.M. is wise and prescient, he will drive on even though horse, foot and artillery confront him. Over them, through them, but not under them is the only way to civil supremacy, popular will and democratic control . . .'[1] Although he admired and appreciated Asquith's wish that home rule should be initiated in a spirit of good will, Burns also believed that Ireland could only be permanently tranquilised by firm measures. 'I would take a shorter cut with the malcontents', he wrote.[2] When J.E.B. Seely resigned at the end of March and Asquith took over the War Office himself, Burns even offered his own services in any capacity thought desirable, a clear hint that he was not averse to going to Ireland himself, even though on a previous visit irate Orangemen had nearly drowned him in the River Lagan.

With civil war looming in Ireland it was understandable that the British public failed to appreciate the grim significance of the June assassination of the Austrian Archduke Ferdinand by a Serbian nationalist. Burns was equally oblivious. Not until the middle of July did his diary make any reference to the tension in the Balkans and the frantic diplomatic efforts being made to avert a headlong clash between the Triple Alliance and the Triple Entente. On 26 July he noted that the war news, while serious, was not critical.[3] But events were already moving with a logic of their own. The following day, as the world lurched nearer to war, dragged by chains of alliances and the activation of irreversible military timetables, Burns spelled out in no uncertain terms his own feelings.

1 Burns Diary, 26 March 1914. B.L. Add. MSS 46336.
2 Ibid. 4 March 1914. He never changed his mind. 'Asquith should have enforced the Act we passed even to the length of repressing an Orange rising rather than give our enemies abroad the impression of weakness'. Ibid. 21 February 1918. Add. MSS 46340.
3 Ibid. 26 July 1914. Add. MSS 46336.

Why 4 Great Powers should fight over Servia no fellow can understand. This I know, there is one fellow who will have nothing to do
with such a criminal folly, the effects of which will be appalling to
the welter of nations who will be involved. It must be averted by all
the means in our power.

He continued in a tone which once more reveals his clear sense of
calling to be the peculiar advocate of the working classes.

Apart from the merits of the case it is my especial duty to dissociate
myself, and the principles I hold and the trusteeship for the working
classes I carry from such a universal crime as the contemplated war
will be. My duty is clear and at all costs will be done.[1]

On 28 July Austria declared war on Serbia and bombarded Belgrade
the following day. Burns remained convinced that it was a central
European issue from which Britain had to remain aloof and he urged
Morley, too, to stand firm for neutrality at the cabinet meeting on 29
July. On 1 August when Germany declared war against Russia, Burns
lunched with Sir Edward Grey, appealing to him to continue his efforts
for peace, an appeal which could not have endeared him overmuch to a
weary Foreign Secretary who that very day dispatched no fewer than
seventeen telegrams to various European capitals for precisely that
purpose. Ultimately, however, Grey — and Asquith — believed that
Britain had a duty to stand by her Entente allies, particularly France,
should they be attacked by Germany; indeed, they had already given
such an undertaking secretly to the French, and it was on this issue that
the unity of the cabinet threatened to dissolve. Burns was unequivocally
hostile to any British intervention on behalf of France but both he and
the other leading members of the peace party in the cabinet, Morley
and Harcourt, lacked any real weight. Even so, Asquith's chief concern
was to preserve unity at such a time of international crisis and on 2
August he sent J.A. Pease to sound Burns out and to gauge the depth
of his opposition to Britain's involvement. That afternoon, Grey
informed the cabinet of his understanding with France that Britain
would come to her aid in the event of a German fleet entering the North
Sea. The implications of this statement were obvious and the cabinet
received it in total silence. After a second or two, that silence was
broken by a familiar voice. 'Mr Prime Minister', Burns said, 'this
means war and I must resign from the cabinet'. Adding a few words of
gratitude to his colleagues he rose from his seat and walked out of the
government and virtually out of public life as well.[2] Despite the gravity
of the international situation Asquith still made time later in the day
to meet Burns privately to urge him to change his mind. But it was

1 Memorandum on the War Situation, 27 July 1914. Burns Papers. B.L. Add.
MSS 46308, f.130.
2 This is based on Masterman's account in *Sunday Express*, 2 January 1927.

futile; Burns was resolute. Morley joined him in resignation, as did Beauchamp and Simon, though these two changed their minds when Germany launched her attack on France through neutral Belgium.

Despite many hints that he would one day explain in full the reasons for his resignation in 1914, Burns never did so, an omission which produced some very odd assertions later. In 1943, for example, H. Fitzherbert Wright, who had met Burns in a House of Commons cloakroom just after he left the cabinet on 2 August 1914, claimed that Burns told him he resigned because the cabinet was resolved to fight only at sea instead of hitting the Germans on land as well.[1] Yet the real reasons are not hard to work out. Burns was no pacifist, his own frequent youthful resorts to fisticuffs and his later militant line on Ulster show this clearly enough. Indeed, in a curious way, he was as fascinated by military matters as Churchill was. He had been a very vocal member of the cabinet committee established in 1906 to consider Haldane's plans for army reform, and he had also been a regular attender at army manouvres on Salisbury Plain for at least twenty years. The diarist, W.S. Blunt, once asserted that Burns knew intimately the history of every regiment in the British army.[2] Burns's resignation, then, sprang not from any pacifist conviction, but from his belief that Britain was being dragged in to fight a war mainly in the interests of France and Russia. He favoured a policy of splendid isolation and always had done. When Britain had conducted diplomatic talks with Japan in 1911 his comment had been 'very good, though splendid isolation would be better'.[3] Asked in 1915 about his resignation by Lord Fisher he replied simply, 'Splendid isolation, no Balance of Power, no incorporation in Continental System. . . .'[4] For this reason he had been a consistent opponent of the chauvinist sabre rattling against Germany that had erupted periodically in the years before 1914. After the great naval scare of March 1909 Burns had proposed the toast of Anglo-German friendship at a dinner organised by the International Arbitration League, and had taken the opportunity to denounce war-mongering newspapers.[5] When war did come, he blamed it partly on the jingo press and partly on Grey's secret diplomacy which had committed Britain to protect Russian and French interests.[6] His

1 *The Times*, 28 January 1943. It was promptly repudiated by Lord Gainford in ibid. 29 January 1943.

2 W.S. Blunt, *My Diaries, 1888-1914* (1932), 159.

3 Burns Diary, 11 July 1911. B.L. Add. MSS 46333.

4 Ibid. 23 September 1915. Add. MSS 46337.

5 *The Times*, 3 May 1909. See his letter expressing identical sentiments to J. Allen Baker, 9 June 1909. Burns Papers. B.L. Add. MSS 46300, ff.232-4.

6 Burns Diary, 1 and 5 August 1914. B.L. Add. MSS 46336.

very opposition to Grey's cabinet statement of 2 August rested on his ignorance of the secret commitment to help France. The discovery of its existence came as a terrible shock to him and formed a constant theme in his war diaries henceforth. In 1917, for example, he claimed that Britain was increasingly being used as 'the instrument for Russian ambition and French designs'.[1] Seeing Grey in the street one morning towards the end of the war Burns noted that he should have made it clear to both France and Russia that Britain was not in the Entente for purposes of aggression.[2] Frequently during the war Burns made his way over to the Wimbledon home of John Morley and there the two ex-ministers vied with each other in running down the unfortunate Grey for being 'tied to Russia and France beforehand behind the back of Parliament without the consent of Cabinet as a whole . . . therefore drawn into the war by commitments unauthorised'.[3]

But if a basic belief in isolation was the main reason for Burns's resignation it was not the only one. For him, involvement in the war also entailed the violation of values such as economy and humanitarianism which he had always tried to uphold during his ministerial career. In the recurrent cabinet clashes over naval expenditure, for instance, Burns had always been on the side of the restrictionists, going in 1908 to the point of resignation.[4] When at the end of 1913 Churchill was ordered to reduce his estimates which were nearly £3,000,000 up on the previous year, Burns was almost ecstatic. 'Economy has at last seized on [sic] with a vengeance. For 8 years I have preached and practised it but never with the sudden zeal of belated converts'.[5] The war, of course, was a vastly expensive business and this prospect appalled him. In 1914 he forecast that it would cost over £7,000,000,000 before it ended.[6] If anything, however, the probable cost in human terms dismayed him even more. His appreciation of the extent of suffering probably owed much to the fact that, unlike most of his contemporaries, Burns expected a lengthy war. In July 1914 he suggested that the conflict could last four years – almost exactly right and certainly much more realistic than all the talk of a war ended by Christmas. However disagreeably it may have manifested itself at the Local Government

1   Ibid. 6 January 1917. Add. MSS 46339.

2   Ibid. 21 June 1918. Add. MSS 46340.

3   Ibid. 20 July 1918.

4   See *Journals and Letters of Reginald Viscount Esher*, ed. M.V. Brett (1938), II, 283. He had been similarly resolute in 1909. See K. Robbins, *Sir Edward Grey. A Biography of Lord Grey of Falloden* (1971), 196-8.

5   Burns Diary, 16 December 1913. B.L. Add. MSS 46335.

6   A forecast made to a member of the National Liberal Club and published in the *Morning Gazette*, 14 April 1928. See also the notes dated 28 July 1914 in Burns Papers. B.L. Add. MSS 46302, f.293.

Board, Burns did have a great sense of compassion. 'What a waste of life and limb', he lamented in 1915, 'and what a heritage of hate it hands on to our children'.[1] It was hardly surprising that he rejected out of hand a request from the Battersea Recruiting Committee to address rallies on its behalf. In 1916 his concern became more directly personal, for Edgar enlisted in the artillery. Six months later, when his son wrote to say that he had been in the thick of the fighting on the Western Front, Burns's anger and compassion exploded across the pages of his diary. 'Why should millions of mothers' sons be the vicarious sacrifice of proud monarchs, iron emperors, and intriguing diplomats . . . I never see a soldier but what I blame Grey'.[2] Again, his forecast that the war would cost the country a million men was not all that wrong, and he attributed the frightful losses to the bunglings of a class-ridden army, telling Newman that Kitchener was no more than a butcher.[3]

To the end of his life, Burns remained convinced of the rightness of the stand he took against war in 1914. When Rosebery died in 1929 Burns, in remembering him, chose to stress his belief in the necessity of Britain's international isolation.[4] Shortly after Burns's own death in 1943, a former mayor of Battersea, A.G. Pritchard, wrote to the *South Western Star* pointing out that in an interview on what proved to be his death-bed, Burns had still maintained that he was correct to resign in 1914.[5] Yet Burns never spoke out to explain his action, preferring instead to lapse into a self-imposed silence made all the more remarkable because he had previously been so vociferous and combative. Not once did he speak out in public against the war, nor did he participate, other than by voting, in any of the parliamentary debates which it raised, for example, conscription. In no way could this be construed as springing from any lack of courage, either moral or physical. He had exhibited both qualities throughout his life, never more so than at the time of Britain's last major military entanglement, in South Africa. Nor was his silence due to want of opportunity. Burns may not have been a weighty figure in the government but he had been a cabinet minister and his adherence to the peace cause would have been prestigious at least. Leading pacifists rushed to congratulate him on his resignation and it is clear that many were hoping for some sort of lead from him. 'Resign', pleaded Emily Hobhouse, 'and join the ranks of

1 Burns Diary, 25 April 1915. Ibid. Add. MSS 46337.
2 Ibid. 19 June 1916. Add. MSS 46338.
3 Newman Diary, 31 August 1914. Department of Health and Social Security Library. Newman Diary, II.
4 *The Times,* 22 May, 1929.
5 *South Western Star,* 5 February 1943.

labour, the only party likely to save us now'.[1] 'Once more', rejoiced Joseph Clayton, Burns was 'unmuzzled and a leader of the people'.[2] Yet Burns held aloof from the Union of Democratic Control which emerged as the main institutional vehicle of opposition to Britain's involvement, and he repeatedly rejected appeals to denounce the war publicly. Nothing came for example of a proposal from Loreburn that Burns should join with himself and Morley in publishing a letter stating clearly their position.[3] Nor did Burns respond when C.P. Trevelyan urged him to attend the Commons and speak to an anti-war amendment he was moving on the King's Speech at the opening of the 1916 session.[4] In 1917 Lord Lansdowne published a letter highly critical of the war but Burns still refused to be drawn into putting his weight behind it as well. Asked by his friends for an endorsement of Lansdowne's letter he 'remained firm and will give my view when I think most good can be done for all and *without harrying allies'.*[5] Here, it seems, is the clue to Burns's silence, for the comment reveals precisely that same ill-construed but genuinely-held sense of self-importance and loyalty which, according to his own account, had so often prevented him from quitting office prior to the war. This sentiment surfaced frequently in his wartime diary. After hearing Lloyd George speak in April 1915 about the threat to war production caused by drunkeness, he commented — curiously in view of his teetotalism — 'but for my connection with Govt. I would have criticised his implied slander on workmen'.[6] Of course, his self-assessment was wrong. The peace party in the cabinet had been ineffective precisely because it lacked any figure of major importance. Things might have turned out very differently, for example, had Lloyd George supported it. But even so, Burns really believed that any pronouncement from himself would damage the war effort and so he stayed silent. During the first two years this underlying wish to do nothing that would create dissension was reinforced by his admiration and respect for Asquith, whose growing inability to cope with the demands of total war he watched with rising concern.

His dismay was deepened by the fact that if Asquith went there could only be one possible successor — Lloyd George. Burns's long-standing mistrust of him had merely been confirmed by what he saw

1 E. Hobhouse to J. Burns, 4 August 1914. Burns Papers. B.L. Add. MSS 46303, f.15.
2 J. Clayton to J. Burns, 5 August 1914. Ibid. f.33.
3 Lord Loreburn to J. Burns, 26 July 1915. Ibid. ff.171-2.
4 C.P. Trevelyan to J. Burns, 11 February 1916. Ibid. ff.193-4.
5 Burns Diary, 1 December 1917. Ibid. Add. MSS 46339. My italics.
6 Ibid. 29 April 1915. Add. MSS 46337.

as the chancellor's desertion of the peace cause. In fact, although Lloyd George had attended a peace party lunch on 1 August 1914, he had never been an advocate of peace at any price. But in Burns's eyes his support for the war was the crowning act of self-seeking and betrayal, and one for which Burns never forgave him. After listening to Lloyd George outlining the steps he proposed to take in 1915 to raise the money necessary to wage war, Burns commented bitterly that the Welshman had at last been 'confronted with the ghastly tragedy which he more than any other living man has helped to plunge the credulous country into'.[1] His diary records, too, his outrage at the sequence of events that led in 1916 to Lloyd George supplanting Asquith. Burns had long suspected Lloyd George's ambitions for the top position and he thought it unforgiveable that he should exploit the war for this purpose. When Asquith formed his coalition government in May 1915 Burns blamed it on the machinations of Lloyd George. He likened him to Samson and suggested that he had just pulled down the pillars that supported the Liberal Party. Asquith, he noted almost sorrowfully, was suffering for being so indecisive three years ago, and from this time onwards Burns's opinion of the prime minister declined considerably.[2] 'The P.M. has sold his party, deserted his colleagues, misserved his country and destroyed much of his reputation by his surrender to the Tories'.[3] When at the end of the following year Lloyd George finally replaced Asquith as head of the government Burns dispensed with ink and wrote in venom instead.

> The men who made the war were profuse in their praises of the man who kicked the P.M. out of his office and now degrades by his disloyal, dishonest and lying presence the greatest office in the State . . . the Gentlemen of England serve under the greatest cad in Europe.[4]

Such a combination of plotters and renegades, Burns believed, could not possibly generate sufficient trust and loyalty to win the war – but still he would not join the peace movement and risk dividing the nation.[5]

On the outbreak of war people in Britain appeared to be determined to carry on with business as usual. Burns, however, spent the three days that elapsed between his resignation and the appointment of a successor (Runciman) hard at work in his office making plans to offset the distress that was expected to develop from the dislocation of war. That he did so was indicative again of his basic patriotism and also of his

1 Ibid. 4 May 1915.
2 Ibid. 19 May 1915.
3 Ibid. 28 May 1915.
4 Ibid. 8 December 1916. Add. MSS 46338.
5 Ibid. 18 December 1916.

concern for humanity. So, too, was his acceptance of both a place on the government committee established to consider the prevention of distress, and the chairmanship of the committee charged with organising relief in London. The government committee contained Herbert Samuel as President of the Local Government Board, Birrell, Mckinnon Wood, Herbert Lewis, Masterman, J.A. Pease, Walter Long, Ramsay MacDonald, Wedgwood Benn, George Murray, and Mrs Tennant, company in which Burns played a relatively minor role.[1] Generally, however, he adopted a strictly *laissez-faire* line, for example in his efforts to preserve the flow of food supplies. A week or so after the war began he met representatives of the bakery, sugar, and butchery trades and appealed to them to pool their stocks, 'play the game and pull the populace through their difficulties by being public spirited'.[2] In very much the same vein he wrote to *The Times,* pointing out that there was considerable unemployment in the furniture trade but that it could be alleviated if people placed their orders for new furniture now rather than in the following spring.[3] This was tempered by his efforts to ensure, however, that workers were not being laid off unnecessarily, particularly in government departments like the Post Office where both he and MacDonald were 'anxious for an assurance that the reduction of staff has not been in excess of the reduction of actual work that has taken place'.[4] He also suggested that the committee undertake a survey to see how many jobs could be saved by ending all overtime working.

As chairman, however, Burns played a much more prominent role in the London relief committee and it was not long before his attempts to apply *laissez faire* principles there led him into conflict with his old protagonists, Mrs Webb and Charles Masterman, who were also members. In London many clerks, warehousemen, and labourers had been laid off once war broke out, while other firms had given their employees notice or put them on short time working. This created much distress as many families suddenly found themselves with reduced incomes or even no income at all. But Burns wanted to minimise interference in the natural working of the economy, putting a premium on self-help, restricting relief to a minimum, and making soup kitchens and other relief works very much a last resort. He therefore began by adopting a very *ad hoc* procedure for distributing the funds available to him, much to the disgust of Mrs Webb who wanted a much more scientific

1 All of course were politicians except George Murray who was the Commissioner of Customs and Excise. Mrs Tennant had been a factory inspector and was wife of the Under-Secretary of State for War.
2 Burns Diary, 10 August 1914. B.L. Add. MSS 46336.
3 *The Times,* 12 September 1914.
4 H. Samuel to L. Hobhouse, 24 August 1914. PRO MH 57/197.

approach relating the monies allocated to the various London boroughs to their particular degree of distress. So, too, did Masterman who protested bitterly to Samuel and pleaded for a much greater degree of systematisation to be forced on Burns. [1] Their attitude prompted Burns into some very scathing comments about 'sentimentalists and professional philanthropists . . . these Vivisectors of the poor, these Pauper vaccinators and statistical ghouls who regard life as a hunting ground for social facts'.[2] But even those who shared Burns's desire to prevent abuse of the relief facilities were concerned by his attitude. A member of the Shoreditch Committee, for example, wrote to Simon complaining that they had had to reject many genuine applications because of Burns's parsimony. He added that he had prepared an outline scheme of relief and sent a copy to Burns a month before but had not even received an acknowledgement.[3] Burns feared that if he ended his *ad hoc* approach he would lose all control over the allocation of funds which might then be distributed too lavishly or find their way into the pockets of malingerers. This was why he was determined to keep to an absolute minimum the relief to be paid in London. There was a great deal of discontent anyway with the scales which the government committee considered in the early days of the war, but in London Burns's committee, in the teeth of all the labour representatives, recommended scales substantially lower than those recommended by the Charity Organisation Society and those paid by the War Office to soldiers' families. At the end of September after repeated clashes with Mrs. Webb, Burns emerged victorious, 'our London scale being practically adopted with *what we wanted most, no reference to rent at all*'.[4] It was a harsh decision to opt for relief scales without allowing for rents, which were rising rapidly, but Burns believed that their inclusion would involve the relief funds in large and unknown liabilities. Although Mrs Webb had support from Masterman and Harry Gosling it was not sufficient to outweigh the restrictionists like the Lord Mayor, the chairman of the L.C.C., and the notorious anti-socialist, Herbert Jessel, all of whom backed Burns. So, too, did the officials of the Local Government Board whose Intelligence Department was providing the committee with all its information, and Burns's hand was further strengthened by the fact that, apart from Masterman, he was the only London committee member who also sat on the government committee.

1   C.F.G. Masterman to H. Samuel, 7 September 1914. Ibid. 57/195.
2   Burns Diary, 10 and 18 August 1914. B.L. Add. MSS 46336.
3   E. Konstam to J. Simon, 24 September 1914. PRO MH 57/183.
4   Burns Diary, 30 September 1914. B.L. Add. MSS 46336. Italics in the original.

By the beginning of 1915 the economy had pretty well taken up the slack in the labour market and the London committee adjourned its meetings for a month. This permitted Burns to turn his attention briefly to a dock dispute which had caused Runciman some trouble. When the committee reconvened it was to consider further cuts in relief. 'The fact is', Burns observed at the beginning of February, 'there is a shortage of men and soon will be a shortage of women for all forms of productive work. I am strongly in favour of closing down nearly all the relief agencies and reversing the monies now beginning to be wasted . . . '[1] Although 'the monstrous regiment of women' continued to resist, the logic of events was clearly on Burns's side.[2] As total war with its all consuming requirements pushed up the demand for labour so the need for relief steadily diminished. In March 1915 the workrooms established in London for unemployed women were shut down. The following month it was announced that Hollesley Bay was to become a home for disabled servicemen. There remained, of course, a small irreducible residual, useless even in wartime, but Burns felt they were too few to warrant the continued existence of specialist relief agencies. In August, therefore, he wrote to Asquith, resigning from both the government and London committees, suggesting that such work as now remained to be done could be carried out quite adequately by the relevant departments of the Local Government Board.[3]

But if Burns had turned his back on the London relief committee he had in no way turned his back on the capital's politics. On the contrary, the welfare of London became his main interest for the rest of the war. In the years immediately before 1914 he had expressed some anxieties in his diary that London Conservatism and its associated business interests were reviving. Now he felt that commercial interests against which he had fought on the London County Council were beginning to reassert themselves under the cover of war, a suspicion first aroused by the appearance in February 1915 of a bill (subsequently withdrawn) to set up a company to provide the London area with electricity. When the scheme was resurrected towards the end of the war Burns took a leading part in a meeting of London M.P.s and Progressive Councillors and urged them to resist the efforts of what he called 'the octopus gang' to 'expropriate and expel the local authorities whose power and light installations are doing well by consumer and ratepayer'.[4] For the same reason he intervened noisily, though unsuccessfully, in debates on

1 Ibid. 6 February 1915. Add. MSS 46337.
2 Ibid. 26 January 1915.
3 J. Burns to H.H. Asquith, 20 August 1915. Burns Papers. B.L. Add. MSS 46282, ff.179-80.
4 Burns Diary, 25 September 1917. Ibid. Add. MSS 46339.

the Statutory Undertakings (Charges) Bill in 1917, a measure designed to permit various public utilities to raise their prices which had been subjected to rigorous wartime controls.

Burns's concern was not only to protect the principle of municipalisation but also to prevent all considerations of amenity and welfare being swept aside by commercialism. For this reason he was busy behind the scenes in 1918 organising opposition to a bill which would have allowed the Brentford Gas Company to build a new works on 125 acres of riverside Chiswick. Even more indicative of this concern was his parliamentary support for L.C.C. elements trying to block a scheme mooted by the South Eastern Railway Company to strengthen the bridge running across the Thames to Charing Cross. Burns took the view that this might well inhibit any future improvement in the area, specifically the pulling down of the bridge, which he regarded as an architectural monstrosity, the transfer of Charing Cross Station to the south side of the river, and the construction of a new road bridge linking it with the north bank stations somewhere near Trafalgar Square. 'It is really a monstrous thing', he wrote, 'that the very finest point of the river . . . should be occupied by this ugly railway bridge and the unutterable meanness of Charing Cross Station'.[1] In July 1916 the bill's opponents succeeded in getting the second reading deferred for six months, aided by a powerful speech from Burns who claimed that the company's plan violated the canon of public taste as well as ruining a fine riverside view.[2] He further promised, if the bill was postponed, to do his best to get the interested parties together to thrash the matter out and to this end a conference was arranged at the Mansion House for the end of December. The delegates decided that the question was too complex to be dealt with while the war was on but still suggested that the relevant local authority might consider the scheme. Accordingly the L.C.C. called a meeting in January 1917 which really endorsed the Mansion House decision that the matter should be deferred until after the war. Shortly afterwards, however, the company made a slight alteration in its bill, adding a sterilisation clause. This stated that if any public authority subsequently obtained permission to rebuild the station on the south side, no railway company would be able to demand reimbursement for expenditure incurred if the bill became law. What the company was proposing, in other words, was to waive its right to any compensation for the £167,000 it was planning to spend on strengthening the existing bridge, a bribe which some of the bill's opponents found acceptable. Burns was appalled, seeing this as 'treachery. . . to their own duty

1   J. Burns, R.A. Webb, and R. Blomfeld, *The Future of Charing Cross: the Improvement Scheme; Statement of the Case* (1916), 3-4.
2   Hansard, 5th series, LXXXIII, 1303. 3 July 1916.

and policy', and even though the bill was given a second reading in March 1917 by a convincing margin he was determined to continue the fight.[1] Burns and a few other diehards gave evidence to the Lords committee which considered the scheme in July and although the bill was eventually passed, the committee did decide that the bridge could not be widened, nor any work done above the waterline, until three years after the bill became law. (But the bridge still survives, as monstrous as ever, to this day.)

But all this was essentially insignificant for a man who until recently had been at the heart of government, and resignation still left him with plenty of time on his hands. Finding, therefore, that he rather enjoyed showing Edgar and some of his comrades the historic places associated with parliament, he began to deliver freelance lectures to parties of visitors to Westminister, mainly allied soldiers. According to his own account, he addressed so many people that he came near to total exhaustion and had to rest. The lectures afforded an opportunity to exercise his old oratorical skills, but the punch and vitality that had made him such a compelling public speaker in the 1880's and 1890's had gone, worn away by years of 'officialese', to be replaced by a hackneyed style abounding in alliteration and tired clichés.

> Within this towering field of history, this sanctuary of saints, there has grown up from British, Celtic, Roman, Saxon, Danish, Norman, and Tudor times the priceless heritage of the British race known as Westminster Abbey. Revered by the religious, admired by the artistic, the political pilgrim, the social reformer, the humanist find in this ancient sanctuary the Mecca of all their spiritual traditions, the repository of their ideals, the cradle of their liberties, the nursery of their ideals, the seedbed of freedom.[2]

Just occasionally there were flashes of the old sparkle, as when he told an American who was disparaging the Thames, that the river was 'liquid history'.[3]

Peace came finally in November 1918. Burns was pleased enough that the struggle was over, the more so because Edgar had survived, despite suffering severe shell-shock. Now Burns could contemplate a return to the political arena. With the advent of peace, he noted, 'my reticence ends and a new chapter begins. What will it be?'[4] The question was more than a rhetorical one, for the changes induced by the war had left him in a very uncertain position politically. The Liberal Party had turned its back on him as long ago as 1915, resolving not

1 Burns Diary, 22 February 1917. B.L. Add. MSS 46339.
2 Undated note in Burns's own handwriting. Burns Papers. G.L.C. Collection. Box labelled 'Trade Union Pamphlets'.
3 Quoted in S.L. Hughes, *Press, Platform and Parliament* (1918), 283.
4 Burns Diary, 11 November 1918. B.L. Add. MSS 46340.

to support him in view of his opposition to the war and there was a
Coalition Liberal candidate already in the field for the newly created
seat of North Battersea which embraced most of Burns's old constituency. In any case by 1918 the Liberals' loyalties were divided
between Lloyd George and Asquith. An influential section of the party
remained loyal to Asquith but in Burns's eyes the former prime minister
was very much a broken reed. He had rejected several luncheon invitations from the Asquiths after his-resignation and had been indifferent
when Morley urged him to re-establish the Asquith link. It is evident
that Burns never forgave Asquith the indecision which, he believed,
had paved the way for the hated Lloyd George.

This left Labour, for despite the jibes of his less kind critics, there
was never any chance that Burns would join the Tories. In July 1918 he
had accepted the nomination of the Labour League to contest North
Battersea, but by November he was beginning to doubt the wisdom of
this. In part, these doubts were a reflection of the uncertainty in his
mind about the general political situation and his own place in it. He had
welcomed the outbreak of revolution in Russia and more than once
expressed the hope that it would be followed by universal revolution.
Yet at other times he appears to have been fearful of the consequences
of such an upheaval. Towards the end of the war he met Sylvia Pankhurst and told her that when the war ended he would be more
revolutionary than anyone. But immediately she mentioned Russia
'a wave of reserve and impatience seemed to pass over him'.[1] Cole
reports that Burns told him that what Britain needed was a 'straight'
socialist party, 'Hyndman's stuff, my boy, without the frills, and I'm
the man to lead them'.[2] This is confirmed by at least one diary entry
of January 1919 in which Burns suggested that the British Labour Party
was too moderate to be able to defend democracy against the encroach-
ments of big business.[3] Perhaps this was why when Burns was discussing
the trade union movement with Walter Citrine in 1925 he suggested
that his only major political mistake had been to accept office in 1905.[4]
Yet for Burns of all people to imagine that he could lead a more radical
Labour Party was amazing, explicable only in terms of his capacity for
total self-delusion and the generally confused state of his political
thinking in the aftermath of the war. True, the long-standing friction
with Keir Hardie had been somewhat softened in the heat of their
common stand against the war, and when Hardie died in 1915 Burns
had even been moved to praise his old rival. Though in no way changing

1 E. Sylvia Pankhurst, *The Home Front* (1932), 59.
2 Cole, *Burns*, 5.
3 Burns Diary, 23 January 1919. B.L. Add. MSS 46341.
4 W. Citrine, *Men and Work. An Autobiography* (1964), 84.

his view that Hardie had been doctrinaire and narrow Burns did concede that he had been a doughty fighter for the poor and a man of vision.[1] But more generally Burns had been appalled at the way in which so many socialists in Britain (and elsewhere) had sacrificed their political faith to their nationalism. 'National blood is thicker than socialist water', had been his comment.[2] He was even more deeply shocked by the entry of the Labour Party into the coalition governments, a step which, he observed, 'has divided them in parliament, degraded them in the country, and induced contempt amongst those to whom they have surrendered'.[3] Yet in accepting the nomination of the Labour League Burns was really aligning himself with this same Labour Party, for the Labour League had affiliated to the party during the war.

For a few days in November, therefore, Burns wavered about his parliamentary future. Finally at a meeting held in the town hall on 17 November he withdrew. Basing his conclusion on local press reports Kent suggested that Burns backed down because he knew that the coalition candidate would win.[4] It is true that Burns expected the coalition to form the next government and he also knew that population shifts and a redrawing of constituency boundaries had adversely affected his own chances. But to suggest that he ran away does an injustice to his courage, for he had always enjoyed a fight and had never shirked a political challenge. What caused his withdrawal was simply the fact that acceptance of nomination by a body affiliated to the Labour Party involved a declaration of total independence from all other parties and full commitment to the party's parliamentary programme. Such a surrender of the right to act at the dictates of personal conviction in favour of a doctrinally-motivated party whip was anathema to Burns. All his political life he had resisted such a surrender even though it had involved hostility first with the I.L.P. and later with the L.R.C. Now in withdrawing he told party officials that any man who gave the pledge they demanded merely 'degraded his election to Parliament by being the subjective delegate of a section . . . and the creature of a clique. . . .'.[5] Four days after the town hall meeting Burns said goodbye to Mr Speaker, severed his connection with the Labour League after nearly thirty years, and thus brought to an end his long parliamentary career. 'Retirement, even obscurity if they are the rewards of consistence and duty must be faced and endured with courage'.[6]

1 Burns Diary, 26 September 1915. B.L. Add. MSS 46337.
2 Ibid. 29 October 1914. Add. MSS 46336.
3 Ibid. 9 December 1915. Add. MSS 46337.
4 Kent, *Burns,* 258.
5 Burns Diary, 17 November 1918. B.L. Add. MSS 46340.
6 Ibid. 21 November 1918.

188

Of course, there remained the possibility of a re-entry to London politics and a browse through some old L.C.C. papers on Christmas Day 1918 rekindled thoughts in that direction. But it was only a passing whim. Council politics had also changed since 1914 with the birth of the London Labour Party and the disintegration of the old Progressive alliance, and Burns rejected an invitation to contest a council seat in 1919. Often he referred to his hopes of re-entering public life, for instance averring to his retirement as 'temporary' when he opened a swimming pool at Nottingham in 1924.[1] But although he loved in this way to preserve both the mystique of his continued silence and of his withdrawal from politics, the truth was that he had had enough. There is plenty of evidence in his diary that he was finding public life tedious before 1914, clinging to it largely out of an ill-conceived sense of loyalty and self-importance. The war gave him an issue of sufficient magnitude over which to resign, and thereafter he lacked the drive to re-assert himself, even had he been sure of exactly where his future lay. It was only because he lost interest in the Labour League, for so long his own unique personal vehicle, that activists within it had been able to secure its affiliation to the Labour Party during the war. In the early 1920s he received several requests to contest council or parliamentary elections but he refused them all. In 1919, for example, he turned down an invitation to stand in Chelsea for no more serious reason than that it was on the wrong side of the river. Perhaps even more illuminating is the fact that he only considered it at all because of the historical connection between Chelsea and Sir Thomas More.[2] The five year gap in Burns's official life had been sufficient to break down the discipline of a lifetime and he found it easier to continue as a private citizen than to re-enter public life. After all, he had no financial worries. All his life he had practised the thrift he had preached at the Local Government Board, had done no entertaining, and lived so modestly on his ministerial salary that at the beginning of 1914 he had been able to purchase 'Alverstoke', a large house on the north side of Clapham Common. In 1919 Andrew Carnegie left him an annuity of £1,000, providing him with still greater financial security and his socialist critics with capital of a different sort. Even the careful keeping of the diary began to lapse in 1919, gaps appeared with increasing frequency and in May 1920 he finally dried up altogether. The last entry of all gives an excellent insight into his thinking at this time, revealing the enjoyment of hobbies, the hankering for public life, but the lack of any real will to achieve it.

1 *The Times*, 1 September 1924.
2 Burns Diary, 27 December 1919. B.L. Add. MSS 46341.

Books are a real solace, friendships are good but action is better than all. For the moment and for some time great events have been denied me, forward action not come my way. I believe, however, that impending events will call us and we must respond but where, with whom, and how?[1]

Clearly as time passed, so inertia and advancing years made it ever less likely that Burns would become an active politician again. Only once after 1920 was there ever any rumour of him accepting nomination in Battersea again, and that was in 1922. But it originated less in political reality than in the wave of genuine sympathy which swept the locality after the death of Edgar earlier in the year. All his life Burns had doted on his son with a fierce possessiveness that reveals itself time and time again in his diary. His anguish at Edgar's involvement in the war had in no way been diminished by his disappointment at the type of man he turned out to be. Nor did his disappointment do anything to mitigate his grief when Edgar, who had been working with the British War Graves Commission in Rouen, suddenly collapsed and, weakened by shell-shock, died before his father could reach him. It may have sounded sentimental but the *South Western Star* was right in its description of Burns at the funeral. 'By nature he is more emotional than most men; his soul was rocked with grief'.[2] After this loss, he retreated even further into his private world, accepting only a few public engagements.

The 1920s passed into the '30s, for Burns an amalgam of the occasional public appearance (an honorary LLD from Edinburgh University in 1939, for example), much devotion to his hobbies, and regular attendance to his one remaining official duty — the administration of the Strathcona Leper Colony at Chelmsford. His involvement with this institution dated from his time at the Local Government Board when the Company of St Giles, which ran the colony, had sought his assistance. As a minister Burns had been unable to lend his name to any appeal but he had pursuaded Lord Strathcona to bequeath the company £5,000. Burns was made a life trustee and although the colony was only small — in 1920 it housed only four of the estimated one hundred lepers in Britain — Burns attended meetings of the trustees regularly into his seventies. Increasingly, however, fulfilment came from his hobbies. He remained a keen follower of cricket and as late as 1938 he presided at a private dinner party given for the touring Australians at the National Liberal Club. By day he walked a great deal through the streets of his beloved London, browsing for hours in the bookshops. His library, which reached over 12,000 items by the

1 Ibid. 16 May 1920. Add. MSS 46342.
2 *South Western Star,* 30 June 1922.

time of his death, overflowed into most of the rooms in his house, and it included a Shakespeare fourth folio as well as the unique collection of works by More. He was widely and rightly regarded as an expert on London and its history, and frequently reviewed books on the subject for various journals. But although he had been a member of the London Historical Society and had served on the L.C.C.'s Historical Records and Buildings Committee, he never got round to writing the history either of Battersea or of London, both of which he had often resolved to do, further evidence perhaps of his waning self discipline in later life. London did, however, provide the inspiration for the only creative writing to which he did turn his hand, though a surviving fragment of his poetry perhaps indicates why he did not write more.

> Silent flows the river, cleaner than of yore,
> From Teddington to Fanteel (?) Creek against the Nore.
> Some twenty parks and gardens decorate its moving tide
> The harvest of its Council that was our London pride.[1]

At night the billiard room of the National Liberal Club was a favourite haunt. Even in retirement Pattie Burns, it seems, saw little more of her husband than she had during his days of fame. His comment on her death in 1936 was terse and pointed. 'Devoted and well beloved'.[2] Devoted she certainly had been, but there is no way of knowing how well-loved she was. In the last years of his life Burns made some revealing comments to Kent which suggested that he missed her companionship, and occasionally in his diary there were signs of remorse at the way she had been relatively neglected in the interests of his career. Generally, though, his feelings for his wife never came to the surface in the way that they did for his son. After Pattie's death Burns spent even more time at the National Liberal Club, taking most of his meals there, though still receiving a fair number of visitors at home. From 1938 onwards William Kent became one of his most frequent callers, in the course of his many visits picking up lots of the stories that were later to form the basis of his book.

Although he was almost eighty-one when the second world war broke out — in his view, the direct result of the first — Burns obstinately refused to leave his house. By the end of 1941 he was practically bedridden, a combination of old age and the effects of a nearby bomb blast which had thrown him heavily to the ground. By all accounts he was a difficult patient for his niece Mrs Ashton who acted as his nurse. Early in 1943 he was moved, protesting to the last, to Bolingbroke

1   Handwritten and much altered manuscript in Burns's hand. Burns Papers G.L.C. Collection. Box labelled 'Trade Union Pamphlets'.
2   Handwritten note recording his wife's death, 30 October 1936. Burns Papers B.L. Add. MSS 46304, f.232.

Hospital, unaware that in another nearby hospital an old colleague with whom he had continued to correspond intermittently, Ben Tillett, was also slipping surely towards death. The two veterans of the 1889 dock strike died within a week of each other. Burns went first, early on the morning of 24 January. Tillett died a few days later as Burns was being buried. On 4 February a memorial service was held at St Margaret's, Westminster, and although Burns's death passed almost unnoticed in the general turmoil of war, Winston Churchill was represented, Clement Attlee attended on behalf of the Labour Party, and old colleagues like Samuel and McKenna were also present. But it was indicative of his total eclipse that a memorial meeting organised in Battersea itself attracted only about a hundred people, most of them well on in years. A memorial fund raised only £131 and over half of that came from two trade unions. Both incidents might well have offended his fierce pride in an earlier day. Now, of course, they were of no consequence to him at all.

CONCLUSION

It has been commonly concluded that ambition, pride and jealousy were the forces that motivated John Burns and it is impossible to dispute William Kent's claim that 'the most obvious and overwhelming fact, to which all witnesses testify, was his extraordinary egotism'.[1] In his palmy days as a rabble-rouser Burns thrived on the response of the crowd which frequently inspired him to oratorical excesses. All through his political life he exhibited a remarkable knack for catching the public eye, and when M.P.s collapsed or departmental stores caught fire it was invariably Burns who stepped in to control the situation. He clearly revelled in the publicity that attended his activities during the dock strike and he took full advantage of the opportunity afforded by his position as a county councillor and later as a minister to keep himself in the public eye. Egotism is also evident in his accounts of cabinet meetings in which, if his diary were to be believed, he played a prominent and often dominant role. It was a misplaced, but genuinely-held, sense of self-importance that prevented his resignation from the government before 1914, kept him mute about a war against which his soul cried out, and even led him to consider re-entering the labour movement which had long since washed its hands of him.

Yet this is not to agree with that interpretation of Burns which explains his every action and practically every event of significance in his career - the break with Hyndman, his role in helping to muzzle I.L.P. influence within the T.U.C., his hostility towards Hardie and the L.R.C., his entry into the cabinet, and his attitude in office - in terms of his ambition and pride. This view was neatly encapsulated by George Lansbury when he claimed that Burns was 'a workman who has carved his way to power, as someone once said of Mr Disraeli, by the unsparing use of the scalping knife and tomahawk', the implication being that Burns had set out with the intention of securing some form of power and in the drive to achieve it had left his path littered with bloodied rivals and discarded causes.[2] It must be admitted that this view is lent a certain amount of credence by Burns's own tendency to interpret all opposition in strictly personal terms, by his capacity for making venemous comments about opponents, and by his reluctance to forgive rivals. But it is important to notice that none of these traits were really the product of frustrated ambition or affronted pride. They served rather as vents for genuine political differences and his career, too, must be understood in political, not personal, terms.

1 Kent, *Burns,* 357.
2 In a letter to *The Times,* 2 April 1907.

Of course, it must be conceded that for a London working man reared in conditions of poverty there was an undeniable attraction in being an important local figure and even more in being a county councillor. Given Burns's background it would have been strange had he felt no pride or self satisfaction at reaching cabinet rank - witness his increasing use of the royal 'we' in his diary. Yet if his ego was undoubtedly boosted by his success and always attracted by the possibilities of fresh conquests, the initial driving force in his public life, and one which never entirely disappeared, was a deeply-held sense of social injustice which sprang directly from the circumstances of his own upbringing. His socialism, unlike that of most Fabians and Social Democratic leaders, was a matter of personal experience rather than of intellectual conviction. His political views were forged in the mean streets of Battersea which were his playground and by what he had himself undergone in the struggle to support his widowed mother. The advanced radical literature which he read so eagerly and the friendship of Delahaye merely served to confirm his experience. There was more than the self-justification of a power seeker in Burns's frequent references to his 'call' to be the champion of the working classes in their struggle for social improvement. This belief is evident in his diaries, never more so than at the time of his resignation from the cabinet in 1914. Masterman referred to it in 1927 when he wrote that part of Burns still 'cherished the ambition of Tennyson's Ulysses that at the appointed hour and before the end, "some work of noble note may yet be done, not unbecoming men who strove with gods" '.[1] Anyone with a sense of call, however, runs the risk of becoming intellectually arrogant. Because he felt called Burns also tended to assume that he was always right, hence his irritation with those whose views were different to his own.

Social change then, not power *per se,* was what interested Burns, and he was not too concerned about the means of achieving it. For him the end was always more important than the means. Although he called himself a socialist and was quite happy in his early days to accept the idea of revolution - if it was possible and necessary - he was not an advocate of revolution for its own sake, not did he believe that society could be transformed overnight. This was why he sided with Hyndman against the founders of the Socialist League who belittled the S.D.F. programme of palliatives. Yet with very little achieved after three or four years of utterly dedicated work for the S.D.F. Burns came to the conclusion that the organisation was not suitable as a vehicle for social change. Hyndman's insistence on the idea of class war and doctrinal purity was, Burns decided, steering the S.D.F. into a dead end and off the road that led to social amelioration, and so he broke with it, Similar

1 *Sunday Express,* 2 January 1927.

194

feelings prompted his reaction to Hardie and the Independent Labour
Party, for Burns felt that the I.L.P. was merely a northern version of the
S.D.F. For this reason he was highly suspicious of the I.L.P. activists
within the T.U.C. and also of the party's influence - out of all proportion
to its strength - in the Labour Representation Committee. Burns
understood that for Hardie 'the goal was nothing. The Labour movement was everything'.[1] He also happened to believe that Hardie was
totally wrong. Working within the broad Progressive alliance in the
London County Council enabled Burns to advance the workers' cause
and his success there certainly influenced his decision to accept office
in Campbell-Bannerman's cabinet in 1905. This provided him with a
further means of achieving his ends, and Liberalism was also a sufficiently vague creed to permit that freedom of action which was central
to his political outlook. Thus it was not personal ambition alone that
carried Burns into the cabinet, as at least one socialist rival admitted.
Burns, suggested Belfort Bax, had toiled for years and believed that by
throwing in his lot with radical politicians he would be able to secure
those reforms he wished to see, and socialist insinuations against his
character, Bax concluded, were therefore unfair.[2]

Similarly it was Burns's fear that ends were being subordinated to
means that helped to produce the friction with the Webbs. Certainly one
element in this was the suspicion that Burns, as a self-educated man,
felt towards those whose views were based on anything other than
experience. 'Priggish snobbery from the Universities', he once claimed,
'kills more movements and causes than repression ever did'.[3] As far as
the administration of the poor law was concerned Burns warned against
attaching 'too much importance to organisation rather than to getting
rid of the thing they were organised against' lest 'the object was
subordinated to the more efficient working of the machine'.[4] Yet this
was precisely what the Webbs were threatening to do, or so it seemed to
Burns, with their ambitious schemes for demolishing the poor law.
Meeting Mrs Webb in 1917 Burns noted that she was 'grey, old, faint,
yet pursuing her ideals of numbering us all, registering everybody,
regimenting labour, codifying everything, de-individualising us all, and
taking emotion out of character, soul out of body, joy out of work, and
delight that springs from variety out of existence'.[5] On another occasion
he referred to her 'rather chess board view of life'.[6]

1 Kenneth O. Morgan, *Keir Hardie. Radical and Socialist* (1975), 217.
2 Bax, *Reminiscences and Reflexions,* 106.
3 Burns Diary, 23 March 1900. B.L. Add. MSS 46318.
4 *Poor Law Officers Journal. Supplement,* 20 February 1914.
5 Memorandum dated 14 December 1917. Burns Papers. B.L. Add. MSS
46308, f.173.
6 Burns Diary, 12 December 1913. Ibid. Add. MSS 46335.

Thus genuine political differences lay behind Burns's clashes with Hyndman, Hardie, and the Webbs. Further the charge of self-seeking ignores the degree of personal sacrifice that his political work entailed. Even though they were redolent with self-satisfaction there was much truth in thoughts prompted in Burns's mind by reading through some of his old papers. 'My life seems like a romance when sitting here as a minister I read my notes of 1889 diary . . . tired, often ill, often depressed, chronically poor, often hard up'.[1] Standing up for his views had cost Burns most of his time and many jobs, while his rewards had included a great deal of personal abuse from opponents and a six-week jail sentence. Of course, the financial hardships disappeared when he secured cabinet rank but this did not go to his head, for he had never been interested in money as such except insofar as it enabled him to buy the books which he loved. He did not even buy his own house until 1914. Family life, too, had been sacrificed in the interests of his public work. Neither his son nor his wife saw much of him. Most of his spare time was devoted to reading or examining at first hand the various official enterprises with which he was connected. One can only speculate as to how far Edgar's obstinacy and wilfulness were a result of his parent's total involvement in public life and to the latter's attempts at compensation, for Burns was a sentimental and highly indulgent father. Yet Edgar was not permitted to benefit from his father's eminence. Burns had always been a resolute enemy of public graft and was certainly prepared to make no compromises, even for the sake of his own son. It is somewhat ironic that whereas later labour politicians have been pilloried for advocating state education and sending their own children to private schools, Burns was attacked for allowing Edgar to take up the council scholarship he won in 1907, on the grounds that he could afford to pay for the boy's schooling. Radicals, it seems, can never win.

Thus the attempt to portray Burns as a man who swayed before every political wind that blew him nearer to his objective of power does an injustice to his motivation. He wished to see improvements in working-class conditions and was willing to use any convenient tool to that end, be it the revolutionery S.D.F., the Progressive L.C.C., or the Liberal cabinet. To this task he brought, first of all, a tremendous capacity for hard work; witness his propaganda activities for the S.D.F. which often involved him rising in the small hours to deliver speeches before going off to his own work. It was seen, too, in the enormous effort he put into the 1889 dock dispute, and that the stike was so prolonged and ultimately so successful owed much to his enthusiasm and commitment. His habit of personally examining all sides of a particular question does

1   Ibid. 9 September 1912. Add. MSS 46334.

196

much to explain the success of his early council work and his general
dominance in its affairs. It produced good dividends, for example, in
the establishment of trade-union rates and conditions for men employed
on council work and then ultimately in the creation of the Works
Department, Londoners riding in their municipal trams and steamboats,
drinking their purer water, or relaxing in their new parks, had good
cause to be grateful to the Progressives in general and Burns in
particular. Harry Gosling rightly described him as 'one of London's
greatest citizens', while Joseph Clayton told Burns that his work for the
capital would live for ever.[1]

Burns also brought to politics a fundamental honesty and integrity;
Robert Rhodes James is quite unfair in suggesting that the basic
difference between Hardie and Burns was that the latter lacked
integrity.[2] There was no question at all about Burns's personal honesty.
He was disgusted by the 'Tory gold' scandal in 1885 and always took
great care to return gifts which might be construed as bribes. The only
financial aid he ever accepted, other than that provided by the Labour
League, came from George Cadbury who made no effort to extract
favours from Burns in return. Burns carried the same attitude into his
public life. No-one was keener than he in sniffing out corruption in the
council, for he was determined to prevent graft of the sort which, it was
believed, had too frequently sullied the activities of the old Board of
Works. He had no mercy even when those caught in dubious practices
were from his own class, as in the case of the Poplar Guardians, when
they were involved in projects dear to his heart, as in the Works Department affair of 1896, or when they were his own cabinet colleagues, as
at the time of the Marconi scandal.

Politically, too, Burns had an integrity which is often overlooked by
those anxious to suggest that he changed his mind on anything if he
thought that it would bring personal advantage. Home Rule for Ireland
appeared in his first election manifesto in 1885 and was still there in his
last one, issued in December 1910. Privately, he was still taking a very
militant line on this in 1917, believing that Ireland's problems might
have been avoided had the Ulster Protestants been more firmly dealt
with in 1914. Female suffrage and the abolition of hereditary authority
also claimed his lifelong support. Although he was never prepared to
subordinate everything to the suffragette cause (this would have been an
inversion of means and ends) he was genuinely pleased at the passage of
the 1918 act that conferred the vote on women over thirty. For all that

1 H. Gosling, *Up and Down Stream* (1927), 85. J. Clayton to J. Burns
31 October 1936. Burns Papers. B.L. Add. MSS 46304, f.237.
2 R.R. James reviewing Morgan, *Hardie,* in *New Statesman,* 28 March 1975.

he was so proud of his amiable relationship with Edward VII - a relationship which probably says as much about the monarch as about Burns - he never wavered in his belief that the political power of the House of Lords should be ended. He welcomed the disintegrating effects of the world war on the old social order of empires and monarchies.[1] Above all, there was a consistency in Burns's attitude towards war which was not always evident in those who professed to hold a purer version of socialism. Once again, recognition of this comes from a political opponent, Guy Aldred, a sometime member of one of the S.D.F.'s extremist offshoots, the Socialist Labour Party.

> When it comes to the Great War period, and the attitude adopted by Burns during that war, it will be discovered that John Burns possessed an instinctive love of socialism and an understanding not possessed by any of the later parliamentarians . . . When at last a conflict arose between his understanding of principle and his appetite for glory, understanding won . . . John Burns decided that a man styling himself a Socialist could not support war.[2]

Then there was a personal abstemiousness which Burns preached unceasingly to others. He was a lifelong abstainer from tobacco and alcohol. Even when he became a minister his modest life style was in marked contrast to those of many of his colleagues. Burns was a walking embodiment of the virtues of self help — an abstainer, a trade unionist, and a member of several friendly societies. Indeed, the publisher Ernest Cassell even used a picture of the youthful Burns to illustrate his book, *A New Self-help,* published at the beginning of the century. With this went a natural tendency, growing stronger as the years went by, to decry the weaknesses of the flesh in others. His passion for economy also got stronger with time. He was careful with his own money and like all adherents of classical economics believed that the state should be similarly careful. The parsimony which he revealed at the L.G.B. owed nothing to the reactionary influence of his civil servants. It had been publicly apparent from his very first day as a member of the L.C.C.

These essentially puritan values of hard work, honesty, and self denial were also those of the labour aristocracy. If Burns did not share the non-conformist traditions from which so many of the labour aristocrats sprang, he had no doubt as to the validity of their puritanism. 'The day that the Puritan spirit disappears from England', he said in 1907, 'that day we are numbered among the people of the past'.[3] His brand of puritanism was acceptable so long as it was rooted in a real

1 Burns Diary, 18 March 1918. B.L. Add. MSS 46340.
2 G. Aldred, *No Traitor's Gait* (Glasgow, 1955), 133.
3 *Daily Chronicle,* 25 January 1907.

sympathy for the downtrodden, based in his own experience, and seen in his struggle for the dockers and in his parliamentary campaigns for various groups of ill-treated workers. Although he believed that personal vice was often a contributory factor in an individual's poverty, he also appreciated that it was as often a symptom as a cause, and that poverty was frequently a product of a bad environment. This too, rendered his puritanism more palatable. So did his exciting visionary oratory which must rank as one of his greatest contributions to the labour movement. Every revival needs its prophet and this was the role he filled in the socialist upsurge of the 1880s. He spoke in terms that people understood, delivering speeches that were loaded, not with dry academic analyses of society, but with his own experiences which were also those of his hearers. Even his bitterest rivals had to concede that here he had a great talent, never seen to better advantage than at the time of the London dock strike.

Yet over the years Burns changed. Despite his efforts to be involved at grass roots level in the work of the Local Government Board, he increasingly lost touch with the realities of working-class life, something Hardie never did. Increasingly, the personal elements in his speeches was replaced by half-understood and barely digestible statistics. Not surprisingly, his oratory lost its old conviction, the epigrams were stale, and he grew less inclined to make speeches at all. Even his cabinet colleagues laughed behind his back at his laboured style and obsession with figures, both of which were cruelly and anonymously parodied in an account of an imaginary cabinet discussion. Burns is portrayed as having made the following contribution.

> Perhaps I might be allowed to point out to my colleagues that if we do nothing, the effect upon Local Government will be deleterious in the highest degree, if not disastrous. Besides, every shady solicitor in Soho, every tired tramp in Tottenham, every bullying bruiser in Battersea . . . will find his position entrenched and his monopoly fortified by the condonation that we shall have passed, sitting at *this* table, of as flagitious a piece of cunning corruption as it has been my ill-fortune to come across . . . every member of a municipal authority, every member of a Board of Guardians, or of a County, Urban District, Rural District or Parish Council – and there are 144,287 of them in England and Wales alone – will consider that the door has been thrown open . . . to every species of grab, graft, boodle and loot, and that he himself is free to enter in. [1]

His remarkable energy also began to wane. He began at the Local Government with every intention of galvanising a lethargic department and his diary reveals how frustrated he became with his civil servants. Yet after three or four years he apparently abandoned the struggle,

[1] Undated anonymous memorandum. H.L.R.O. Samuel Papers, A/155 (IV), ff.98-9.

and this must go some way towards explaining his relatively poor legislative achievement. After eight years in office he could point to only one major success, the Housing and Town Planning Act of 1909. To some extent, of course, this poor record can be blamed on his departmental officials who were cautious and not very able. The worst was undoubtedly Alfred Adrian and it is interesting that when Morant was discussing the possibilities of himself going to the Local Government Board when Provis retired, he said that 'he would not work with Adrian who wd. have to go'.[1] Burns was also hampered by the absence of any well-developed statistical section within the board, and by the activities of numerous royal commissions. Yet the fact remains that he did little with the reports of these royal commissions when he got them, and his performance did not improve very much even after Adrian left in 1910. The main explanation of Burns's poor legislative achievement at the Local Government Board does lie, therefore in his personality; not in his susceptibility to flattery so much as in his marked intellectual limitations, his lack of any constructive ideas, his inability to exert his will over a poor staff, and in his tendency to become absorbed in trivia. A more energetic president would have become much less involved in the minutiae of running the department and given a more dynamic lead from the top as the records suggest Samuel, his successor, was trying to do when war broke out.

Almost in spite of himself, therefore, Burns lapsed into being a president who was generally content to keep the machine ticking over, lacking either the energy or intellectual sharpness to use his office as the means to the ends which he wished to achieve. In any case, by the time he entered office in 1905 those ends had become more than a little vague. True there was a certain flexibility evident in his approach to several matters, for example the poor law which he was quite happy to see handed over to the municipalities, and his willingness to allow experiments in unemployment relief. But this initial flexibility did not survive for very long in the reactionary atmosphere of the Local Government Board, and the arrogance to which he had always been prone, hardened. Lloyd George suggested that he suffered from 'paralysis of the pistol', and it is evident that he became steadily less receptive to new ideas.[2] Even his close friend, Morley, agreed with Lady St Helier that Burns was closed to any idea that did not originate in his own head.[3] Nowhere was this more apparent than in his approach to poverty. Even before he became president of the Local Government

1 Newman Diary, 25 May 1908. Department of Health and Social Security Library. Newman Diary, I.
2 Lloyd George, *Lloyd George*, 120.
3 Fitzroy, *Memoirs*, II, 525.

Board Burns had been veering towards placing greater emphasis on the personal elements in its causation. It was not long before the combination of his own arrogance, reactionary officials, and a conviction that his own environmental outlook was working, served to convince him that all remaining poverty must be the product of defects of character. Such an attitude had been inherent in his outlook; he was not flattered into it as is usually suggested.

This hardening of his attitudes coincided, however, with a major realignment in Liberal thinking about social problems which emerged as the 'new Liberalism'. Burns would not have been out of place in a nineteenth-century Liberal administration – he had been a great admirer of Gladstone – but the 'new Liberalism' with its stress on state intervention left him sadly adrift on the right of the party. His belief that the municipality rather than the state was the right body to deal with social problems was increasingly outdated. 'If I were a minister again', he said in 1919, 'my chief task would be to strike off all the shackles that fetter local initiative. An over-drilled, an over-inspected nation, and bureaucratised departments mean a routine machine'.[1] Burns found it increasingly difficult to find his place in a society which seemed to be questioning all his values and became ever more isolated, both within the party and the cabinet. Only his sense of call and love of publicity prevented him resigning before 1914.

Thus shorn of its compassion, its vision, its oratory, its energy and flexibility, Burns's puritanism degenerated into a rather repugnant combination of self-satisfied censoriousness tinged with what threatened to become a very despotic approach to policy. 'Can nothing be done about John Burns?', demanded one irate correspondent of George Lansbury, '[his] dismal, sordid, hazardous outlook is to foster manly independence. John Burns has said so, so it must be right and he is the guardian (the God-ordained custodian) of the proud spirit of the poor ... no use writing a bitter note to the Daily News about this little tin-wheel god'.[2] What contributed still more to this impression was that Burns, because he couldn't cope with the intellectual demands of piloting bills through the House of Commons, turned more towards administrative means of implementing policy. It must be admitted that here his achievement was more impressive. Under Burns, the L.G.B. made substantial headway in the fight against T.B., infant mortality, and several other diseases. A greater degree of variety and specialisation was introduced into the administration of the poor law, such that even

1 *The Times,* 27 November 1919.
2 Lady R. Cavendish Bentinck to G. Lansbury, 11 February 1911. B.L.P.E.S. Lansbury Papers, L. 3, f.175.

the supporters of the Prevention of Destitution Committee had to confess that poor law administration had been marked in recent years by 'certain vague humanitarian tendencies'.[1] If Burns is to get the brickbats for his legislative failures it is perhaps only fair to give him the credit for the department's administrative achievement. Although personal calculations entered into Asquith's decision to retain Burns in 1908 and then to put him at the Board of Trade in 1914, both decisions also owed something to the prime minister's belief in Burns's administrative abilities.

They owed something as well to Burns's general popularity as a political figure in the country at large. Critical as many of them were of Burns's performance at the Local Government Board, most of his cabinet colleagues recognised the breadth of his appeal which lay in his ability to deal equally with King and commoner. At the one level his courage and artless display of self disarmed aristocratic suspicion; at the other he was able to inspire intense devotion in Battersea, especially among the officials of the Labour League. In office he generated strong personal feelings even in a man like Charles Masterman, who disagreed with him fundamentally on a whole range of political issues. Yet most of John Burns's relationships were essentially superficial. He could give himself utterly to a crowd or a principle in a way which he could not, or would not, at an individual level. In his papers there are few indications of any real lasting friendships. Only H.W. Massingham, J. Allen Baker, and John Morley were ever at all close to him. With Baker he went to America for lengthy political tours. Massingham was Burns's regular companion in the 1890s at cricket and tennis and when his wife, Emmie, died in 1905 it was to Burns that Massingham turned for comfort. John Morley was the one man in the Liberal cabinet to whom Burns talked at all freely and their mutual, rather old-fashioned, radicalism was reinforced by their common love of books. By no means blind to Burns's faults, Morley still held him in the highest esteem, particularly during the First World War. 'My dear Burns', he wrote in 1916, 'I shall not soon, nor ever, forget your visit here tonight. I am more melted than for many a long day past. The breadth of social survey and foresight, the angry vision of this hideous war . . . it all makes me proud that I hold the hand of such a comrade in a great piece of history'.[2]

But these few instances are the exceptions that prove the rule, for generally Burns was far too self-centred to be able to develop real friendship. There is no doubt that he needed popularity — there was

1 *Poor Law Officers Journal*, 15 March 1912.
2 John Viscount Morley, *Memorandum on Resignation* (1928), xi.

nothing he loved better than holding court at the centre of a group of admiring listeners at the National Liberal Club — but he did not appear to require close personal relationships in the same way. Emotionally he seems to have been extremely self-contained. Once he became an active politician he rarely bothered with his numerous brothers and sisters, and only his own son seems to have been capable of exerting any emotional pull on him. Burns never made much effort to cultivate friendship deliberately for its own sake. He never entertained and his isolation after 1918 owed something to the fact that while he had many acquaintances he had few real friends. Time after time he allowed political differences to become matters of personality because he did not regard friendship very highly. This happened in the case of Lord Rosebery when disagreements over imperialism soured the genuine friendship they had formed during the first years of the London County Council. Massingham's disillusionment with his ministerial record caused Burns to turn his back on this old friend. Neither did Burns do much to preserve his friendship with Baker once it had outlived its original political usefulness. Perhaps because it could not answer back to expose his weaknesses and illusions, Burns's diary became his main confidant, passively sharing in his setbacks and triumphs.

What, finally, of Burns's place in the British labour movement? Inevitably, perhaps, he invites comparison with Keir Hardie. Both had similar backgrounds, both shared all the assumptions of the labour aristocrats, and both sought in the 1890s to mould the movement's tactics in accord with their own particular views. Both probably had equally hazy ideas of the socialist millennium towards which they were moving. But, for Burns, arrival there was much more important than the means of transport, hence his decision to abandon the labour movement altogether and join the Liberals in 1905. Hardie never got the chance to realise his vision. Burns made his own opportunity and took a few faltering steps towards it. Like a whole line of British socialists after him, he discovered that the detailed process of realising the vision frequently tended to obscure its main outlines. His radicalism, already much diluted by 1905, could not survive the tedium of committees, involvement with the mundane realities of departmental administration, and the resourcefulness of opponents. Yet if the achievement was relatively· minor, it might be considered that the effort was worth making, for social improvement needs not only its visionaries but also its builders. 'Labour biography', it has been suggested, 'until quite recently, was a sort of Pilgrim's Progress in which the Shining Ones, who died in the faith, were gathered within the city, and the defaulters along the way, MacDonald, Snowden, Burns etc. —

were consigned to Hell'.[1] If John Burns has been thus condemned it is for one reason only — he believed with all his heart that faith without works was dead.

---

1 C. Harvie reviewing Morgan, *Hardie,* in *Welsh History Review* 8 (1976), 118.

BIBLIOGRAPHY

1. *Manuscript Sources*   4. *Newspapers*
2. *Minutes, Manifestos and Reports*   5. *Books*
3. *Official Papers and Reports*   6. *Articles*
                                     7. *Theses*

1. *Manuscript Sources*

H.H. Asquith	Bodleian Library
Lord Avebury	British Library
W.H. Beveridge	British Library of Political and Economic Science
A. Birrell	University of Liverpool Library
R. Blatchford	Manchester Central Reference Library
A.J. Braithwaite	British Library of Political and Economic Science
J. Bryce	Bodleian Library
J. Burns	Battersea Public Library
J. Burns	British Library
J. Burns	Greater London Council Record Office
S. Buxton	C/o Mrs J. Clay
H. Campbell-Bannerman	British Library
L. Courtenay	British Library of Political and Economic Science
Lord Crewe	University of Cambridge Library
R.B. Cunninghame Graham	National Library of Scotland
W.H. Dickinson	Greater London Council Record Office
C. Dilke	British Library
Master of Elibank	National Library of Scotland
A. Emmott	Nuffield College Library
Lord Gainford	Nuffield College Library
H. Gladstone	British Library
Lord Grey	Public Record Office
R.B. Haldane	National Library of Scotland
E. Hamilton	British Library
L. Harcourt	Bodleian Library
G. Lansbury	British Library of Political and Economic Science
D. Lloyd George	Beaverbrook Library

J. Ramsay MacDonald	British Library of Political and Economic Science
R. McKenna	Churchill College Library
T. McKinnon Wood	Bodleian Library
G. Newman Diary	Ministry of Health and Social Security Library
G. Newman Papers	Wellcome History of Medicine Library
Lord Passfield	British Library of Political and Economic Science
A. Ponsonby	Bodleian Library
Lord Ripon	British Library
Lord Rosebery	National Library of Scotland
W. Runciman	University of Newcastle Library
H. Samuel	House of Lords Record Office
J.A. Spender	British Library
C.P. Trevelyan	University of Newcastle Library

2. *Minutes, Manifestos and Reports*

Comité Revolutionnaire du Prolétariat, *A La classe ouvrière* (Paris, 1874)
Independent Labour Party, *Annual Reports*
Industrial Remuneration Conference, *Report* (1885)
Labour Party, *Annual Reports*
L.C.C. Bridges Committee, *Minutes*
L.C.C. Contracts Committee, *Minutes*
L.C.C. Fire Brigade Committee, *Minutes*
L.C.C. General Purposes Committee, *Minutes*
L.C.C. Main Drainage Committee, *Minutes*
L.C.C., *Minutes of Proceedings*
L.C.C. Parliamentary Committee, *Minutes*
L.C.C. Rivers Committee, *Minutes*
L.C.C. Standing Committee, *Minutes*
L.C.C. Stores Committee, *Minutes*
L.C.C. Technical Education Committee, *Minutes*
L.C.C. Works Committee, *Minutes*
Social Democratic Federation, *Annual Reports*

3. *Official Papers and Reports*

Hansard
Local Government Board, *Annual Reports*
Public Record Office   CAB 37
                        HLG 46
                        LAB 7
                        MEPO 2
                        MH 4,29,48,51,55,56,57,60,63,78,80

Report from Standing Committee A on the Notification of Births Bill, *British Parliamentary Papers* VII (1907)

Report from Standing Committee A on the Public Health Bill, *British Parliamentary Papers* VII (1907)

Report from Standing Committee B on the Housing, Town Planning etc. Bill; with the Proceedings of the Committee, *British Parliamentary Papers* IX (1908)

Report to the President of the Local Government Board on the Poplar Union by J.S.Davy C.B., [Cd. 3240] *British Parliamentary Papers* CIV (1906)

Report of the Royal Commission on the Poor Laws and the Relief of Distress, [Cd. 4499] *British Parliamentary Papers* XXXVII (1909)

4. *Newspapers*

Battersea Labour Gazette
Battersea Vanguard
Clarion
Commonweal
Daily Chronicle
Daily News
Democrat
Justice
Labour Elector
Labour Leader
Labour Record and Review
Lambeth Post

Pall Mall Gazette
Poor Law Officers Journal
Practical Socialist
Reynold's Newspaper
South London Press
South Western Star
Star
The Times
Wandsworth and Battersea District Times
Workman's Times

5. *Books*

(Here and in the footnotes place of publication is London unless otherwise stated.)

W. Ashworth, *The Genesis of Modern British Town Planning* (1954)

E.B. Baker and P.J. Noel Baker, *J. Allen Baker M.P.: A Memoir* (1927)

W.H. Beveridge, *Power and Influence; an Autobiography* (1953)

H.N. Bunbury (ed.), *Lloyd George's Ambulance Wagon. Being the Memoirs of William J. Braithwaite, 1911-12* (1957)

J.L. Brand, *Doctors and the State* (Baltimore, 1965)

K.D. Brown, *Labour and Unemployment, 1900-1914* (Newton Abbot, 1971)

J. Burgess, *John Burns. The Rise and Progress of a Right Honourable* (Glasgow, 1911)

208

R. Churchill, *Winston S. Churchill. Young Statesman, 1901-1914* (1967)

G.D.H. Cole, *John Burns* (1943)

M. Cole (ed.), *Beatrice Webb's Diaries, 1912-1924* (1952)

M. Cole, *The Story of Fabian Socialism* (1961)

J.B. Cullingworth, *Town and Country Planning in England and Wales* (1964)

A. Fitzroy, *Memoirs* (1925)

A.G. Gardiner, *John Benn and the Progressive Movement* (1925)
    Prophets, Priests, and Kings (1908)

F. Gould, *Hyndman, Prophet of Socialism, 1842-1921* (1928)

J. Harris, *Unemployment and Politics. A Study in English Social Policy, 1886-1914* (Oxford, 1972)

A.F. Havighurst, *Radical Journalist. H.W. Massingham, 1860-1924* (Cambridge, 1974)

H. Haward, *The London County Council from Within* (1932)

P. Henderson (ed.), *The Letters of William Morris to his Family and Friends* (1950)

E. Hughes, *Keir Hardie* (1956)

H.M. Hyndman, *Further Reminiscences* (1912)
    The Record of an Adventurous Life (1911)

W. Kent, *John Burns. Labour's Lost Leader* (1950)

H. Lee, *Social Democracy in Britain* (1935)

J. Lovell, *Stevedores and Dockers* (1969)

T. Mann, *Memoirs* (1923)

L. Masterman, *C.F.G. Masterman* (1939)

A. McBriar, *Fabian Socialism and English Politics, 1884-1914* (Cambridge, 1962)

J. McCarthy, *British Political Portraits* (1903)

G.F. McCleary, *The Early History of the Infant Welfare Movement* (1933)
    The Maternity and Child Welfare Movement (1935)

K.O. Morgan, *Keir Hardie. Radical and Socialist* (1975)

G. Newman, *The Building of a Nation's Health* (1939)

A. Newsholme, *Fifty Years in Public Health* (1935)
    The Last Thirty Years in Public Health (1936)

H. Pelling, *The Origins of the Labour Party* (Oxford, 1965)

S. Pierson, *Marxism and the Origins of British Socialism: the Struggle for a New Consciousness* (1973)

H. Roseveare, *The Treasury* (1969)

W. Sanders, *Early Socialist Days* (1927)

W. Saunders, *History of the First London County Council* (1892)

F. Sheppard, *London, 1808-1970: The Infernal Wen* (1971)

H.L. Smith and V. Nash, *The Story of the Dockers' Strike* (1889)

E.P. Thompson, *William Morris. Romantic to Revolutionary* (1955)

P. Thompson, *Socialists, Liberals and Labour. The Struggle for London, 1885-1914* (1967)

B. Tillett, *Memories and Reflections* (1931)

C. Tsuzuki, *H.M. Hyndman and British Socialism* (Oxford 1961)

B. Webb, *My Apprenticeship* (1950)
  Our Partnership (1948)

S. and B. Webb, *English Poor Law Policy* (1910)
  History of Trade Unionism (1907)

J. Wilson, *A Life of Sir Henry Campbell-Bannerman* (1973)

6. Articles

F. Bealey, 'Keir Hardie and the Labour Group', *Parliamentary Affairs* 10 (1956-7)

K.D. Brown, 'John Burns at the Local Government Board: A Reassessment', *Journal of Social Policy* 6 (April 1977)
  'London and the Historical Reputation of John Burns', *The London Journal* 2 (November 1976)

J.A.M. Caldwell, 'The Genesis of the Ministry of Labour', *Public Administration* 37 (1959)

G.E. Cherry, 'Influences of the Development of Town Planning in Britain', *Journal of Contemporary History* 4 (1968)

R. Davidson, 'Llewellyn Smith, the Labour Department and Government Growth, 1886-1909, *Studies in the Growth of Nineteenth Century Government,* ed. G. Sutherland (1972)

A.E. Duffy, 'Differing Policies and Personal Rivalries in the Origins of the Independent Labour Party', *Victorian Studies* 6 (1962)
  'The Eight Hour Day Movement in Britain, 1886-1893', *Manchester School of Economic and Social Studies* 36 (1968)

F. Honigsbaum, 'The Struggle for the Ministry of Health', *Occasional Papers in Social Administration* 37 (1970)

R. Macleod, 'The Frustration of State Medicine, 1880-1899', *Medical History II* (1967)
  'Treasury Control and Social Administration: A Study of Establishment Growth at the Local Government Board, 1871-1905', *Occasional Papers in Social Administration* 23 (1968)

A. MacNalty, 'The Medical Department of the Local Government Board', *Journal of the Royal Institute of Public Health* 2 (1948)

V. Markham, 'Robert Morant. Some Personal Reminiscences', *Public Administration* 28 (1950)

J. Minett, 'The Housing, Town Planning etc. Act, 1909', *The Planner* 60 (1974)

W.A. Ross, 'Local Government Board and After: Retrospect', *Public Administration* 34 (1956)

S. Shipley, 'Club Life and Socialism in Mid-Victorian London', *History Workshop Pamphlet* 5 (1971)

7. *Theses*

J.A.M. Caldwell, 'Social Policy and Public Administration, 1909-1911' (Nottingham Ph.D., 1956)

J. Stevens, 'The London County Council Under the Progressives, 1889-1907' (Sussex M.A., 1966)

K. Young, 'The London Municipal Society, 1894-1963: A Study in Conservatism and Local Government' (London Ph.D., 1973).

INDEX

Adrian, A., 111, 128, 140, 147, 152, 158, 199
Amalgamated Society of Engineers, 9, 15, 16, 39, 55, 88, 89, 99
American Federation of Labor, 49, 78
Askwith, G., 173
Asquith, H.H., 30, 63, 75, 104, 106, 133, 141, 149, 155, 157, 158, 159, 162, 163, 164, 166, 174, 175, 183; and Lloyd George, 148, 165, 179-80, 186; and unemployment, 120, 135, 142-4; retains Burns in cabinet, 136-8, 172, 201
Aveling, E., 14, 27, 65

Baker, J.A., 86, 104, 201, 202
Balfour, A.J., 103, 104, 108, 162
Barnes, G., 88, 99, 162
Battersea, 1, 2, 6, 7, 9, 15, 20, 24, 40, 41, 42, 52, 54, 63, 76, 80, 82, 93, 94, 95, 129, 148, 153, 155, 167, 190, 191, 193, 201; Labour League, 52, 63, 64, 65, 81, 82, 94, 95, 100, 115, 154, 186, 187, 188, 196, 201; Labour Party, 154; Liberal and Radical Association, 51, 52, 80, 153, 154; Social Democratic Federation, 34, 38, 40, 50, 80, 155, 160
Beauchamp, Lord, 150, 176
Benn, A. Shirley, 108, 153, 155
Benn, J., 59, 67, 86
Besant, Annie, 18, 27, 31, 34, 42
Beveridge, W.H., 129, 138, 173
Blatchford, R., 73, 75, 88
Board of Trade, 2, 112, 126, 138, 142, 164, 172, 174, 201
Boer War, 86, 90-1, 93, 94, 113
Bright, John, 13, 17, 36, 92
Broadhurst, Henry, 55, 78
Bryce, J., 71, 139
Budget (1909), 147-9, 153, 154
Burgess, J., 1, 3, 4, 12, 17, 38, 64, 106, 162
Burns, Alexander (Jr.), 10, 23
Burns, Alexander (Sr.), 6, 8
Burns, Barbara, 6, 96
Burns, Edgar, 106, 124, 161, 170, 178, 185, 189, 195
Burns, John, assessments of, 1-4, 110, 192. Career: early life, 1-7; Africa, 10, 12-3; marriage, 11; arrested, 9, 22, 28; and S.D.F., 12, 14-6, 26, 35-9, 41, 50, 62, 192, 193; Dock strike (1889), 44-52; and T.U.C., 56, 70, 73, 77-9; eight hour movement, 69-70, 72, 88; Fabian Society, 76-7; L.C.C. work, 42, 56-61, 64, 65-8, 84-6; trips

ROYAL HISTORICAL SOCIETY
STUDIES IN HISTORY

Already published

Frank F. Foster,	**The Politics of Stability : A Portrait of the Rulers of Elizabethan London**
Rosamond McKitterick,	**The Frankish Church and The Carolingian Reforms, 789 - 895**

Copies obtainable on order from
Swift Printers Ltd., 1-7 Albion Place, Britton Street, London EC1M 5RE